Adolescent Pregnancy and Childbearing

Findings from Research

Catherine S. Chilman
School of Social Welfare
University of Wisconsin
Milwaukee, Wisconsin

U.S. DEPARTMENT OF
HEALTH AND
HUMAN SERVICES
Public Health Service
National Institutes of Health

NIH Publication No. 81-2077
December 1980

For sale by the Superintendent of Documents, U.S. Government
Printing Office, Washington, D.C. 20402

This book is dedicated to the memory of Frederick S. Jaffe,
November 27, 1925 - August 16, 1978.

Foreword

The Center for Population Research, National Institute of Child Health and Human Development (NICHD), has had a continuing interest in early pregnancy and childbearing. The effects of an early birth are felt not only by the young mother, but also by her child, the father, other family members involved, and society as a whole. Although birth rates have declined among adolescents, they have declined more slowly than for older women and, until 1973, increased for the youngest adolescents. A growing percentage of births to adolescents are out-of-wedlock and, increasingly, out-of-wedlock births are concentrated among adolescents. Evidence indicates high levels of unintended pregnancy and childbearing among adolescents.

Given the wide-ranging effects of this continuing problem, the Center for Population Research sponsored two conferences intended to assess the current knowledge about adolescent childbearing and to identify areas in which further research is needed. The first conference, cosponsored by the Center and the Alan Guttmacher Institute, addressed the consequences of adolescent pregnancy and childbearing. The second conference focused on the determinants of adolescent pregnancy and childbearing. The chapters in this book consist mainly of conference papers that initiated extensive efforts by the Center to encourage and support studies of the causes and consequences of adolescent sexuality, contraceptive, and fertility behavior.

Contents

List of Figures

List of Tables

Conference on Determinants of Adolescent Pregnancy and Childbearing
May 4, 1976

Sponsored by the U.S. Department of Health, Education, and Welfare
Center for Population Research
National Institute of Child Health and Human Development

PARTICIPANTS

Dr. Catherine Chilman
School of Social Welfare
University of Wisconsin
Milwaukee, Wisconsin 53201

Dr. George Cvetkovich
Department of Psychology
Western Washington State
  College
Bellingham, Washington 98225

Dr. Kingsley Davis
International Population and
  Urban Research
University of California
Berkeley, California 94720

Dr. Elizabeth Douvan
Department of Psychology
University of Michigan
Ann Arbor, Michigan 48104

Ms. Virginia Ernster
School of Public Health
University of California
Berkeley, California 94720

Dr. Frank F. Furstenberg, Jr.
Department of Sociology
University of Pennsylvania
Philadelphia, Pennsylvania 19104

Mr. Frederick S. Jaffe
Alan Guttmacher Institute
Planned Parenthood Federation
  of America
515 Madison Avenue
New York, New York 10022

Dr. David J. Kallen
Department of Human Development
Michigan State University
East Lansing, Michigan 48824

Dr. John F. Kantner
Population and Family Health
Johns Hopkins University
School of Hygiene & Public
  Health
615 North Wolfe Street
Baltimore, Maryland 21205

Ms. Virginia Ktsanes
School of Public Health and
    Tropical Medicine
Tulane University
New Orleans, Louisiana 70112

Dr. Richard Lincoln
Alan Guttmacher Institute
Planned Parenthood Federation
    of America
515 Madison Avenue
New York, New York 10022

Dr. Kristin Luker
Department of Sociology
University of California
LaJolla, California 92037

Mr. Paul J. Placek
Health Resources Administration
Rockville, Maryland 20852

Dr. Harriet Presser
International Institute for Study
    of Human Reproduction
Columbia University
New York, New York 10032

Dr. Alice Rossi
Department of Sociology
University of Massachusetts
Amherst, Massachusetts 01002

Dr. William Simon
Institute for Urban Studies
University of Houston
Houston, Texas 77004

Dr. Charles F. Westoff
Office of Population Research
Princeton University
Princeton, New Jersey 98540

Dr. Paul Williams
Department of Sociology
University of Rochester
Rochester, New York 14627

Center for Population Research—NICHD

Dr. Wendy Baldwin
Social Demographer
Behavioral Sciences Branch

Mr. Arthur Campbell
Deputy Director
Center for Population Research

Dr. Jerry W. Combs, Jr.
Chief
Behavorial Sciences Branch

Dr. V. Jeffrey Evans
Economist
Population and Reproduction
    Grants Branch

Dr. Gloria Kamenske
Psychologist
Behavioral Sciences Branch

Dr. Earl E. Huyck
Social Demographer
Behavioral Sciences Branch

Conference on Consequences of Adolescent Pregnancy and Childbearing
October 29 – 30, 1975

Cosponsored by the U.S. Department of Health,
Education, and Welfare
Center for Population Research

National Institute of Child Health and
Human Development
and
The Alan Guttmacher Institute of
the Planned Parenthood Federation of America

PARTICIPANTS

Ms. May Aaronson
Program Specialist
Center for Studies of Child &
  Family Mental Health
Parklawn Building, Room 15C12
Rockville, Maryland 20852

Ms. Linda Ambrose
Alan Guttmacher Institute
1666 K Street, N.W.
Washington, D.C. 20006

Mr. Jim Chamberlin
Youth Coordinator
Population Crisis Committee
Suite 200, 1835 K Street, N.W.
Washington, D.C. 20006

Dr. Catherine Chilman
  (Rapporteur)
Professor and Research
  Coordinator
School of Social Welfare
University of Wisconsin
Milwaukee, Wisconsin 53201

Dr. John Clausen
Institute of Human
  Development
University of California
1203 Tolman Hall
Berkeley, California 94720

Ms. Lolagene Coombs
Population Studies Center
University of Michigan
1225 South University Avenue
Ann Arbor, Michigan 48104

Dr. Henry P. David
Trans-National Family Research
    Institute
8307 Whitman Drive
Bethesda, Maryland 20034

Ms. Joy Dryfoos
Alan Guttmacher Institute
Planned Parenthood Federation
    of America
515 Madison Avenue
New York, New York 10022

Dr. Thomas J. Espenshade
Assistant Professor, Population
    & Manpower Research Center
Institute for Social Research
Florida State University
Tallahassee, Florida 32306

Dr. Ruth Faden
Assistant Professor
School of Hygiene & Public
    Health
Johns Hopkins University
615 North Wolfe Street
Baltimore, Maryland 21205

Ms. Janet Forbush
National Alliance Concerned
    with School-Aged Parents
7315 Wisconsin Avenue, Room
    211-W
Bethesda, Maryland 20014

Dr. Frank F. Furstenberg, Jr.
Department of Sociology
University of Pennsylvania
3718 Locust Street
Philadelphia, Pennsylvania 19104

Dr. Susan Gustavus
Associate Professor of Sociology
University of Cincinnati
Cincinnati, Ohio 45221

Dr. Andre Hellegers
Professor of Obstetrics and Gy-
    necology
Georgetown University Hospital
3800 Reservoir Road, N.W.
Washington, D.C. 20007

Dr. Reuben Hill
Regents' Professor of Family
    Sociology
Minnesota Family Study Center
1014 Social Sciences Building
Minneapolis, Minnesota 55455

Mr. Frederick S. Jaffe
Alan Guttmacher Institute
Planned Parenthood Federation
    of America
515 Madison Avenue
New York, New York 10022

Dr. John F. Kantner
Population and Family Health
Johns Hopkins University
School of Hygiene & Public
    Health
615 North Wolfe Street
Baltimore, Maryland 21205

Dr. Hylan G. Lewis
372 Central Park West
Apt. 17X
New York, New York 10025

Dr. E. James Lieberman
6451 Barnaby Street, N.W.
Washington, D.C. 20015

Dr. Richard Lincoln
Alan Guttmacher Institute
Planned Parenthood Federation
    of America
515 Madison Avenue
New York, New York 10022

Dr. Jane A. Menken
Office of Population Research
Princeton University
Princeton, New Jersey 08540

Dr. Warren B. Miller
Assistant Professor
Department of Psychiatry &
  Behavior Science
School of Medicine
Stanford University
Stanford, California 94305

Dr. Phyllis Piotrow
Executive Director
Population Crisis Committee
1835 K Street, N.W. Suite 200
Washington, D.C. 20006

Dr. Harriet Presser
International Institute for Study
  of Human Reproduction
Columbia University
New York, New York 10032

Dr. Ann Rosewater
Children's Defense Fund
1520 New Hampshire Avenue,
  N.W.
Washington, D.C. 20036

Dr. Alice Rossi
Department of Sociology
University of Massachusetts
Amherst, Massachusetts 01002

Dr. Kenneth W. Terhune
Institute for Survey Research
Temple University
Philadelphia, Pennsylvania 19121

Dr. James Trussel
Office of Population Research
Princeton University
Princeton, New Jersey 08540

Dr. Charles F. Westoff, Confer-
  ence Chairman
Associate Director
Office of Population Research
Princeton University
5 Ivy Lane
Princeton, New Jersey 08540

Ms. Elizabeth M. Whelan
Executive Director
Demographic Materials, Inc.
165 West End Avenue
New York, New York 10023

Dr. Paul Williams
Department of Sociology
University of Rochester
Rochester, New York 14627

Federal Government Personnel

Mr. George E. Hall
Chief, Social Statistics Branch
Policy Division, Office of
  Manpower and Budget

Mr. Carl S. Schultz
Director of Population Affairs
Office of the Secretary, U.S.
  DHEW

Dr. Gooloo Wunderlich
Director
Division of Health Data Policy,
  U.S. DHEW

Center for Population Research—NICHD

Dr. Wendy Baldwin
Social Demographer
Behavioral Sciences Branch

Mr. Arthur A. Campbell
Deputy Director

Dr. Jerry W. Combs, Jr.
Chief, Behavioral Sciences
  Branch

Dr. Earl E. Huyck
Social Demographer
Behavioral Sciences Branch

Dr. Gloria Kamenske
Psychologist
Behavioral Sciences Branch

Dr. Sidney H. Newman
Behavioral Sciences Administra-
  tor
Population and Reproduction
  Grants Branch

Growth and Development Branch—NICHD

Dr. Sigmund Dragastin
Health Sciences Administrator

Dr. James Kavanagh
Acting Chief

Dr. John McKigney
Health Sciences Administrator

Chapter 1

Trends in Teenage Childbearing in the United States

Arthur A. Campbell

Center for Population Research, NICHD

The birth rate changes so rapidly among girls from ages 13 to 19 that it is almost meaningless to treat trends in childbearing among teenagers as a coherent phenomenon. The birth rate is close to zero at age 13, but at age 19 it is approaching its maximum value (generally reached at ages 21 to 23 in the United States). Accordingly, this paper describes trends for single years of age, insofar as the basic data permit.

TRENDS IN AGE-SPECIFIC BIRTH RATES

At the youngest end of the childbearing span, births to women under age 15 are shown as a group. The majority of births to women in this age group occur to those aged 14 (81 percent in 1975); therefore, in calculating birth rates, the denominator is the number of women aged 14. As shown in table 1–1, the birth rate for this group has doubled in the past 47 years—from 3.4 births per 1,000 women in 1930–1934 to 6.7 in 1977. At age 15 the birth rate almost doubled during the same period (from 10.9 to 18.2). At ages 16 and 17 the relative increases were smaller, and at ages 18 and 19 the birth rates increased sharply in the postwar period to reach their highest values in 1955–1959 and then dropped, so that the values observed in 1977 were below those observed in the 1930's. In fact, the trend of the birth rate among women aged 18 and 19 is very similar to that observed for older women. Only among the younger teenagers (ages 14 to 17) are recent birth rates markedly higher than those observed in the early 1930's. The youngest members of this group (ages 14 and 15) have shown the greatest percentage increases.

The trends in teenage childbearing are similar for white and nonwhite women, as shown in tables 1–2 and 1–3, although the levels of the age-specific birth rates are substantially higher for

3

Table 1-1. — *Births per 1,000 women aged 14 to 19 by single years for all women : United States, 1920-1976*

Period	14	15	16	17	18	19
1920-1924	3.6	11.9	28.6	57.9	93.1	125.4
1925-1929	3.9	12.3	28.5	55.6	86.9	114.0
1930-1934	3.4	10.9	25.2	48.6	75.3	99.0
1935-1939	3.7	11.5	26.0	49.0	75.0	97.9
1940-1944	4.0	12.7	27.8	52.2	81.7	109.2
1945-1949	4.9	15.5	34.1	63.7	99.4	133.0
1950-1954	5.9	19.3	43.1	79.7	123.1	162.6
1955-1959	6.0	20.1	45.7	85.8	136.2	184.0
1960-1964	5.4	17.8	40.2	75.8	122.7	169.2
1965	5.2	16.5	36.0	66.4	105.4	142.4
1966	5.3	16.4	35.5	64.8	101.8	136.1
1967	5.3	16.5	35.3	63.2	97.5	129.5
1968	5.7	16.7	35.2	62.6	95.7	125.2
1969	6.0	17.4	35.8	63.1	95.7	124.5
1970	6.6	19.2	38.8	66.6	98.3	126.0
1971	6.7	19.2	38.3	64.2	92.4	116.1
1972	7.1	20.1	39.3	63.5	87.1	105.0
1973	7.4	20.2	38.8	61.5	83.1	98.5
1974	7.2	19.7	37.7	59.7	80.5	96.2
1975	7.1	19.4	36.4	57.3	77.5	92.7
1976	6.8	18.6	34.6	54.2	73.3	88.7
1977	6.7	18.2	34.5	54.2	73.8	89.5

Sources: For 1920-1973, reference 1, p. 37. For 1974-1977, National Center for Health Statistics, unpublished tabulations.

the nonwhite population. Both groups showed the greatest increases at ages 14, 15, and 16.

Trends in the proportion of girls who have borne a child before reaching their 17th birthdays are shown in figure 1–1. The proportion of white girls who had a baby by age 17 remained relatively constant around 3 percent until the postwar period, when it rose to about 5 percent in the late 1950's. Since then it has declined to a level around 4 percent. Trends in the proportion of nonwhite women who had a baby by age 17 have risen from 9 percent in 1917 to around 12 percent during World War II, and to 15 percent in the 1950's. This proportion declined to 13 percent in the 1960's, rose again to 15 percent in the early 1970's, and declined to 13 percent by 1978.

Table 1-2. — *Births per 1,000 women aged 14 to 19 by single years for white women : United States, 1920-1976*

Period	14	15	16	17	18	19
1920-1924	2.1	8.2	22.8	49.8	84.7	117.2
1925-1929	2.2	8.3	22.5	47.4	78.6	106.3
1930-1934	2.0	7.5	19.9	41.3	67.6	91.5
1935-1939	2.0	7.5	19.8	40.5	66.1	89.8
1940-1944	2.0	7.8	20.5	42.5	71.6	100.5
1945-1949	2.6	9.8	25.7	53.0	89.0	124.1
1950-1954	3.2	12.8	33.4	67.8	111.5	153.1
1955-1959	3.6	14.1	36.7	74.7	125.2	174.8
1960-1964	3.1	12.3	32.0	65.7	112.4	160.6
1965	2.7	10.5	27.2	55.6	93.9	131.8
1966	2.8	10.5	26.4	53.3	90.0	125.5
1967	2.7	10.1	25.8	51.4	85.1	118.7
1968	2.9	10.5	25.7	50.7	83.0	114.1
1969	3.2	11.1	26.5	51.2	82.8	112.8
1970	3.6	12.6	29.0	54.3	85.2	114.0
1971	3.7	12.4	28.6	51.8	79.5	103.9
1972	4.1	13.2	29.5	51.2	74.4	93.2
1973	4.3	13.6	29.5	50.0	70.9	87.1
1974	4.3	13.5	28.9	48.7	69.0	85.5
1975	4.4	13.4	28.1	46.9	66.3	82.2
1976	4.2	12.8	26.6	44.3	63.0	78.8
1977	4.1	12.6	26.4	44.1	63.0	79.3

Sources: For 1920-1973, reference 1, p. 64. For 1974-1977, National Center for Health Statistics, unpublished tabulations.

Among all groups combined, the proportion of women aged 17 who had borne a child before reaching their 17th birthdays was 5.5 percent in 1978. The proportion of women aged 20 who had borne a child before reaching age 20 was 22.2 percent.

LEGITIMACY STATUS

Estimates of the illegitimacy rate (the number of illegitimate births per 1,000 unmarried women) are available for the United States since 1940. At that time there were 7.4 illegitimate births per 1,000 unmarried women aged 15 to 19, as shown in table 1–4. The rate rose steadily during and after World War II, climbing most rapidly in the late 1960's. By 1978 the rate had reached 26.0.

Table 1-3. — *Births per 1,000 women aged 14 to 19 by single years for nonwhite women : United States, 1920-1976*

Period	14	15	16	17	18	19
1920-1924	13.3	35.4	65.0	108.9	146.0	177.6
1925-1929	15.4	39.3	69.5	111.0	142.5	165.6
1930-1934	14.0	35.7	63.8	101.2	130.6	152.8
1935-1939	15.8	40.8	71.7	111.4	140.2	158.9
1940-1944	17.7	46.0	79.0	120.8	153.2	171.5
1945-1949	19.8	51.9	89.2	134.1	170.3	193.3
1950-1954	23.1	59.8	103.7	155.3	197.3	224.2
1955-1959	22.4	58.8	103.2	156.8	206.9	243.3
1960-1964	20.5	53.6	94.7	144.1	191.0	226.1
1965	20.4	52.6	92.4	139.5	183.7	214.2
1966	20.5	52.7	92.0	138.4	180.3	208.7
1967	21.3	54.2	93.3	136.8	176.2	202.0
1968	21.9	54.3	92.2	135.4	172.7	196.1
1969	22.4	54.4	91.8	134.9	172.9	195.5
1970	23.8	58.0	96.3	139.3	175.8	197.7
1971	23.6	57.6	95.3	135.8	169.1	187.9
1972	24.1	58.2	95.6	133.7	161.5	175.0
1973	24.5	57.0	91.9	126.5	152.3	164.0
1974	22.8	53.6	86.8	120.4	145.0	156.5
1975	22.1	51.2	82.3	114.5	138.9	151.0
1976	20.5	48.6	77.6	108.0	130.4	143.6
1977	20.0	47.4	77.0	107.4	131.3	145.3

Sources: For 1920-1973, reference 1, p. 91. For 1974-1977, National Center for Health Statistics, unpublished tabulations.

Illegitimacy rates by color are shown in tables 1–5 and 1–6. Between 1940 and 1977 the illegitimacy rate for white girls quadrupled (from 3.3 to 13.6); the corresponding rate for nonwhite girls doubled by 1972, but since that time it has fallen by 7 percent.

The generally upward trend in illegitimacy rates for women aged 15 to 19 paralleled that for older women until the latter half of the 1960's, when the illegitimacy rates for women above age 20 declined sharply. For example, the illegitimacy rate for nonwhite women aged 20 to 24 dropped by 32 percent between 1965 and 1976. The corresponding rate for white women dropped by 28 percent. Whatever forces were bringing about this trend in the older

Figure 1—|1|—Percentage of women who have borne one or more children by age 17, by race: United States, January 1, 1917–1978

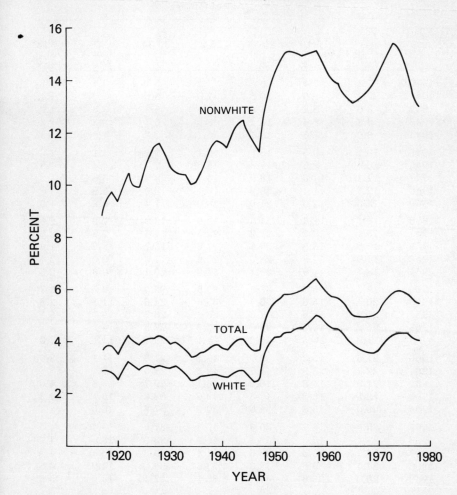

ADOLESCENT PREGNANCY

Table 1-4. *Estimated illegitimacy rates, by age of mother : United States, 1940-1976*

Year	All ages 15-44[a]	Age of mother					
		15-19	20-24	25-29	30-34	35-39	40-44[b]
1940	7.1	7.4	9.5	7.2	5.1	3.4	1.2
1941	7.8	8.0	10.5	7.8	6.0	3.7	1.4
1942	8.0	8.2	11.0	8.4	6.3	3.8	1.2
1943	8.3	8.4	11.4	8.8	6.7	3.8	1.3
1944	9.0	8.8	13.1	10.1	7.0	4.0	1.3
1945	10.1	9.5	15.3	12.1	7.1	4.1	1.6
1946	10.9	9.5	17.3	15.6	7.3	4.4	1.8
1947	12.1	11.0	18.9	15.7	9.2	5.6	1.8
1948	12.5	11.4	19.8	16.4	10.0	5.8	1.6
1949	13.3	12.0	21.0	18.0	11.4	6.8	1.9
1950	14.1	12.6	21.3	19.9	13.3	7.2	2.0
1951	15.1	13.2	23.2	22.8	14.6	7.6	2.2
1952	15.8	13.5	25.4	24.8	15.7	8.2	1.9
1953	16.9	13.9	28.0	27.6	17.3	9.0	2.4
1954	18.7	14.9	31.4	31.0	20.4	10.3	2.5
1955	19.3	15.1	33.5	33.5	22.0	10.5	2.7
1956	20.4	15.6	36.4	35.6	24.6	11.1	2.8
1957	21.0	15.8	37.3	36.8	26.8	12.1	3.1
1958	21.2	15.3	38.2	40.5	27.5	13.3	3.2
1959	21.9	15.5	40.2	44.1	28.1	14.1	3.3
1960	21.6	15.3	39.7	45.1	27.8	14.1	3.6
1961	22.7	15.9	41.7	46.5	28.3	15.4	3.9
1962	21.9	14.8	40.9	46.7	29.7	15.6	4.0
1963	22.5	15.2	40.3	49.0	33.2	16.1	4.3
1964	23.0	15.8	39.9	50.2	37.2	16.3	4.4
1965	23.5	16.7	39.9	49.3	37.5	17.4	4.5
1966	23.4	17.5	39.1	45.6	33.0	16.4	4.1
1967	23.9	18.6	38.3	41.4	29.2	15.4	4.0
1968	24.4	19.8	37.3	38.6	28.2	14.9	3.8
1969	25.0	20.6	37.4	38.1	27.4	13.6	3.6
1970	26.4	22.4	38.4	37.0	27.1	13.6	3.5
1971	25.6	22.4	35.6	34.7	25.3	13.3	3.5
1972	24.9	22.9	33.4	31.1	22.8	12.0	3.1
1973	24.5	22.9	31.8	30.0	20.5	10.8	3.0
1974	24.1	23.2	30.9	28.4	18.6	10.0	2.6
1975	24.8	24.2	31.6	28.0	18.1	9.1	2.6
1976	24.7	24.0	32.2	27.5	17.8	8.9	2.5
1977	26.0	25.5	34.7	28.5	17.2	8.3	2.4

[a]Rates computed by relating total illegitimate births regardless of age of mother to unmarried women aged 15 to 44 years.
[b]Rates computed by relating illegitimate births to mothers aged 40 and over to unmarried women aged 40 to 44 years.

Sources: For 1940-1973, reference 2. For 1974, reference 3. For 1975, reference 4. For 1976, reference 5. For 1977, reference 6.

Table 1-5. — *Estimated illegitimacy rates, by age of mother : White women, United States, 1940, 1950, and 1955 to 1977*

Year	All ages 15-44[a]	Age of mother					
		15-19	20-24	25-29	30-34	35-44[b]	
1940	3.6	3.3	5.7	4.0	2.5	1.2	
1950	6.1	5.1	10.0	8.7	5.9	2.0	
1955	7.9	6.0	15.0	13.3	8.6	2.8	
1956	8.3	6.2	16.3	14.0	9.2	3.0	
1957	8.6	6.4	16.6	14.6	10.5	3.0	
1958	8.8	6.3	17.3	15.8	10.8	3.4	
1959	9.2	6.5	18.3	17.6	10.7	3.6	
1960	9.2	6.6	18.2	18.2	10.8	3.9	
1961	10.0	7.0	19.7	19.4	11.3	4.2	
1962	9.8	6.5	20.0	19.8	12.6	4.3	
1963	10.5	7.0	20.8	22.0	14.2	4.6	
1964	11.0	7.3	21.2	24.1	15.9	4.8	
1965	11.6	7.9	22.1	24.3	16.6	4.9	
1966	12.0	8.5	22.5	23.5	15.7	4.9	
1967	12.5	9.0	23.1	22.7	14.0	4.7	
1968	13.2	9.8	23.1	22.1	15.1	4.7	
1969	13.5	10.0	23.0	22.4	15.1	7.6	2.0
1970	13.9	10.9	22.5	21.1	14.2	7.6	2.0
1971	12.5	10.3	18.8	18.6	13.3	7.2	1.9
1972	12.0	10.5	16.7	16.6	12.1	6.4	1.6
1973	11.9	10.7	15.6	16.1	10.7	5.9	1.7
1974	11.8	11.1	15.2	14.9	9.6	5.5	1.5
1975	12.6	12.1	15.7	15.1	10.0	5.4	1.5
1976	12.7	12.4	16.0	14.4	10.2	5.5	1.4
1977	13.7	13.6	17.7	14.7	9.5	4.8	1.4

[a] Rates computed by relating total births regardless of age of mother to women aged 15 to 44 years.
[b] Rates computed by relating births to mothers aged 35 and over to women aged 35 to 44.

Sources: Same as table 1–4.

Table 1-6. — *Estimated illegitimacy rates, by age of mother: Nonwhite women, United States, 1940, 1950, and 1955-1977*

Year	All ages 15-44[a]	15-19	20-24	25-29	30-34	35-44[b]	
1940	35.6	42.5	46.1	32.5	23.4	9.3	
1950	71.2	68.5	105.4	94.2	63.5	20.0	
1955	87.2	77.6	133.0	125.2	100.9	25.3	
1956	92.1	79.6	143.5	132.7	113.7	27.0	
1957	95.3	81.4	147.7	142.6	115.1	30.3	
1958	97.8	80.4	153.2	161.2	110.5	32.5	
1959	100.8	80.8	167.8	168.0	106.5	34.9	
1960	98.3	76.5	166.5	171.8	104.0	35.6	
1961	100.0	77.6	169.6	172.7	112.0	37.4	
1962	97.5	74.1	163.6	172.7	115.2	35.5	
1963	97.1	73.8	161.8	171.5	124.3	34.4	
1964	97.2	74.0	164.2	168.7	132.3	34.5	
1965	97.6	75.8	152.6	164.7	137.8	39.0	
1966	92.8	76.9	139.4	143.8	119.4	33.8	
1967	89.5	80.2	128.2	118.4	97.2	28.9	
1968	86.6	82.8	118.3	104.4	80.6	25.2	
1969	86.6	85.6	116.6	98.0	73.5	34.7	10.6
1970	89.9	90.8	121.0	93.8	69.8	32.0	10.7
1971	90.6	92.4	121.0	93.3	65.7	32.2	10.4
1972	86.9	92.7	113.1	84.5	56.3	29.0	8.2
1973	84.2	89.7	108.9	82.4	56.4	26.2	7.2
1974	81.5	88.8	104.3	78.8	51.6	23.3	6.7
1975	80.4	88.1	103.8	75.3	48.7	20.1	7.0
1976	78.1	84.6	103.1	76.8	44.3	18.8	6.9
1977	79.4	86.4	105.6	77.8	44.6	18.6	6.6

[a]Rates computed by relating total births regardless of age of mother to women aged 15 to 44 years.
[b]Rates computed by relating births to mothers aged 35 and over to women aged 35 to 44.

Sources: Same as table 1-4.

ages did not affect fertility at the younger ages to the same extent.

FACTORS AFFECTING THE TREND IN THE ILLEGITIMACY RATE AMONG TEENAGERS

Whether a birth is classified as legitimate or illegitimate depends on the marital status of the mother at the time the birth occurs, and not at the time conception occurs. Accordingly, many legitimate children are conceived before marriage and born after marriage. Therefore, the illegitimacy rate varies not only in response to changes in the proportion of girls who conceive out of wedlock, but also in response to changes in the proportion of pregnant girls who marry before the birth of a child.

To determine how these two factors have changed, O'Connell and Moore[7] of the U.S. Bureau of the Census estimated the distribution of first births at ages 15 to 19 by marital status at conception and marital status at birth on the basis of retrospective data from the June 1978 Current Population Survey. Estimates from their analysis in table 1–7 show that between the periods 1963–1966 and 1975–1978, both the increase in the proportion conceiving before marriage and the reduction in the proportion of pregnant women who marry before the first child is born have contributed to the rise in the proportion of first births classified as illegitimate.

Table 1–7 clearly shows that the majority of conceptions resulting in first births at ages 15 to 19 occur before marriage. The proportion has risen substantially since the mid-1960's. Table 12–7 also shows that the proportion of pregnant women who marry before their first birth at ages 15 to 19 has declined since the 1960's, both for white and black women.

The rise in the proportion of premaritally conceived births probably is due to an increase in the prevalence of sexual intercourse before marriage. Between 1971 and 1976, the proportion of never-married women aged 15 to 19 who ever had sexual intercourse increased from 26.8 to 34.9 percent.[8]

At the same time a greater proportion of unmarried teenagers reported using contraception "always" (18.4 percent of the sexually experienced never-married women in 1971 and 30.0 percent in 1976). They were using more effective methods in 1976, and they were using all methods with greater regularity. The proportion reporting that they were contraceptively protected at the time of most recent intercourse was 45.4 percent in 1971 and 63.5 percent in 1976. Thus, although the prevalence of sexual intercourse has risen, the effectiveness with which contraception is used by unmarried teenagers seems to have improved. This apparent improvement is partially offset, however, by an increase in the proportion who

Table 1-7. — *Percent distribution of first births by marital status at time of birth and conception for births at ages 15 to 17 and 18 to 19, by race : 1963-1966 and 1975-1978*

| Year | Total | Premarital conceptions | | | Postmarital conceptions | Percent of premaritally conceived births legitimated |
		Total	Premarital births	Legitimated births		
		White women aged 15-17				
1975-1978[a]	100.0	80.3	35.5	44.8	19.7	55.9
1963-1966	100.0	55.7	19.9	35.8	44.3	64.3
		White women aged 18-19				
1975-1978	100.0	52.5	20.8	31.7	47.5	60.4
1963-1966	100.0	35.9	8.6	27.2	64.1	76.0
		Black women aged 15-17				
1975-1978[a]	100.0	97.7	92.9	4.8	2.2	4.9
1963-1966	100.0	89.3	72.9	16.4	10.7	18.4
		Black women aged 18-19				
1975-1978	100.0	85.1	75.8	9.3	14.8	10.9
1963-1966	100.0	66.6	41.8	24.7	33.4	37.1

[a] Excludes births to women aged 15 to 17 and unmarried at the time of the survey in June 1978. This source of bias tends to understate the proportion with a premarital conception and to overstate the proportion who legitimate a premaritally conceived birth for the period 1975-1978.

Source: Reference 7.

report never using contraception: from 17.0 percent in 1971 to 25.6 percent in 1976.

Despite the trend toward more and better contraception, the proportion of sexually active single women under age 20 who became pregnant was about the same in 1971 (29.8 percent) and 1976 (28.3 percent).[9] Fewer premarital pregnancies resulted in live births in 1976, however, because higher proportions of single women obtained abortions. In other words, this study suggests that the only progress in the control of fertility among unmarried teenagers between 1971 and 1976 came about through increased reliance on abortion.

REFERENCES

1. National Center for Health Statistics. *Fertility Tables for Birth Cohorts by Color: United States, 1917–73,* U.S. DHEW Publ. No. (HRA) 76–1152. Washington: U.S. Government Printing Office, 1976.
2. National Center for Health Statistics. *Vital Statistics of the United States, 1973,* Vol. I. *Natality.* Washington: U.S. Government Printing Office, 1977, pp. 1–30.
3. National Center for Health Statistics. "Advance Report: Final Natality Statistics, 1974." *Monthly Vital Statistics Report.* Vol. 24, No. 11, Suppl. 2, February 13, 1976, p. 11.
4. National Center for Health Statistics. "Advance Report: Final Natality Statistics, 1975." *Monthly Vital Statistics Report.* Vol. 24, No. 10, Supplement, December 30, 1976, p. 14.
5. National Center for Health Statistics. "Advance Report: Final Natality Statistics, 1976." *Monthly Vital Statistics Report.* Vol. 26, No. 12, Supplement, March 29, 1978, p. 17.
6. National Center for Health Statistics. "Advance Report: Final Natality Statistics, 1977." *Monthly Vital Statistics Report.* Vol. 27, No. 11, Supplement, February 5, 1979, p. 19.
7. O'Connell, M. and Moore, M., "The Legitimacy Status of First Births: A Retrospective Study, 1939–42 to 1975–78," *Fam. Plann. Perspec.* 12(1), 1980 (in press).
8. Zelnik, M. and Kantner, J. F., "Sexual and Contraceptive Experience of Young Unmarried Women in the United States, 1976 and 1971," *Fam. Plann. Perspec.* 9(2):55–71, 1977.
9. Zelnik, M. and Kantner, J. F., "First Pregnancies to Women Aged 15–19: 1976 and 1971," *Fam. Plann. Perspec.* 10(1):12–13, 1978.

Chapter 2

Psychosocial Development and the Social Problem of Teenage Illegitimacy

George Cvetkovich and Barbara Grote
Western Washington University

A recent news story reported that the pastor of a small Florida church has begun collecting and destroying rock music records to protect the moral decay of youth. "Rock music appeals to the flesh," claims the minister. "Out of 1,000 girls who become pregnant, 984 committed fornication while rock music was being played." More than $2,200 has been collected to purchase records to burn (*Rolling Stone*, Nov. 26, 1976).

Regrettably, this example typifies the level of much present thinking with respect to the social problems of teenage illegitimacy. However, meaningful responses to teenage illegitimacy demand more complex concepts of the problem. In particular, what seems to be essential is a concept that is both broad enough to include a number of different factors simultaneously and pliable enough to consider the behavior in question in the light of everyday occurrences. This concept would include at least four perspectives:

1. Biological perspective that would consider the change in the teenager's physical ability to conceive and carry a child to term.
2. An individual difference perspective that would consider personality and other individual characteristics that may place some teenagers at greater contraceptive risk than others.
3. A life cycle perspective that would consider the emotional, intellectual, and social development that characterizes adolescence as a unique developmental period.
4. A generational perspective that would consider how members of one particular cohort are similar to each other and are different from other cohorts. This perspective would consider, for example, changes in attitudes toward

15

premarital sex that were developing in the 1960's. On a
broader level, this generational perspective would blend
into a cultural perspective that would consider similarities
shared by individuals as members in a social group.

Providing evidence linking these perspectives is not our goal.
Our research, however, suggests that looking at these different
levels is conceptually important.

AMERICAN PUBLIC HEALTH
ASSOCIATION PROJECT

Our research, part of a project coordinated by the American
Public Health Association, provides an opportunity to examine
some implications of a multiperspective approach to the social
problem of teenage illegitimacy.[a] The purpose of the study was to
identify, on the basis of psychosocial factors, those teenagers who
are most likely to be at contraceptive risk at some time during
their early sexual careers. The project, planned as a longitudinal
study, has recently completed its first year. In that year, a total
of 684 teenagers between the ages of 15 and 18 participated in the
study. Of the participants, 94 percent were aged 16 or 17. The
teenagers were residents of two large metropolitan areas
(Washington, D.C., and Atlanta, Ga.) and one smaller community
(Bellingham, Wash.). The sample consisted of 195 white males, 253
white females, 117 nonwhite males, and 119 nonwhite females. A
majority of the nonwhite sample (92 percent) was black and will
be referred to as such.

The information collected on each participant consisted of a
battery of self-administered questionnaires and an interview.
Approximately 1 to 1-1/2 hours was spent with each participant.

Analysis

Two preliminary analyses have been completed on the first-
year data. As a step toward instrument refinement, a cluster
analysis of each of the subtests of the questionnaire was completed
separately for males and females. A second analysis consisted of
subjecting these clusters, along with a few individual questionnaire
items and some personal and family information collected during
the interview, to a stepwise multiple regression procedure to

[a]The other researchers involved in the project, in addition to the authors, are: E.
James Lieberman and Sarah Brown (American Public Health Association), Warren
Miller (Laboratory of Behavior and Population, Palo Alto, Calif.) Paul Poppen
(George Washington University, Washington, D.C.), and Fred Crawford (Emory Uni-
versity, Atlanta, Ga.). The study was supported by grant R01 HD09813, Center for
Population Research, National Institutes of Health.

determine which variables functioned as the best discriminators of the criterion behavior of sexual activity and contraceptive use.

Two sets of regressions were performed. The first set used independent variables that could be broadly construed as pertaining to individual characteristics. These variables included self-reports of personal characteristics, sex knowledge and certainty, family role attitudes, sexual attitudes, motives for sexual involvement, age at puberty, age at first intercourse, and satisfaction with sexual intercourse. The second set of regressions was completed on those variables considered situational in nature: friends' and parents' attitudes toward premarital sex, perception of the prevalence of sexual activity among peers, relationship to family, attitude toward school, parents' education, religious involvement, and family mobility. Because race was found to be significantly related to both sexual activity and contraceptive use for males ($r=0.43$ and 0.29, respectively; $P<0.01$) and to sexual activity for females ($r=0.25$; $P<0.01$), separate analyses were completed for each sex and race. A more complete description of the variables used in the regression analysis is given in appendix A. The exact item content of the variables in tables 2-1 to 2-6 appear in appendix B.

Three criterion behaviors were utilized. Did the teenager ever have sexual intercourse? What contraceptive protection was used by those who had intercourse during the 3 months just prior to the interview? What overall protection was used since first intercourse? Measures of contraceptive protection included clinically proven methods (the pill, intrauterine device, foam, diaphragm, and condom) as well as rhythm and withdrawal if evidence indicated that they were used correctly and conscientiously.

The results of these analyses are presented in tables 2-1 to 2-6. These tables show the steps of each regression analysis that yielded a significant discriminator of the relevant criterion variable. All of the variables shown were significant at the 0.05 level or better. The multiple R^2 presented for each variable indicates the amount of variance in the criterion variable accounted for by linear association with the independent variables entered into the regression equation up to and including that step. The β-weights reported with each independent variable are the standardized regression coefficients extracted on the last step completed and, of course, indicate the relative predictive importance of each of the independent variables. The sign of β shows the direction of relationship between the criterion variable and the independent variable entered on that step.

Sexual Activity

The teenagers' reports on their sexual activity indicate a high similarity for three of the four groups studied. White and black

ADOLESCENT PREGNANCY

Table 2-1.—*Results of stepwise regression for all females*

Race and step	Variables[a]	R^{2b}	β^c
White[d]	Individual		
1 ..	Sexual liberalism: 1 = liberal; 7 = conservative; $\bar{x}$ = 4.16	0.32	−0.61
2 ..	Sexual motives (desire to please partner): 1 = no; 2 = yes; $\bar{x}$ = 1.37	0.37	0.25
3 ..	Sexual motives (affiliation): 1 = no; 2 = yes; $\bar{x}$ = 1.56	0.39	−0.16
4 ..	Conventional sex role: 1 = agree; 7 = disagree; $\bar{x}$ = 5.07	0.41	−0.12
5 ..	Self-report (competence): 1 = low; 7 = high; $\bar{x}$ = 4.28	0.42	−0.11
6 ..	Self-report (confusion over sex): 1 = agree; 7 = disagree; $\bar{x}$ = 3.84	0.43	0.11
	Situational		
1 ..	Estimate of percent nonvirgin female peers: $\bar{x}$ = 47.91	0.23	0.31
2 ..	Perception of female friends' sexual liberalism: 1 = liberal; 7 = conservative; $\bar{x}$ = 3.47	0.32	−0.26
3 ..	Importance of religion: 1 = very important; 7 = not at all; $\bar{x}$ = 3.34	0.37	0.17
4 ..	Consistency of rule enforcement by mother: 1 = consistent; 7 = inconsistent; $\bar{x}$ = 3.03	0.39	0.15
5 ..	Number of changes in residence: 0 = none; 6 = 11 or more; $\bar{x}$ = 2.71	0.40	0.11
Non-white[e]	Individual		
1 ..	Sexual liberalism: 1 = liberal; 7 = conservative; $\bar{x}$ = 4.10	0.33	−0.47
2 ..	Sexual motive (desire to please partner): 1 = no; 7 = yes; $\bar{x}$ = 1.38	0.40	0.29
3 ..	Self-reported confusion over sex: 1 = agree; 7 = disagree; $\bar{x}$ = 2.59	0.43	0.18
	Situational		
	Importance of religion: 1 = very important; 7 = not at all; $\bar{x}$ = 2.59	0.15	0.37
	Perceived sexual liberalism of mother: 1 = liberal; 7 = conservative; $\bar{x}$ = 4.81	0.21	−0.25

[a] Criterion variable is sexual activity: 1 = virgin; 2 = nonvirgin.
[b] The multiple R^2, presented for each variable, indicates the amount of variance in the criterion variable accounted for by linear association with the independent variables entered into the regression equation up to and including that step. All R^2 values are significant at or below the 0.05 level.
[c] The β-weights reported with each independent variable are the standardized regression coefficients extracted on the last step completed. They indicate the relative predictive importance of each of the independent variables. β shows the direction of relationship between the criterion variable and the independent variable entered on that step.
[d] N = 253 (36 percent nonvirgin).
[e] N = 119 (63 percent nonvirgin).

Table 2-2.—*Results of stepwise regression for all males*

Race and step	Variables[a]	R^{2b}	β^c
White[d]	Individual		
1 ..	Sexual liberalism: 1 = liberal; 7 = conservative; $\bar{x}$ = 3.51	0.22	-0.38
2 ..	Sexual motives (pleasure): 1 = no; 2 = yes; $\bar{x}$ = 1.60	0.26	0.17
3 ..	Sexual motives (lack of control): 1 = no; 2 = yes; $\bar{x}$ = 1.44	0.28	0.15
4 ..	Conventional sex role: 1 = agree; 7 = disagree; $\bar{x}$ = 3.88	0.29	-0.13
	Situational		
1 ..	Estimate of percent nonvirgin male peers: $\bar{x}$ = 43.86	0.20	0.35
2 ..	Perception of male friends' sexual liberalism: 1 = liberal; 7 = conservative; $\bar{x}$ = 2.64	0.27	-0.21
3 ..	Church attendance: 1 = more than once a week; 5 = never; $\bar{x}$ = 3.49	0.30	0.19
Non-white[e]	Individual		
1 ..	Conventional sex role: 1 = agree; 7 = disagree; $\bar{x}$ = 3.18	0.07	-0.27
2 ..	Sexual liberalism: 1 = liberal; 7 = conservative; $\bar{x}$ = 3.32	0.12	-0.23
3 ..	Father's education: $\bar{x}$ = 12.14 years	0.15	-0.39

[a] See footnote a in table 2-1.
[b] See footnote b in table 2-1.
[c] See footnote c in table 2-1
[d] N = 195 (51 percent nonvirgin).
[e] N = 117 (92 percent nonvirgin).

females and white males report similar ages of first intercourse (the mean ages are 15.3, 15.2, and 15.2 years, respectively) and number of partners (the mean numbers are 2.0, 2.1, and 2.2, respectively). Black males are the exceptional group in that they report an average age of 11.75 years at first intercourse and a mean number of partners as 3.9.

As is seen in tables 2–1 and 2–2, there is a high similarity among all groups of teenagers in the variables that discriminate sexually active from virgin teenagers. Sexual liberalism stands out in this respect. Those teenagers who are sexually active are more likely to agree that premarital sexual activity is acceptable.

Two points should be kept in mind with regard to sexual liberalism. First, acceptance of premarital intercourse is not

Table 2-3.—*Results of stepwise regression for nonvirgin females*

Race and step	Variables[a]	R^{2b}	β^c
White[d]	Individual		
1 ..	Self-report (dissocial trait): 1 = agree; 7 = disagree; $\bar{x}$ = 3.72	0.11	−0.32
2 ..	Birth control attitude (trust both partners to use birth control: 1 = agree; 7 = disagree; $\bar{x}$ = 5.32	0.16	0.22
	Situational		
	None significant at 0.05 level	[e]—	—
Non-white[f]	Individual		
1 ..	Birth control attitude (important to use birth control after marriage): 1 = agree; 7 = disagree; $\bar{x}$ = 2.19	0.17	0.31
2 ..	Self-report (better to enjoy oneself now, even though one might be hurt later): 1 = agree; 7 = disagree; $\bar{x}$ = 4.89	0.24	−0.31
3 ..	Birth control attitude (trust both partners to use birth control): 1 = agree; 7 = disagree; $\bar{x}$ = 4.55	0.29	0.23
	Situational		
1 ..	Feelings toward school: 1 = like; 5 = dislike; $\bar{x}$ = 2.20	0.10	0.32

[a] Criterion variable is contraceptive use last 3 months: 1 = 100 percent; 2 = 90 percent; 3 = > 50 percent; 4 = < 50 percent; 5 = never protected.
[b] See footnote b in table 2-1.
[c] See footnote c in table 2-1.
[d] N = 91 ($\bar{x}$ = 2.27; standard deviation = 1.67).
[e] Not applicable.
[f] N = 75 ($\bar{x}$ = 2.21; standard deviation = 1.67).

extremely high even among the sexually active. For active white females, for instance, the mean attitude was 3.08, "somewhat approve" (compared with 4.8, "somewhat disapprove," for the white female virgins).

Second, these items ask the teenager to approve of premarital sex in the abstract (i.e., for "a man," "a woman"). It does not follow directly that even the sexually active have accepted premarital sex for themselves in the sense that they see themselves as sexually active persons who plan to have intercourse on a regular basis. This distinction helps to clear up what is otherwise a paradox of teenage attitudes toward premarital sex and failure to use contraceptives.

Table 2-4.—*Results of stepwise regression for nonvirgin males*[a]

Race and step	Variables	R^{2b}	β^c
White[d]	Individual		
1 ..	Self-report (self-esteem): 1 = high; 7 = low; $\bar{x}$ = 3.23	0.08	0.18
2 ..	Sex knowledge (average of five items): 1 = right; 2 = wrong; $\bar{x}$ = 1.22	0.13	0.32
3 ..	Birth control attitude (birth control depends on the situation): 1 = agree; 7 = disagree; $\bar{x}$ = 4.47	0.17	0.28
4 ..	Satisfaction with sexual intercourse: 1 = always; 5 = never; $\bar{x}$ = 2.00	0.22	0.32
5 ..	Sexual motives (pleasure): 1 = no; 2 = yes; $\bar{x}$ = 1.71	0.30	0.32
6 ..	Birth control attitude (riskiness): 1 = agree; 7 = disagree; $\bar{x}$ = 4.84	0.35	−0.23
Non-white[e]	Individual		
1 ..	Birth control attitude (there are problems with birth control): 1 = agree; 7 = disagree; $\bar{x}$ = 4.33	0.23	−0.21
2 ..	Birth control attitude (birth control is available): 1 = agree; 7 = disagree; $\bar{x}$ = 2.81	0.27	0.29
3 ..	Self-report (do not trust others): 1 = agree; 7 = disagree; $\bar{x}$ = 3.86	0.31	−0.21
4 ..	Birth control attitude (birth control use depends on the situation): 1 = agree; 7 = disagree; $\bar{x}$ = 3.35	0.35	−0.21
	Situational		
1 ..	Mother's education: $\bar{x}$ = 11.70 years	0.07	−0.26

[a] Criterion variable is contraceptive use last 3 months: 1 = 100 percent; 2 = 90 percent; 3 = > 50 percent; 4 = < 50 percent; 5 = never protected.
[b] See footnote b in table 2-1.
[c] See footnote c in table 2-1.
[d] N = 99 ($\bar{x}$ = 2.45; standard deviation = 1.57).
[e] N = 108 ($\bar{x}$ = 3.37; standard deviation = 1.46).

As tables 2–1 and 2–2 show, the sexually active not only are more sexually liberal, but are more likely to accept traditional family sex roles. The sexually active appear to be liberal, but not liberated. A number of theorists have speculated on the psychological development during the adolescent years[1,2] and hypothesized that a period of stereotyped sex-role perception is a

Table 2-5.—*Results of stepwise regression for nonvirgin females*

Race and step	Variables[a]	R^{2b}	β^c
White[d]	Individual		
1 ..	Age at first intercourse: $\bar{x}$ = 15.34 years	0.13	−0.44
2 ..	Age at puberty: $\bar{x}$ = 11.93 years	0.21	0.30
	Situational		
1 ..	Perceived strictness of mother: 1 = strict; 7 = lenient; $\bar{x}$ = 4.22	0.06	−0.24
2 ..	Estimate of percent nonvirgin female peers: $\bar{x}$ = 63.59	0.12	0.24
Non-white[e]	Individual		
1 ..	Birth control attitude (birth control use depends on the situation): 1 = agree; 7 = disagree; $\bar{x}$ = 4.00	0.09	−0.37
2 ..	Certainty of answers to sex knowledge items: 1 = certain; 2 = uncertain; $\bar{x}$ = 1.37	0.15	−0.25
	Situational		
1 ..	Perception of female friends' sexual liberalism: 1 = liberal; 7 = conservative; $\bar{x}$ = 3.32	0.13	0.35

[a] Criterion variable is contraceptive protection since becoming sexually active: 1 = always protected; 2 = one or more incidences of unprotected intercourse.
[b] See footnote b in table 2-1.
[c] See footnote c in table 2-1.
[d] N = 91 ($\bar{x}$ = 1.68).
[e] N = 75 ($\bar{x}$ = 1.77).

typical aspect of the development of gender identity. Magnifying the differences between the sex roles makes the job of identifying one's own role cognitively easier.

Our data suggest that some adolescents turn to sexual intercourse in the process of grappling with their sexual identity. The Jessors[3], who have speculated about the symbolic nature of sexual intercourse for many adolescents, argue that adolescent smoking, drinking, drug use, and sexual activity are acts of rebellion against authority. These actions are attempts to establish adult status for the teenagers. If this explanation is correct, it may tie the occurrence of sexual activity for some adolescents directly to an important transition in adolescent development. The adolescent virgin, who has a less stereotyped perception of sex roles, may be more mature and may have already passed through the stage of sex-role stereotyping. The question that then arises is, "Why does a virgin not become sexually active during adolescence?" The age at which virgins resolved their gender identity may be part of the answer. The data suggest that virgins

Table 2-6.—*Results of stepwise regression for nonvirgin males*

Race and step	Variables[a]	R^{2b}	β^c
White	Individual		
1 ..	Age at first intercourse: $\bar{x}$ = 15.22 years	0.10	-0.22
2 ..	Sexual motive (reason for avoiding sexual involvement): 1 = no; 2 = yes; $\bar{x}$ = 1.32	0.15	-0.27
3 ..	Birth control attitude (birth control use depends on the situation): 1 = agree; 7 = disagree; $\bar{x}$ = 4.47	0.19	0.49
4 ..	Birth control attitude (riskiness): 1 = agree; 7 = disagree; $\bar{x}$ = 4.84	0.24	-0.25
5 ..	Birth control attitude (birth control should be available to teenagers): 1 = agree; 7 = disagree; $\bar{x}$ = 1.66	0.27	0.27
6 ..	Self-report (carelessness): 1 = agree; 7 = disagree; $\bar{x}$ = 3.49	0.31	-0.22
7 ..	Birth control attitude (should trust both partners to use birth control, but mostly it is the woman's responsibility): 1 = agree; 7 = disagree; $\bar{x}$ = 5.51	0.35	-0.25
8 ..	Birth control attitude ("If a woman uses birth control, it changes how a man feels about her."): 1 = agree; 7 = disagree; $\bar{x}$ = 5.51	0.38	0.19
	Situational		
1 ..	Number of changes in residence: 0 = none; 6 = 11 or more; $\bar{x}$ = 2.98	0.09	0.31
Non-white[e]	Individual		
1 ..	Sexual motive (pleasure): 1 = no; 2 = yes; $\bar{x}$ = 1.69	0.09	0.33
2 ..	Birth control attitude (birth control depends on the situation): 1 = agree; 7 = disagree; $\bar{x}$ = 3.35	0.15	-0.33
	Situational None significant at the 0.05 level	[f]—	—

[a] Criterion variable is contraceptive protection since becoming sexually active: 1 = always protected; 2 = one or more incidences of unprotected intercourse.
[b] See footnote b in table 2-1.
[c] See footnote c in table 2-1.
[d] N = 99 ($\bar{x}$ = 1.69).
[e] N = 108 ($\bar{x}$ = 1.89).
[f] Not applicable.

complete this task of adolescence at an earlier age, perhaps at a time when heterosexual social relationships, as well as the likelihood of resolving the identity problem through sexual intercourse, were less important. Other variables point out further differences between sexually active and virgin adolescents.

One variable was the motive of the sexually active female toward sexual involvement. Specifically, sexually active females were more likely to become sexually involved because they couldn't say "No" or wanted to please and satisfy a boyfriend or because it seemed like it was expected of her. These reasons support the popular image of the teenage woman "giving in" to pressure from her boyfriend.

The two most powerful situational predictors of activity for the white female and male adolescents were the estimate of the percentage of sexually active same-sex peers and the perception of sexual liberalism of same-sex friends. Together, these variables account for 32 percent of the variance in sexual activity for white females and 27 percent of the variance for white males. This corroborates, for white teenagers, the almost universal description of adolescents as highly sensitive to real or imagined pressure from the same-sex peer group. Furthermore, with the exception of black males, the virgins seem to be more religious than those who are sexually active. This situation is expected because almost all religions discourage premarital sexual intercourse.

In conclusion, sexually active adolescents have fewer reservations about premarital sexual intercourse, sexually active females are more susceptible to pressure from their boyfriends, and white teenagers perceive their same-sex peers as being more accepting of (perhaps even expecting) premarital sexual intercourse. It has been speculated that partly because of these factors, adolescents are likely to use sexual intercourse as one means of defining their sexual identity. In contrast, virgins are more likely to be religious and to think of premarital sexual intercourse as an unacceptable behavior. Indeed, white females most often cite affiliation motives as factors that influence their sexual involvement. Finally, white virgins, like sexually active whites, perceive their same-sex peer group to be supportive of their position. Perhaps because of these factors, it seems that virgins are more likely to have developed a mature sexual identity without engaging in sexual intercourse.

Contraceptive Protection

Contraceptive protection during the 3 months preceding the interview was rated in terms of the percentage of incidences of intercourse in which some effective form of contraception was known to be used by either partner. The important variables that separate women who were more protected from those who were less protected were found to relate to the woman's self-perceptions and her beliefs about interpersonal trust in heterosexual relationships (table 2–3).

For white women, the most powerfully discriminating individual variable was a cluster of items labeled "dissocial trait." The exact content of this cluster is given in appendix B and includes self-report items (such as, "I get enjoyment out of doing certain things that are wrong when I know I might get caught," "I am willing to try almost anything once," and "How I behave depends completely on the people I am with and the situation I am in"). White women, who are better protected, disagree with these items. The better protected black women showed a similar self-perception. In their case the discrimination was made on the basis of disagreement to the item, "I prefer to enjoy myself thoroughly with someone, even though I will be hurt and disappointed later."

A word of caution is in order with respect to interpretation of these self-perceptions as personality characteristics. Although the items mentioned will probably bring to mind a particular type of teenage woman, such an image may not be correct. No evidence has been found that these characteristics represent enduring personality characteristics. Responses to the self-report items may be very specific to the general topic of sexual activity and contraceptive use. These items were embedded in the context of the larger questionnaire and the interview, and the respondents were aware of the purpose of the study. Thus, they may have had the broad topics of sex and contraceptive use in mind when answering these items.

As mentioned earlier, the better protected among both black and white women also were distinguished on the basis of their beliefs toward heterosexual trust relative to contraceptive use. Specifically, the more protected women were more likely to agree that either sex could trust the opposite sex "to take care of birth control." This trust about contraception contrasts with the anxiety and suspicion expressed by the Bellingham, Wash., sample of adolescent women who were asked, "What did you consider when you thought about having sexual intercourse?" Women's responses to this question fell into two groups: concerns about their partners (Did he love her? What would he think about her? Would he enjoy himself? Would he tell other people?), and concerns about what others might think if they found out the woman was sexually active.

Concern about pregnancy often was only acknowledged when the women were directly asked the question, "Were you concerned about getting pregnant?" Common answers were: "Oh yes, that too." "I didn't think about it until later." "Not until my period

was late." When asked, "What do you think it is like for an
unmarried high school girl to become pregnant?" a very frequent
answer was, "It would be awful because then everyone would
know what she had been doing."

Other evidence of this concern with the opinions of others
was found in the analysis of the second measure of contraceptive
behavior. This variable was dichotomous and indicated whether an
adolescent had ever had unprotected intercourse at any time since
becoming sexually active (tables 2–5 and 2–6). Of a woman's
overall contraceptive protection, two of the discriminators dealt
with her perception of other people. For white females, the
discriminator was the estimate of sexual activity among female
peers. The always protected women, on the average, made a more
accurate (lower) estimate of how many young women their age
were sexually active than did the less protected. This result may
indicate an acceptance of one's sexual behavior that allows an
objective analysis of peer activity. The less protected women may
feel they have to rationalize behavior they do not fully accept by
overestimating the proportion of peers who are sexually active—a
version of the age-old adolescent argument: "Everyone is doing it!"

The discriminator for black women was perception of the
sexual liberalism of female friends. In contrast, the always
protected thought their friends were more sexually liberal than the
sometimes unprotected thought. Thus, the protected could be
expected to believe that they had more social acceptance for their
decision to have sexual intercourse. In summary, it appears that
the less protected women of both races are unable to accept their
own sexual activity. This lack of acceptance prevents women from
using contraceptives.

One final point can be made to support the importance of the
woman's social perceptions in the matter of contraceptive use. A
subanalysis based on the 54 sexually active women in the
Bellingham, Wash., sample, shows a strong relationship between
contraceptive protection and the degree (or average degree, in the
case of multiple partners) of social intimacy with the sex
partner(s). Social intimacy was scored on a scale ranging from
fiance (or steady boyfriend), friend (or occasional date) to casual
acquaintance (pickup or stranger). Contraceptive protection was
based on the percentage of times the woman or her partner had
used effective birth control throughout her sexual career (not just
over the preceding 3 months). The more intimate the woman's
relationship to her partner(s), the more likely she was to have
been protected ($r = 0.29$, $P < 0.01$). Interestingly, if only female-
initiated birth control is analyzed, this relationship is not found.
Thus, social intimacy affects the degree to which the woman is
protected but does not indicate that she will necessarily be the one
doing the protecting. Several possible explanations for this

situation can be offered. In an emotionally intimate relationship, there may be less anxiety and guilt about sexual intercourse, facilitating a rational assessment of the need for protection. Communication, including discussion of birth control, might be more open between intimate partners, and the male simply may be more concerned for his girlfriend's welfare and, therefore, be more responsible about birth control.

As can be seen from the final proportion of variance accounted for among females, our conceptualization of the determinants of female contraceptive protection is far from complete. Although both individual and situational variables separately can account for as much as 43 percent of the variance for females on the virgin-active criterion (table 2–1), considering contraceptive protection over the last 3 months, the individual variables used account for only 16 and 29 percent of the variance for white and black women, respectively (table 2–3). The situational variables were even less powerful. None was significant for white women. Attitude toward school (the better protected liked school more) accounted for 10 percent of the variance for blacks. On the dichotomous measure of overall protection (table 2–5), the individual variables were similarly weak, accounting for 21 and 15 percent of the variance for whites and blacks, respectively. The situational variables accounted for only 12 and 13 percent of variance for whites and blacks, respectively.

Among males, the power of the individual variables to predict contraceptive vigilance, as measured by either criterion, was much stronger. A cumulative variance of 35 percent was accounted for on recent protection for whites and blacks (table 2–4). For overall protection (table 2–6), 38 percent of the variance was accounted for among white males, but only 15 percent among blacks. This latter fact, however, may result from the fact that only 11 percent of black males were always protected. Thus, the distribution on this dichotomous criterion variable is highly skewed. A reason for an increased explained variance relative to contraceptive protection for males than for females may be that birth control use is a much more straightforward analytic matter for males.

Two variables differentiate the better contraceptors[b] (tables 2–4 and 2–6). The better protected of both races tend not to give "pleasure" motives as influencing their sexual involvement (see appendix B for items included in pleasure motives). They also tend

---

[b]Although this phrase may be sexist, it is the least awkward expression. It refers, of course, to the males whose partners were better protected. The term "contraceptive use" is not entirely appropriate. It connotes direct action, although with this measure it cannot be ascertained to what extent the male or female was directly responsible for the degree of contraception practiced by the couple.

to agree with a number of items that indicate birth control information and materials are available to them.

For white males, there were several other powerful discriminators. On both measures, the better contraceptors disagreed with items, implying that it is sometimes all right to chance a pregnancy. These males did not relegate the responsibility for birth control to the woman. Better contraceptors reported higher self-esteem (including interpersonal and heterosexual social skills), and disagreed that they were careless or irresponsible. They reported a later age at first intercourse, were more likely to identify reasons for avoiding sexual involvement, and gave their sexual experiences a satisfactory or better rating.

Better contraceptors among black males perceived fewer problems with birth control (ineffectiveness, side effects, expense or difficulty of obtaining materials, or inconvenience). Perhaps, like the better protected females, they were more trusting of others.

For white males, protection is rather neatly related to responsible attitudes toward birth control: Knowing that contraceptive methods are available, making an accurate assessment of the risks of unprotected coitus, and being unwilling to take such risks. A self-perception of responsibility coupled with high interpersonal skills and sexual self-control also are important. For black males, responsible and positive attitudes toward birth control seem to be the most important determinates of contraceptive protection, along with a degree of interpersonal trust and sexual self-control.

Sex education programs that emphasize sexual and contraceptive knowledge and attitudes seem best suited to increasing male contraceptive protection. Regrettably, this force is countered by strong cultural attitudes that deemphasize the responsibility of males in contraceptive matters.

Race Differences

Current results do not account for the widely reported differences in illegitimacy rates between black and white women. The samples of women in this study are quite similar in age at first intercourse and number of partners. The studies suggest that black women are actually the victims of a number of factors that appear to produce the large reported differences.

The likelihood is high that a young unmarried black woman's child will be recorded as illegitimate. Racist practices encountered in paternity recording, the manner in which a woman presents herself at the admissions desk at a hospital or clinic, and greater use of public hospitals by blacks may be factors for illegitimacy reporting.[4] Recent decreases in racial differences in illegitimacy may be largely the result of decreases in institutionalized racism in the keeping of public health records.

Young black women are at greater biological risk of pregnancy than are white women. National Health Survey data show, for instance, that at age 11, the percentage of black women having started their menstrual periods is nearly twice that of white females (21 percent compared with 12 percent).

Black women are likely to have the least contraceptively responsible partners. Black males are the most sexually active of the groups studied. They have the highest percentage of intercourse, lowest age of first intercourse, and greater number of partners. The black woman is the least protected of the four studied groups. Of the black males, 89 percent report having had unprotected intercourse at least once. This figure is only 69 percent for white males. This male diversity, however, does not produce a large racial difference in protection among females. Among black women, 77 percent report having had at least one incidence of unprotected intercourse; white females report 68 percent. In terms of degree of protection during the last 3 months, the effect of race on female contraceptive protection is even less. A sizeable race effect also exists among males: The mean for black males is 3.37 (on the average, protected about 50 percent of the time); the mean for white males is 2.45, indicating a higher degree of protection (on the average, protected more than 50 percent but less than 90 percent of the time). There is no reported difference in protection between white females and black females. The means are 2.27 for whites and 2.21 for blacks. This degree of protection is very similar to that reported by white males.

The fact that contraceptive protection was rated on the basis of whether the person used a method or knew that his or her partner was using a method could explain the disparity between the levels of protection reported by black males and black females. Possibly, many black females are protecting themselves. The males, assuming that birth control is the woman's responsibility, do not know whether their partners are protected.

APPENDIX A

Description of Variables Used in Regression Analysis

Each questionnaire subtest was cluster analyzed for males and females separately. A "coefficient of belongingness" of 2.5 was used to determine what items within an instrument were highly intercorrelated. Cluster scores, along with individual items that did not enter into any of the clusters but were significantly correlated with one or more criterion variables, were used as the "individual" independent variables in the regression analyses performed for each criterion variable.

A description of each variable used in the regression analyses follows. The variables labeled *(Active)* are those that were used with the sexually active sample. The first given set of variables include "individual" variables used in the first set of regressions (the top part of the tables for each subsample); the second set of variables include "situational" variables (the bottom part of the tables for each subsample). Because separate cluster analyses were done for males and females, some variables for females do not appear for males, and vice versa; they are labeled appropriately. When no indication of sex is given, the variable was the same for both sexes.

Individual Independent Variables

Female self-concept: A nine-item cluster of self-reported personal characteristics describing attitude toward self includes several items concerning interpersonal and social skills and a dimension of future orientation. Example items: "I am generally well satisfied with myself;" "I find it easy to carry on discussions with other people, even those I do not know;" and "I have made general plans for most of my future."

Female self-report (dissocial trait): See appendix B for detailed description.

Female mistrust: Two items indicating interpersonal mistrust: "Anyone who completely trusts anyone else is asking for trouble" and "I avoid people who are unpredictable."

Sexual liberalism: See appendix B for items.

Sexual manipulation: Two-item cluster: "Many men will lie in order to get a woman to have sex with them" and "Many women will use sex to get something from a man."

Sex knowledge and certainty: Two separate variables. See appendix B items.

Age at puberty for females: Mean self-reported age of the beginning of breast development, appearance of pubic hair, and beginning of menstruation.

Conventional sex role: See appendix B for items.

Female sexual motives concerning sexual control: A five-item cluster of motives, three for sexual involvement and two against involvement: "I got excited and just got carried away" and "I did not have a place with privacy to go with him."

Female sexual motive (desire to please): See appendix B for detailed description.

Female sexual motive (affiliation): A four-item cluster, two items for sexual involvement and two items against: "I was lonely" and "I did not know him well enough."

Female reasons for avoiding sexual involvement: A five-item cluster: "I felt it was wrong" and "I was concerned about my reputation."

Self-report (confusion over sex): See appendix B for items.

Male future orientation: A somewhat confusing five-item cluster extracted for males includes two clear-cut future orientation items: "I know pretty well what I will be doing in a few years time" and "I have made general plans for most of my future life," but also two "low Machiavellian" items: "Most people are good and kind" and "You should always be honest no matter what." Also includes one item indicating low self-concept: "Most people can do things better than I can."

Male—"Many people find it difficult to have me around": A single-item variable.

Male—"Even after I have started to feel better I have no trouble remembering to take my medicine": A single-item variable.

Male—"Even when I am really enjoying myself, I keep my responsibilities in the back of my mind": A single-item variable.

Male—"The best way to get along with people is to tell them things that make them happy": A single-item variable.

Female heterosexual assertiveness: "I never get too concerned about making my boyfriend mad at me."

"I think most people worry too much": A single-item variable for males and females.

"I prefer to enjoy myself thoroughly now even though I may be hurt and disappointed later": A single-item variable that appears in table 2–3 for females, but was not a significant regression variable for males.

Sexual satisfaction (Active): The degree of physical satisfaction with sexual intercourse, except for the first few incidences, was asked during the interview.

Age at first sexual intercourse (Active).

Male birth control attitude (riskiness) (Active): See appendix B for items.

Birth control attitude (use depends on the situation) (Active): See appendix B items.

Birth control attitude (birth control is available) (Active): See appendix B items.

Male self-report (self-esteem): See appendix B for items.

Male self-report (dissocial trait): A four-item cluster similar to, but less inclusive than, the analogous variable for females: "I am willing to try almost anything once" and "I get a certain enjoyment out of mixing with a reckless crowd."

Male self-report (carelessness): See appendix B for items.

Male self-report (distrust): See appendix B for items.

Age at puberty for males: Mean self-reported age of the occurrence of first "wet dream," appearance of pubic hair, and voice changing.

Male family role attitudes: See appendix B for items.

Male sexual motive (reasons for avoiding sexual involvement): See appendix B for items.

Male sexual motives (lack of control): A two-item cluster: "I got excited and just got carried away" and "I was under the influence of alcohol or some drug."

Male sexual motives (pleasure): See appendix B for items.

Female heterosexual communication: A single-item variable: "I am the kind of woman who expresses herself quite openly with a man."

Female—"I often worry that other people disapprove of me": A single-item variable.

Female—"When I am unsure what to do, I will often just wait and see what works out": A single-item variable.

Female competence: See appendix B for items.

Birth control attitude (there are problems with birth control) (Active): See appendix B for detailed description.

Birth control attitude ("If a woman uses birth control, it changes how a man feels about her.") (Active): See appendix B for items.

Female—Birth control is available: A seven-item cluster almost identical to the "male—birth control is available" variable.

Female—Birth control attitude (riskiness) (Active): Same content as "male—birth control attitude (riskiness)" but not a significant variable for females.

Female—Birth control attitude (trust both partners to use birth control) (Active): See appendix B for detailed description.

Female—Birth control attitude (should trust both partners to use birth control, but mostly it is the woman's responsibility) (Active): See appendix B for detailed description.

Female—Birth control attitude (important to use birth control after marriage) (Active): See appendix B for detailed description.

Sex education (Active): Asked during the interview, and scored yes or no: "Have you had sex education in school as a course or as part of a course?"

Situational Independent Variables

All variables are the same for males and females.

Perceived sexual liberalism of mother: See appendix B for items.

Perceived sexual liberalism of father: Same items as in "perceived sexual liberalism of mother."

Perception of male's friends' sexual liberalism: See appendix B for items.

Perception of female's friends' sexual liberalism: See appendix B for items.

Feelings toward mother (or mother-figure): A five-point rating issued during the interview, ranging from "only good feelings" to "only bad feelings."

Feelings toward father (or father-figure): Same content as previous variable.

Perceived strictness of father (or father-figure): A seven-point rating scale issued during the interview ranging from "very strict" to "very lenient."

Perceived strictness of mother (or mother-figure): Same content as previous variable.

Consistency of rule enforcement by father: A seven-point rating scale issued during the interview, ranging from "very consistent" to "very inconsistent."

Consistency of rule enforcement by mother: Same content as previous variable.

Estimate of percent nonvirgin-female peers: An estimate made during the interview of the percentage of female peers who have had sexual intercourse at least once.

Estimate of percent nonvirgin-male peers: Same content as previous variable.

Feelings toward school: A five-point rating scale issued during the interview, ranging from "strongly like" to "strongly dislike."

Length of residence at present address: Asked during the interview: "How many years the participants had lived at their current address?"

Number of changes in residence: Asked during the interview: "How many times the participants had moved during their whole lives?"

Church attendance: Asked during the interview: "How often did the participant attend church services or functions, such as Bible study, youth group, etc.?"

Importance of religion: Asked during the interview: "Aside from church attendance, how important is religion to you personally?"

Father's education: Asked during the interview: "What is the highest grade of school completed by your father?"

Mother's education: Same content as previous variable.

APPENDIX B

Item Content of Variables

The following are the items that form the clusters significantly related to one or more criterion variables, and thus appear in tables 2–1 to 2–6. Also given is the exact content of single-item variables that appear in the tables. The items that were reversed have been noted, and it is indicated when certain items within a cluster or certain clusters refer only to one sex.

Self-Reported Personal Characteristics Inventory

The clustering of the 34-item Self-Reported Personal Characteristics Inventory yielded these clusters and two single-item variables that appear in tables 2–1 to 2–6.

(1) Female dissocial trait
  (a) I get a certain enjoyment out of doing some things that are wrong when I know I might get caught.
  (b) What annoys me one day may make me laugh the next.
  (c) I often worry that other people disapprove of me.
  (d) How I behave depends completely on the people I am with and the situation I am in.
  (e) Sometimes I just don't take things seriously until I have been hurt a little.
  (f) I often need to be reminded of things.
  (g) I get a certain enjoyment out of mixing with a reckless crowd.
(2) Male carelessness (similar to female dissocial trait but less inclusive)
  (a) Sometimes I don't take things seriously until I have been hurt a little.
  (b) I often worry that other people disapprove of me.
  (c) I often need to be reminded of things.
(3) Male self-esteem
  (a) I avoid people who are unpredictable.
  (b) I find it easy to carry on discussions with other people, even those I do not know.
  (c) I have the kind of personality everyone admires.
  (d) I believe I am physically very attractive.
  (e) I feel as though I have a definite influence on the people around me.
  (f) I am the kind of man who expresses himself quite openly with a woman.
  (g) I have more friends than most people.

(4) Male mistrust (do not trust others)
   (a) Anyone who completely trusts anyone else is asking for trouble.
   (b) Sometimes you have to hurt other people to get what you want.
(5) The single-item competence variable: Most people can do things better than I can. (agree = low competence; disagree = high competence).
(6) The single-item variable: I prefer to enjoy myself thoroughly with someone, even though I will be hurt and disappointed later.

Sexual Motives Instrument

The Sexual Motives Instrument gave nine possible reasons for sexual involvement with the following instructions:

Below is a list of motives or reasons for getting sexually involved with a girlfriend (boyfriend). By sexual involvement, we mean anything from kissing and petting to sexual intercourse. Please put a check mark in front of each reason which has ever influenced you to become sexually involved or, at least, desire sexual involvement.

Nine reasons for avoiding sexual involvement were given with these instructions:

Below is a list of reasons for avoiding sexual involvement with a girlfriend (boyfriend). Please put a check mark in front of each reason which has ever influenced you to avoid becoming sexually involved.

A cluster analysis of the 18 reasons yielded these clusters:

(1) Females—desire to please
   (a) Couldn't say "No."
   (b) Wanted to please and satisfy my boyfriend.
   (c) Seemed like it was expected of me.
(2) Females affiliation
   (a) Reasons for involvement.
      (i) Wanted to be close and be held.
      (ii) Was lonely.
   (b) Reasons for avoiding involvement: Did not know him well enough.
(3) Males—Pleasure
   (a) Reasons for involvement.
      (i) Wanted to please and satisfy my girlfriend.
      (ii) Felt sexy and wanted to receive some pleasure.
   (b) Reasons for avoiding involvement: Did not have a place with privacy to go with her.
(4) Males—Lack of control
   (a) Reasons for involvement.
      (i) Was under the influence of alcohol or some drug.
      (ii) Couldn't say "No."

(b) Reasons for avoiding involvement
  (i)   Did not have birth control method available.
  (ii) Felt I was not ready for it.
  (iii) Was concerned about my reputation.
  (iv) Was afraid my parents might find out.
  (v)   Did not know her well enough.

Sex Knowledge and Certainty of Sex Knowledge Instrument

The items in the Sex Knowledge and Certainty of Sex Knowledge Instrument scores were given with these instructions:

Read each statement in this section and then circle True or False. Next circle Certain, if you are sure of your answer, or Uncertain, if you are uncertain of your answer or if you have guessed.

(1) A young woman can get pregnant the very first time she has sexual intercourse. (True)
(2) If the man pulls out of the woman (withdraws his penis) before he comes (ejaculates or has climax), she cannot get pregnant. (False)
(3) A woman can get pregnant even though she does not get excited during sexual intercourse. (True)
(4) If you only have sex once in a while, your girlfriend will not get pregnant. (False)
(5) The "safe time" to have intercourse (the time when pregnancy is *least* likely) are the days just before and during the woman's menstrual period. (True)

The sex knowledge variable is the average score (correct or incorrect) in these five items.

The certainty variable is the average certainty (certain or uncertain) for these five items.

Parents-Friends-Self-Attitudes and Own Sexual Attitudes Instruments

The cluster analysis of the Parents-Friends-Self-Attitudes and Own Sexual Attitudes Instruments yielded these clusters:

(1) Perception of others' (mother, father, male friends, or female friends) sexual liberalism
  (a) It is all right for a young man to have sexual intercourse with someone he loves or has very good feelings about but to whom he is not married.
  (b) It is all right for a young woman to have sexual intercourse with someone she loves or has very good feelings about but to whom she is not married.

    (c) (Reversed) If a young man gets his girlfriend pregnant, they should get married.

    (d) Having a legal abortion is a good way to cope with a premarital pregnancy.

(2) Own sexual liberalism including participants' own attitudes to the preceding four items plus the following items

    (a) It is all right for a young man to have sexual intercourse with someone he likes but does not know well.

    (b) It is all right for a young woman to have sexual intercourse with someone she likes but does not know well.

    (c) (Reversed) I want the person I marry to be a virgin.

    (d) It is a good idea to experiment sexually before marriage.

    (e) It is easy for me to become sexually excited.

    (f) Self-reported confusion over sex: Sometimes it is hard for me to understand how I feel about sex.

Family Role Attitudes Instrument

The cluster analysis of the nine-item Family Role Attitudes Instrument yielded one cluster for females and an almost identical cluster for males:

(1) Conventional sex role

    (a) (Reversed) A husband and wife should spend equal time in raising the children.

    (b) There is nothing more fulfilling to a woman than having children.

    (c) It is difficult for a man to spend a lot of time with his family and still be masculine.

    (d) There is nothing more fulfilling to a man than having children.

    (e) A woman should devote a lot of her time to satisfying her husband.

    (f) It is difficult for a woman to have a regular job or career and still be feminine.

    (g) A man should be the boss around the home.

(2) For males only: Having a challenging job or career is just not enough to make a man happy.

(3) For females only: (Reversed) Being a housewife and homemaker is just not enough to make a woman happy.

Contraceptive Attitude Questionnaire

The 24-item Contraceptive Attitude Questionnaire yielded several clusters that were significant regression variables:

(1) Males—Availability
   (a) It is hard to talk to your girlfriend about what methods of birth control the two of you could use.
   (b) Where I live, teenagers can easily get birth control materials without their parents knowing about it.
   (c) If I wanted to get a good method of birth control, I know where I could go.
   (d) If I wanted to get advice from someone about the different methods of birth control, I know to whom I would go.
   (e) The only source of information about birth control methods available to me is my friends.
   (f) The whole idea of birth control is embarrassing to me.
(2) Males—Riskiness
   (a) It can sometimes be important to show your love by taking a chance on getting pregnant.
   (b) Sometimes, when a birth control method is not available, you just have to take a chance and count on good luck.
   (c) Planning ahead about what kind of birth control method to use can spoil the fun of sex.
(3) Males—There are problems with birth control
   (a) It really is too hard for me to find the time and transportation to get a good method of birth control.
   (b) I might avoid getting a good birth control method if it meant being examined by a doctor.
   (c) No birth control methods really work well enough.
   (d) I am unlikely to use a birth control method because I do not believe that I am really fertile.
   (e) Good methods of birth control cost too much for me to buy.
   (f) I would not want my friends to know that I was getting a birth control method.
   (g) The side effects of the good birth control methods are a real problem.
(4) Males and Females—Trust both partners to use birth control
   (a) A woman can trust a man to take care of birth control.
   (b) A man can trust a woman to take care of birth control.
   (c) It is mostly up to the woman to take care of birth control. (This item is for males only.)

(5) Males and Females—Birth control use depends on situation
   (a) How carefully I used birth control would depend on
        how much I wanted to marry my girlfriend.
   (b) How carefully I used birth control would depend on
        how much I wanted my girlfriend to have a baby.

The following single items were significant regression
variables:

(1) For females: It is very important to use birth control
    after marriage until you have decided to start a family.
(2) For males
   (a) Good methods of birth control should be available to
        teenagers even without their parents' consent.
   (b) If a woman uses birth control, it changes how a man
        feels about her.

REFERENCES

1. Erickson, E. *Identity, Youth and Crisis.* New York: Norton,
   1968.
2. Block, S.H. "Conceptions of Sex Role." *Am. Psychol.*
   28(6):512–526, 1973.
3. Jessor, S. and Jessor, R. "Transition from Virginity to Non-
   Virginity Among Youth: A Social-Psychological Study Over
   Time." *Dev. Psychol.* 11(4):473–484, 1975.
4. Ryan, W. *Blaming the Victim.* New York: Vintage, 1971.

DISCUSSION

The following people were the major participants in the
discussion: K. Davis, A. Rossi, W. Simon, C. Chilman, E. Douvan,
D. Kallen, K. Luker, H. Presser, and V. Ernster. The major topic
of discussion was the possible interpretations of the findings and
suggestions for further research concerning adolescent premarital
intercourse and contraceptive use.

The particpants were intrigued by the seemingly conflicting
findings that the sexually active adolescents, compared with those
who had not had intercourse, had higher scores for both liberal
attitudes toward sex behavior and traditional sex role orientations.

The concept that traditional sex role orientations were largely
caused by a more concrete stage in cognitive development was
questioned. Today's adolescents are exposed to many ideas of sex
role equality. These findings need to be further analyzed in terms
of the socioeconomic status of the respondents' parents. Traditional
sex role attitudes are more characteristic in blue collar families.
The tendency toward premarital coitus by age 16 or 17 may be
stronger in females from lower social class backgrounds. Some

considered this a moot point that requires further study. Cvetkovich and his research associates, it was suggested, should look at subgroups of adolescents, because there is great heterogeneity in the adolescent population. This subgroup consideration should include differentiation between adolescents who have had only one or two sex partners and those who have had many.

In attempting to discover why some adolescents have premarital intercourse and some do not, attention should be paid to the level of sexual attractiveness of females. (Interestingly, the discussion barely touched on the same trait in males). Evidence from a few studies suggests that physically attractive females are more likely to date earlier and more frequently, have premarital intercourse earlier, and marry earlier. Physical attractiveness rests partly on the psychosocial development and the dating, love, and sex experiences of the female. As she becomes psychophysically stimulated and has fulfilling love-sex relationships, she is apt to be more outgoing and at ease with the opposite sex and more motivated to make herself attractive. Self-perceptions of being attractive have been correlated with dating frequency and participation in premarital intercourse. The cause and effect relationships are difficult to determine in this situation.

The speculation that unattractive females are more apt to engage in premarital sex to "get a man" and desire pregnancy to affirm their sense of feminine adequacy finds only slight confirmation in the research.

The part played by puberty at age of first intercourse was briefly discussed. Little research has been done on this subject. A specific timing measure of male sexual maturation is extremely difficult to find because this process extends over several years and is marked by a variety of events (development of pubic hair, first ejaculation, voice change, and growth spurt). Although time of first ejaculation is often used as a measure, it is considered less than satisfactory.

The meaning of the finding that high measures of intrapersonal trust, in general, are correlated with effective contraceptive use was discussed. Questions were raised as to whether trust or contraceptive effectiveness come first. Some thought that trust is central to forming intimate interpersonal relationships and that such relationships are conducive to contraceptive effectiveness. It is not clear how, or whether, interpersonal trust is related to good heterosocial and communication skills and to contraceptive use among males. An ability to communicate with the opposite sex was particularly important in the use of contraceptives.

Questions were raised as to the reliability of findings that over 90 percent of black males were sexually active by age 16.

This finding does seem to be in line with the few available studies that include black males. In respect to the inclusion of males in this research, Cvetkovich had reported no more difficulty in getting male than female subjects in the Bellingham, Wash., sample. Yet greater difficulties were encountered with the Washington, D.C. and Atlanta, Ga., samples.

The need for longitudinal research was emphasized, partly in terms of the contribution such studies can make in yielding greater clarity about the cause-consequence dilemma. The American Public Health Association study reported in the Cvetkovich paper is planned as a 3-year project, in which the sample will be followed over this time period.

A study of men and women between the ages of 40 and 50 should be undertaken to find retrospective information concerning dating, sexual, fertility, family planning, and marriage experiences. The study may include their children.

A study to look at the fertility control experiences of women born between 1900 and 1910 (a time of very low birth rates) is now underway.

In respect to the Cvetkovich paper, it was reported that tests of the reliability of the questionnaire are now being conducted. It was recommended that further information be sought about the experiences adolescents actually had in trying to get contraceptives and that findings for the three study sites be compared to learn if there were any differences between them.

Chapter 3

Sexual and Contraceptive Experience of Young Unmarried Women in the United States, 1976 and 1971

Melvin Zelnik and John F. Kantner
The Johns Hopkins University

In the spring and early summer of 1971, a study was conducted with a national probability sample of women aged 15–19 living in households and in college dormitories in the continental United States. The sampled population included women of all marital statuses and races. The sampling procedures involved stratification by race to ensure a substantial and disproportionate number of interviews with black respondents but not with other nonwhites.

One of the major purposes of that study was to provide for teenagers estimates of the prevalence of premarital intercourse, the use and nonuse of contraception, pregnancy, and the manner in which pregnancies were resolved. The study also attempted to determine how knowledgeable teenage women were about contraception and the menstrual cycle.[1]

A similar but independent study was carried out in the spring and early summer of 1976, again with a national probability sample of women aged 15–19 who lived in households in the continental United States. As before, the sampled population covered women of all marital statuses and races. As with the 1971 study, the sampling procedures used in 1976 involved stratification by race to ensure a substantial number of interviews with black respondents. Following our previous practice, we use the term white to refer to whites plus nonwhites other than blacks.

This article is an overview from the 1976 study of certain aspects of sexual knowledge, the prevalence of premarital sexual experience, and contraceptive practices. The findings relate to never-married women aged 15–19 in 1976. Where the data permit, comparisons were made with 1971.

The 1976 study did not include women living in college dormitories. For the sake of comparison, therefore, the 1971 study which included such women has been appropriately retabulated. Another point of difference from our previous practice is the presentation here of the unweighted data when dealing separately with each race. Because of differences in the weighting schemes employed in 1971 and 1976, we prefer to make comparisons from the unweighted data where appropriate. Obviously, in examining distributions for the total population (i.e., whites and blacks combined), weighted estimates must be employed since blacks are disproportionately represented in the samples. The weights for the 1971 sample were computed from the 1970 census counts of females aged 14 to 18, by single years of age and race, for each of the 45 geographical and residential strata of the sampling scheme. The weights for the 1976 sample were computed for each respondent, incorporating PSU, SSU, segment, household and eligible selection probabilities plus adjustments for household screening and interview nonresponse.

Although restriction of the discussion to unmarried women greatly simplifies the exposition, it can lead in some instances to biased or misleading estimates. For example, a valid estimate of the prevalence of premarital intercourse or premarital pregnancy among a cohort of women must include ever-married as well as never-married women.

Two differences between the 1971 and 1976 studies may have a minor bearing on the findings. In the 1971 study, age eligibility[a] was determined at the time the household was screened; young women whose age at last birthday was 15–19 were eligible to participate in the study. Although interviewing usually proceeded immediately after screening, screening itself extended over a 3–4-month interval. As a result, the respondents represented more than 60 months of births, but no events could occur to them at an age greater than their reported current age. In the 1976 study, age eligibility was based on having been born between March 1956 and February 1961, with those born between March 1956 and February 1957 classified as age 19, those born between March 1957 and February 1958 as age 18, and so forth. As a result of this procedure, respondents represent exactly 60 months of births. However, since interviewing occurred over a 4-month span, recent events could have occurred to a respondent at an age greater than her age at the time eligibility was established. For example, a respondent born in March 1960 is classified in the study as age 15, since her birth date falls between March 1960 and February 1961. If such a respondent were interviewed any time after March 1976,

---

[a]In both studies, the sole criterion of eligibility was age, with the restriction that only one eligible female could be selected (randomly) from any one household.

she would have turned 16, although still classified as 15. This could produce anomalous results in some instances; thus, if she first had intercourse in May 1976, her age at first intercourse would be 16. Such anomalies can occur only for respondents whose birth dates fall in the earlier months of the years as here bounded and would be of importance only for events which occurred to them after attaining their survey age.

Although we do not regard this matter as serious, the two samples are not strictly comparable in respect to age.

The other difference between the two studies is in the manner of asking some of the questions. In the 1971 study, questions presumed to be more "sensitive" were included in a self-administered questionnaire; in 1976, all questions were asked by an interviewer. The two procedures might have a differential impact on the quality of the answers, but our impression is that such impact is negligible. The procedure used in 1976 allows for greater complexity in the design of the questionnaire, making it possible to tie events together more satisfactorily. The presumed price for this benefit is some loss of privacy for the informant, but as will become apparent in discussing the results of a randomized response procedure used in reference to one of the most sensitive issues, that concerning sexual experience, respondents appear to be remarkably candid in their answers to the direct question on sexuality as asked by the interviewer.

PREVALENCE OF PREMARITAL INTERCOURSE

Evidence from various studies indicates that the level of sexual activity among young Americans has been increasing. Much of this evidence comes from studies of selected groups, particularly of high school and college students. A decade or so ago, some students of adolescent behavior believed that it was not sexual behavior that was changing but merely the willingness to talk frankly about it. This view has faded in the face of a steady escalation of the rates of premarital intercourse. It was claimed that the great change in sexual mores occurred after World War I, and that since the mid-1920's, the sexual revolution has been essentially a revolution in candor. No satisfactory data exist for accurately tracing the trend in premarital sexual activity. Data presented by Catherine Chilman suggest that, for white females at any rate, the rise has been especially sharp since the late 1960's.[2] The data from the two surveys show a continued increase during the 1970's—a trend that was foreshadowed in the 1971 survey.[3]

As table 3-1 and figure 3-1 show, 35 percent of the unmarried teenagers in 1976 had experienced sexual intercourse, as compared to 27 percent of a comparable group in 1971—an increase in prevalence of 30 percent. Because the number of

Table 3-1.—*Percent of never-married women aged 15-19 who have ever had intercourse, by age and race, 1976 and 1971*

Age	Study year and race											
	1976					1971					Percent increase 1971-1976		
	All	White		Black		All	White		Black		All	White	Black
		%	N	%	N		%	N	%	N			
15-19	34.9	30.8	1,232	62.7	654	26.8	21.4	2,633	51.2	1,339	30.2	43.9	22.5
15	18.0	13.8	276	38.4	133	13.8	10.9	642	30.5	344	30.4	26.6	25.9
16	25.4	22.6	301	52.6	135	21.2	16.9	662	46.2	320	19.8	33.7	13.9
17	40.9	36.1	277	68.4	139	26.6	21.8	646	58.8	296	53.8	65.6	16.3
18	45.2	43.6	220	74.1	143	36.8	32.3	396	62.7	228	22.8	35.0	18.2
19	55.2	48.7	158	83.6	104	46.8	39.4	287	76.2	151	17.9	23.6	9.7

Note: *In this and subsequent tables:* Base excludes those for whom no information was obtained on intercourse; this amounted in 1971 to 1.2 percent of the never-married blacks and 1.3 percent of the whites; and, in 1976, to 0.9 percent of the blacks and 0.7 percent of the whites. Percentages for whites and blacks are computed from unweighted data (Ns in tables); percentages for total sample are computed from weighted data and thus may sometimes appear to be inconsistent with figures by race. Figures for 1971 differ from earlier published reports because they exclude women living in group quarters. Except where indicated, the base excludes women who did not respond to the question analyzed in the table.

teenagers increased over the 5 years, the absolute growth in prevalence was even greater. The increase in premarital sexual experience occurred between 1971 and 1976 for both blacks and whites at each year of age. The proportionate change is about the same for both races at age 15, but is two times greater overall for whites than for blacks. As a result, although blacks continue to show higher rates of prevalence than whites, the relative differences are smaller in 1976 than in 1971. In total, 63 percent of unmarried black teenagers interviewed in 1976 report having had sexual intercourse, as compared to 31 percent of comparable whites. By age, the proportion sexually experienced rises in 1976 from 18 percent at age 15 to 55 percent at age 19. The increase in the prevalence of intercourse is accompanied by a slight downward shift, averaging 4 months, in the age at first intercourse.

The increase of 30 percent in the level of premarital sexual activity between 1971 and 1976—with due allowance for sampling errors, minor elements of noncomparability in the two samples, and a possible increase in candor over the 5 years—represents clear evidence that more young women are today engaging in premarital intercourse than in years past. The conclusion that there has been a marked increase in the prevalence of sexual experience among teenage women holds when the comparisons are standardized for age.

Figure 3–1.—*Percent of never-married women aged 15–19 who have ever had intercourse, by age, 1976 and 1971*

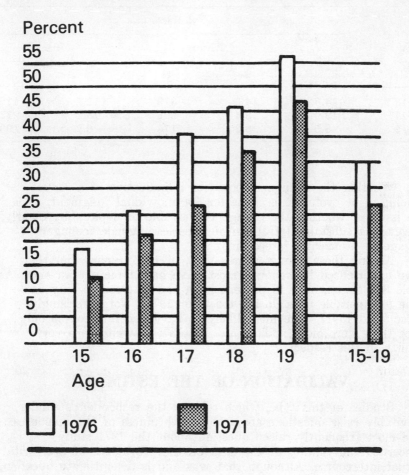

Table 3-2.—*Percent of sexually experienced never-married women aged 15-19 who had intercourse only once, by age and race, 1976*

Age	All	Race			
		White		Black	
		%	N	%	N
15-19	14.8	14.3	379	12.7	410
15-17	19.9	18.4	206	18.4	217
18-19	8.6	9.3	173	6.2	193

Whether the change in behavior is indicative of a sexual revolution or evolution is a matter for individual judgment, as is the issue of whether the change is desirable or deplorable. Clearly, however, a substantial fraction of American female teenagers engage in premarital intercourse.

Among those young women who, in 1976, report that they have experienced intercourse, most have had it more than once. As table 3–2 shows, only 15 percent have had intercourse only one time (comparable data do not exist for 1971). Not surprisingly, those aged 15–17 were more likely to have had intercourse only once than were older adolescents. Blacks and whites are very similar in this respect.

VALIDATION OF THE ESTIMATE

Studies of this type, which rely on the respondent's candor, inevitably raise questions about the truthfulness of the responses. The most frequently raised question about the 1971 study concerned the validity of the data on the prevalence of premarital sexual intercourse. Although that was and is a legitimate question, there was no definitive way of answering it. The overall quality of the data from the 1971 study and its internal consistency suggest that the data on premarital sexual activity were reasonably good, but no stronger defense for the estimates can be made.

The 1976 study included an application of the randomized response technique (RRT) to provide another estimate of the proportion of respondents who had experienced intercourse.

Ideally, when the RRT is used, the total sample should be randomly split into two groups; one group should be asked the direct question (of interest) and the other should be subjected to the RRT. Each group would thereby provide an independent estimate of the behavior in question. If the RRT provides an unbiased estimate and is consistent with the population estimate derived from responses to the direct question, then the validity of the latter is supported. Unfortunately, the RRT procedure provides an estimate of a population parameter; it does not provide any information (about the behavior of interest) at the individual level. Thus, respondents subjected to the RRT cannot be included when the behavior of concern is related to individual characteristics. To prevent that "loss" of cases, this study did not follow the ideal but costly procedure of splitting the sample. Instead, all unmarried respondents were both asked a direct question on whether they had ever had intercourse and subjected to the RRT.

Basically, the RRT is a procedure for arriving at an estimate of the level of some form of behavior (usually sensitive or clandestine) among a group of respondents without revealing to the interviewer whether they have or have not engaged in that behavior. In effect, the respondent "plays a game" that determines whether he or she will answer a sensitive or an innocuous question without the interviewer knowing which question is being answered. The rules of the game determine the probability of the selection of the sensitive question. The respondent simply answers yes or no to the question determined by the game. The interviewer, who does not know which question is being answered, records only a yes or no answer. Given the known probability of selection of the sensitive question and the proportion of yes answers, it is possible to arrive at an estimate of the proportion who are responding affirmatively to the sensitive question, i.e., who have engaged in that behavior. The estimation procedure depends upon knowing for the innocuous question the distribution of expected yes and no answers.[b]

The estimate of the proportion who have had intercourse provided by the RRT is 44.1 percent, with a standard error of 1.6

[b]For further discussions see: J. R. Abernathy, B. G. Greenberg and D. G. Horvitz, "Estimate of Induced Abortion in Urban North Carolina," *Demography*, 7:19, 1970.

[c]This percentage, which is based (as is the estimate from the RRT) on an unweighted combination of the data for both races, is greater than the value shown in Table 1 for the weighted total. There is no way to weight the RRT responses. However, if the RRT calculation is made separately for each race, the results again are very close to those obtained by the direct question:

Percent who had intercourse

Race	RRT	(SE)	Direct
White	33.6	(2.0)	30.8
Black	64.1	(2.6)	62.7

percent. The unweighted estimate from the direct question on sexual intercourse, 41.8 percent,[c] falls comfortably within the 95 percent confidence interval of 40.9–47.3 percent. Thus, it appears that a direct question on sexual intercourse addressed to young unmarried women aged 15 to 19 in 1976 elicited truthful responses. To the degree that the initial question on sexual intercourse has been answered truthfully, it seems reasonable to assume that subsequent questions on other aspects of sexual behavior have been answered truthfully also.

KNOWLEDGE OF RISK

The 1971 study indicated that fewer than two out of five unmarried women aged 15 to 19 had a generally correct notion about the period of greatest risk of contraception during the menstrual cycle. Only 16 percent of blacks correctly perceived that the period of greatest risk is about 2 weeks after the period begins, in contrast to 40 percent of the whites (see table 3–3). Among whites, there was a direct relationship between age and knowledge of the period of risk, and those who were sexually experienced were more knowledgeable than those who were not. On the other hand, blacks showed no variation in knowledge by age, and those with sexual experience were no more knowledgeable than those without such experience.

Proportionately more of the teenage respondents in 1976 knew the time of greatest risk than was the case in 1971; however, the increase is small, especially for whites. Overall, 41 percent of unmarried women aged 15 to 19 in 1976 have a correct notion of the period of greatest risk—up by only 3 percentage points from 1971. As in 1971, sexually experienced whites are better informed about the risk of pregnancy than their age peers who have not had intercourse. Among blacks, misinformation is widespread and bears little relationship to sexual experience or age. The continued high level of misinformation and ignorance about the period of greatest risk during the menstrual cycle may be surprising in light of the recent attention to sex education.

SEX EDUCATION

In an attempt to determine how effective sex education is in informing women about the menstrual cycle, each respondent was asked if she had ever had any formal classroom instruction in sex education and, if so, whether the course included information about the monthly menstrual cycle. If a respondent reported that she had not had formal classroom instruction in sex education in school, she was asked if she had ever had such a course somewhere else. Of

Table 3-3.—*Percent of never-married women aged 15-19 who correctly perceived the time of greatest pregnancy risk within the menstrual cycle, by age, race and sexual experience, 1976 and 1971*

	Race and sexual experience																				
	All			White						Black						
	Total	Experienced	Not experienced	Total		Experienced		Not experienced		Total		Experienced		Not experienced	
Age				%	N	%	N	%	N	%	N	%	N	%	N
1976															
15-19	40.6	47.3	36.9	43.9	1,194	53.2	365	39.8	829	23.5	646	24.0	405	22.8	241
15	29.5	33.5	28.6	30.5	272	40.5	37	28.9	235	22.7	132	17.6	51	25.9	81
16	33.5	42.8	30.3	39.8	289	50.8	65	36.6	224	18.0	133	17.4	69	18.8	64
17	47.0	51.7	43.7	48.0	271	51.0	98	46.2	173	26.6	139	28.4	95	22.7	44
18	49.2	52.7	46.3	52.6	215	57.0	93	49.2	122	22.3	139	23.1	104	20.0	35
19	48.6	46.7	51.1	56.5	147	59.7	72	53.3	75	29.1	103	29.1	86	29.4	17
1971															
15-19	37.6	41.6	36.1	40.2	2,624	50.2	562	37.5	2,062	16.0	1,333	16.3	681	15.8	652
15	28.6	32.8	28.0	29.5	640	41.4	70	28.1	570	16.1	341	14.4	104	16.9	237
16	34.0	35.3	33.7	36.7	659	41.4	111	35.8	548	15.4	319	15.6	147	15.1	172
17	38.7	41.6	37.6	42.7	644	51.8	141	40.2	503	16.3	295	16.8	173	15.6	122
18	44.5	46.7	43.2	48.9	395	56.2	128	45.3	267	15.0	227	16.9	142	11.8	85
19	48.5	45.8	50.8	54.6	286	55.4	112	54.0	174	18.5	151	17.4	115	22.2	36

those who reported having had a course in sex education, more than 90 percent said they had had the course in school.

Table 3–4 shows, for those who had a course that included such information and for those who didn't, the proportions who know the period of greatest risk of contraception.

The table does not include a breakdown by sexual intercourse status, since for both blacks and whites the proportions having had a course that covered the menstrual cycle were not very different for the sexually active and the sexually inactive. Among blacks, 75 percent of the sexually experienced had had such a course in comparison with 70 percent of those who hadn't had intercourse; for whites, the figures were 67 and 64 percent, respectively.

The data in table 3–4 indicate that those who had a sex education course in which the menstrual cycle was discussed are more knowledgeable than those who have not had such a course, but the differences are not great. Only a little over one-fourth of blacks who have had a course correctly identify the period of greatest risk during the menstrual cycle, and slightly fewer than half of the whites who have had a course can correctly identify that period. We do not know much about the competence of the instruction, or about the duration or content of these courses; but these data do suggest that, as in other areas of education, the transfer of knowledge in formal settings may be likened to carrying water in a basket.

THE GEOGRAPHY OF SEX

Has premarital sex among young women become more common because the opportunities for it have increased? The automobile, assorted wayside attractions, by-the-hour motels, in short, the world of a mobile teenage society, removes adolescents from the purview of concerned adults. In an earlier time, parental influence was palpable if not present in the parlors and on the porches of small-town America, and it was represented by proxy on Main Street and in the corner store. Whether this is fact, romantic reconstitution or some of both, there is a pervasive belief that control of the young has become seriously weakened in a society in which children are more and more at large and the home is less and less the center of their activities. The situation is exemplified by solemn mayors announcing that it is 11 p.m. and asking worried parents at their TVs the question many cannot answer.

The geography of premarital sex has received little attention from those who study such matters, perhaps because they feel that they know where such acts occur, or perhaps also because of the conviction that it doesn't really matter because love, whether of the durable or disposable variety, will find a way. In the 1976

Table 3-4.—Percent of never-married women aged 15-19 who correctly perceived the time of greatest pregnancy risk within the menstrual cycle, by age, race and exposure to sex education, 1976

	Race and exposure to sex education														
Age	All			White						Black					
	Total	Had course	No course*	Total		Had course		No course*		Total		Had course		No course*	
	%	%	%	%	N	%	N	%	N	%	N	%	N	%	N
15-19	40.6	44.6	31.8	44.0	1,199	47.6	786	37.3	413	23.5	650	26.3	475	16.0	175
15-17	36.7	41.3	27.5	39.5	836	43.0	532	33.2	304	22.4	407	24.8	298	15.6	109
18-19	49.1	51.3	43.3	54.6	363	57.1	254	48.6	109	25.5	243	28.8	177	16.7	66

*Includes a small number who had a sex education course which did not discuss the menstrual cycle.

survey, each sexually active respondent was asked where sexual intercourse occurred the first time and the most recent time. For those who had intercourse only once, of course, first and most recent are the same events. More than three out of four white and black respondents report that they have had intercourse in their own or their partner's home, or in the home of a friend or relative, regardless of whether it was the first, most recent, or only time that they had intercourse (see table 3–5). The partner's home is especially favored. If intercourse does not occur in someone's home, then blacks are more likely to go to a motel or hotel; whites, on the other hand, are more likely to have intercourse in an automobile or "elsewhere," which translates generally as some part of the "great outdoors"—an option somewhat less open to blacks, who are more urban.

The changes in locale between first and most recent intercourse are in the direction of increased use of either the respondent's or the partner's home, and less reliance on the home of a friend or relative. With few exceptions, place of intercourse shows no systematic variation by current age, although with increasing age, blacks tend to place greater reliance on motels, and whites, decreasing reliance on the automobile, both in regard to first and last intercourse. There is a high degree of consistency among blacks in the locale of the first and most recent intercourse. These observations pertain only to those who had intercourse more than once. From half to two-thirds have had sex in the same kind of place. Whites exhibit a greater tendency than blacks to change locales, except where the first encounter occurred at the partner's home (not shown).

A closer examination of where sex takes place, taking account of the female's age at the time, reveals that the initiation of sex among those under age 13 occurs most often in the girl's home; at age 13, the home of a friend or relative becomes the most likely place; from age 14 on, the partner's home becomes increasingly important so that from age 17 on, half or more of all first sexual encounters occur there (not shown). The partner's home is the most likely place for the most recent intercourse to have occurred regardless of the girl's age at the time (excluding those who have had intercourse only once).

The girl's home becomes increasingly important as the locale for the most recent intercourse as her age increases. Thus, for four out of five sexually experienced unmarried females who have had more than one encounter with sex, the choice seems to lie in the answer to "my place or your place?" with his place having the edge.

"Home" is an elastic and dynamic concept. Not only has there been a sharp increase in single-person households and households containing an unmarried couple, but more and more homes are in

Table 3-5.—*Percent distribution of sexually experienced never-married women aged 15-19, according to place of occurrence of selected episodes of intercourse, by race, 1976*

	Episode of intercourse and race								
	First			Only once			Most recent		
Place of occurrence	All	White (N=323)	Black (N=348)	All	White (N=53)	Black (N=51)	All	White (N=324)	Black (N=350)
Respondent's home	16.3	15.2	20.7	12.4	15.1	21.6	23.0	22.8	26.0
Partner's home	41.6	44.0	38.5	41.5	35.8	51.0	51.2	50.0	44.8
Relative/friend's home	21.4	19.8	21.0	24.8	24.5	15.7	11.6	13.0	9.7
Motel/hotel	5.2	2.2	13.5	0.6	0.0	5.9	6.4	3.4	16.0
Automobile	9.5	11.1	4.9	13.8	17.0	3.9	6.1	8.3	2.6
Other	6.0	7.7	1.4	6.9	7.6	1.9	1.7	2.5	0.9
Total	100.0	100.0	100.0	100.0	100.0	100.0	100.0	100.0	100.0

effect zero-person households during much of the time. It is thus often a relatively easy matter to find a home that is reliably vacant at an opportune time. It is no more than ironic speculation, but one wonders to what extent the upsurge in employment among married women that has helped to reduce their own fertility may have been a factor in the sexual liberation of their children.

FREQUENCY OF INTERCOURSE

The 1971 study revealed that most never-married, sexually experienced teenage women had intercourse infrequently. As measured by the frequency of intercourse during the month preceding the survey, approximately two in five abstained. Race made no difference. Teenagers in 1976 appear even more abstemious (see table 3–6). About half of the never-married, sexually experienced respondents had not had intercourse during the month prior to the survey, and fewer than 3 in 10 had had intercourse as many as 3 times in the month. The data shown in table 3–6 include those who have had intercourse only once. Most of them had that experience more than 4 weeks prior to the survey. When they are removed from consideration, the modal frequency is still zero for both blacks and whites.

Thus, the increase since 1971 in the proportion of young unmarried women who have had sex has not been paralleled by an increase in the frequency of such behavior among the initiated. Blacks and whites are very similar with respect to degree of sexual activity; whites who had sex at all during the reference period had it somewhat more often.

THE MALE PARTNER

Most sexually experienced unmarried women in the 1971 survey tended to confine themselves to one partner (see table 3–7 and figure 3–2). Whites and blacks were quite similar except that whites were considerably more likely than blacks to have had six or more partners. By 1976, both whites and blacks at each age show less exclusivity in the choice of sexual partners. The change in general is greater among blacks than among whites. Thus, whereas in 1971 more than 61 percent of sexually experienced whites and blacks had had only one partner, in 1976 this was true of only 53 percent of comparable whites and 40 percent of blacks.

Such an increase in the number of partners might occur if intercourse were beginning at younger ages than was true five years before—that is, if the period of sexual experience was lengthened. The median age at first intercourse has declined by about 4 months (see table 3–8), but it is unlikely that this fact

Table 3-6.—Percent distribution of sexually experienced never-married women aged 15-19, according to frequency of intercourse in the four weeks preceding interview, by age and race, 1976 and 1971

Number of times	All			Race and age					
				White			Black		
	15-19	15-17	18-19	15-19	15-17	18-19	15-19	15-17	18-19
1976				(N=378)	(N=206)	(N=172)	(N=404)	(N=214)	(N=190)
0	47.6	51.0	43.5	49.2	53.4	44.2	49.3	55.1	42.6
1-2	25.4	30.1	19.6	21.2	24.3	17.4	29.2	28.5	30.0
3-5	11.7	10.3	13.4	12.2	10.7	14.0	14.1	10.8	17.9
>6	15.3	8.6	23.5	17.4	11.6	24.4	7.4	5.6	9.5
Total	100.0	100.0	100.0	100.0	100.0	100.0	100.0	100.0	100.0
1971				(N=528)	(N=299)	(N=229)	(N=641)	(N=392)	(N=249)
0	39.6	41.5	37.7	38.3	39.8	36.2	40.1	42.4	36.6
1-2	30.2	34.5	25.7	30.1	34.4	24.5	34.0	33.9	34.1
3-5	17.4	15.4	19.5	17.6	15.4	20.5	17.6	16.6	19.3
>6	12.8	8.6	17.1	14.0	10.4	18.8	8.3	7.1	10.0
Total	100.0	100.0	100.0	100.0	100.0	100.0	100.0	100.0	100.0

Table 3-7.—Percent distribution of sexually experienced never-married women aged 15-19, according to number of partners ever, by age and race, 1976 and 1971

Number of partners	All			White			Black		
	15-19	15-17	18-19	15-19	15-17	18-19	15-19	15-17	18-19
1976				(N=372)	(N=203)	(N=169)	(N=398)	(N=213)	(N=185)
1	50.1	54.0	45.3	52.9	54.7	50.9	40.2	47.9	31.3
2-3	31.4	31.5	31.3	28.0	31.0	24.2	42.0	35.7	49.2
4-5	8.7	8.4	9.1	7.8	6.4	9.5	11.8	11.7	11.9
≥6	9.8	6.1	14.3	11.3	7.9	15.4	6.0	4.7	7.6
Total	100.0	100.0	100.0	100.0	100.0	100.0	100.0	100.0	100.0
1971				(N=541)	(N=308)	(N=233)	(N=648)	(N=400)	(N=248)
1	61.5	66.5	56.1	61.6	66.5	54.9	61.4	64.2	56.9
2-3	25.1	22.7	27.7	22.9	20.8	25.7	28.9	27.8	30.6
4-5	7.8	5.9	9.9	8.5	6.5	11.2	6.9	6.0	8.5
≥6	5.6	4.9	6.3	7.0	6.2	8.2	2.8	2.0	4.0
Total	100.0	100.0	100.0	100.0	100.0	100.0	100.0	100.0	100.0

Age and race

Figure 3-2.—*Percent of sexually experienced never-married women aged 15–19, by number of partners ever, 1976 and 1971*

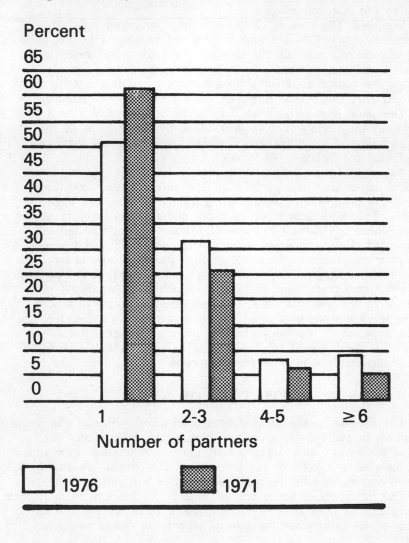

could be the entire explanation. We have no other clues as to this rather substantial increase except possibly an increase in the tendency to postpone marriage.

Whatever the reason, it appears that proportionately more unmarried female teenagers are having intercourse; they are initiating sex earlier; and, on the average, they have had more partners, but without any increase in frequency of sexual activity. Perhaps the reason that coital frequency has not increased is that more partners mean that relations are somewhat less established.

The male partner at first intercourse is generally 2 to 3 years older than the female (not shown). More the 85 percent of the first partners of black teenage females are themselves teenagers; for whites, the figure is 73 percent.

As might be expected, the partner at the most recent intercourse is older than the partner at first intercourse. More than half of the most recent partners, regardless of race, are aged 20 or older. This high proportion of older males is due in part to the predominance of 18- and 19-year-old females among the sexually experienced. However, even among women aged 17 and younger, a little over one-quarter of the black male partners, and nearly one-third of the white, are 20 or older. What is important is the fact that older males are more difficult to reach with organized programs than are younger ones, most of whom are still in school. If we include male partners aged 19, because most of these, too, are out of high school, the proportion of girls who were aged 17 or younger at most recent intercourse and whose partner was 19 or older was nearly 50 percent for both races.

INITIATION OF SEX

The decline in age at first intercourse from 16.5 to 16.2 years (as shown in table 3–8)—a decline that occurs at virtually each age—is consistent with the apparent general relaxation in sexual behavior observed both in the increase in the proportion who have had intercourse and in the relative increase in number of partners.

The initiation of sex bears no relation to the age at menarche for whites, but does show some systematic tendency for blacks, among whom the earlier the age of menarche, the earlier sex begins.

Nearly two-fifths of respondents first experienced intercourse during the summer (not shown).

CONTRACEPTIVE PREVALENCE

From a strictly demographic point of view, the significance of sexual activity depends on whether it occurs at a time when contraception can occur; this, in turn depends a great deal on whether

Table 3-8.—Median age at first intercourse of sexually experienced never-married women aged 15-19, by age and race, 1976 and 1971

Age	Median age, by race											
	1976					1971						
	All	White		Black		All	White		Black			
	Age	Age	N	Age	N	Age	Age	N	Age	N		
15-19	16.2	16.3	378	15.6	405	16.5	16.5	549	16.0	667		
15	14.7	14.8	38	14.2	51	14.7	14.8	67	14.5	103		
16	15.5	15.6	68	15.4	71	15.9	15.9	109	15.5	140		
17	16.4	16.3	100	15.7	93	16.4	16.5	137	16.1	173		
18	16.8	17.1	96	16.3	105	17.2	17.3	126	16.7	140		
19	17.1	17.3	76	16.2	85	18.0	18.2	110	16.8	111		

and how effectively contraception is employed. Contraceptive use among U.S. teenage women as revealed by the 1971 study was irregular and, except at the older ages, heavily reliant on such conventional methods as the condom and withdrawal and, among blacks, the douche.[4] Most sexually experienced teenage women had used contraception at some time, but at the time of their last intercourse, fewer than half were protected against the risk of conception.

As may be seen in table 3–9 and figure 3–3, that picture has changed remarkably since 1971.[d] For both races, and at all ages, there has been an increase in the percentage of sexually experienced unmarried women who have always used contraception. For all ages, this category of users is up 53 percent for whites and 76 percent for blacks—very substantial increases. Such a change in the regularity of use produces a dramatic rise also in the proportions who were protected at their last intercourse[e] —from 42 to 58 percent for blacks and from 45 to 65 percent for whites. Even the younger respondents, those aged 17 and *under* in 1976, are more likely to have used contraception at last intercourse than were those *over* 17 in 1971.

Moderating this picture of improved contraceptive practice is the fact that the proportion of those who have never used contraception has increased also, though by only 9 percentage points. If we remove those cases who have had intercourse only once,[f] for

---

[d]Information on the use of contraception in 1971 was obtained by means of a self-administered questionnaire with no interchange necessary between the respondent and interviewer. In 1976, this information was obtained by direct question, but the use of cards with lettered response categories required the respondent merely to indicate a letter which corresponded to her answer.

[e]Always-users plus those sometime-users who used contraception at time of last intercourse.

[f]This step can be done for 1976 but not for 1971.

[g]The proportion of those who had intercourse only once and who used contraception is about the same as the proportion of users at first intercourse among those who had subsequent episodes of intercourse. If, as some theorize, the use of contraception is a function of the "commitment" to sex, i.e., to the incorporation of sex into the "self-image," it would seem from the evidence here regarding the early use of contraception that the commitment develops subsequent to sexual initiation. This, indeed, is the view propounded by Constance Lindemann, who sees more frequent sex as indicative of commitment with a self-concept to match, leading not only to more contraception but, ultimately, to the use of medical methods of birth control which require the user to bear witness to her behavior before various authority figures (see reference 6).

Table 3-9.—Percent of sexually experienced never-married women aged 15-19, according to contraceptive use status, by age and race, 1976 and 1971

Age	All				White					Black				
	Never	Some-times	Always	Last* time	Never	Some-times	Always	Last* time	N	Never	Some-times	Always	Last* time	N
1976														
15-19	25.6	44.5	30.0	63.5	24.1	45.8	30.2	64.8	378	25.0	46.1	28.9	58.3	408
15	38.0	32.5	29.5	53.8	36.8	31.6	31.6	55.3	38	47.1	27.4	25.5	35.3	51
16	30.9	38.7	30.5	56.3	36.8	33.8	29.4	50.0	68	21.1	35.2	43.7	69.0	71
17	29.4	41.4	29.3	61.8	25.2	45.5	29.3	64.6	99	32.3	46.2	21.5	57.0	93
18	20.8	49.1	30.1	70.3	20.8	47.9	31.3	71.9	96	17.9	47.2	34.9	66.0	106
19	15.1	54.4	30.5	68.8	9.1	61.0	29.9	74.0	77	16.1	64.4	19.5	55.2	87
1971														
15-19	17.0	64.6	18.4	45.4	18.3	62.0	19.7	45.1	548	16.3	67.3	16.4	41.6	669
15	32.9	47.4	19.7	29.9	36.8	42.6	20.6	29.4	68	27.2	51.4	21.4	31.1	103
16	20.6	58.9	20.5	38.8	20.2	58.7	21.1	38.5	109	21.8	64.8	13.4	34.5	142
17	12.2	70.8	17.0	45.2	14.0	68.4	17.6	46.3	136	11.0	68.6	20.4	44.2	172
18	13.0	70.1	16.9	48.8	13.5	68.3	18.2	47.6	126	11.4	72.3	16.3	48.9	141
19	14.6	66.4	19.0	55.3	15.6	62.4	22.0	56.9	109	13.5	76.6	9.9	46.8	111

Race and use status

*"Last time" includes always-users plus sometimes-users who used contraception at time of last intercourse.

Figure 3–3.—*Percent of sexually experienced never-married women aged 15–19 who used contraception at last intercourse, by age, 1976 and 1971*

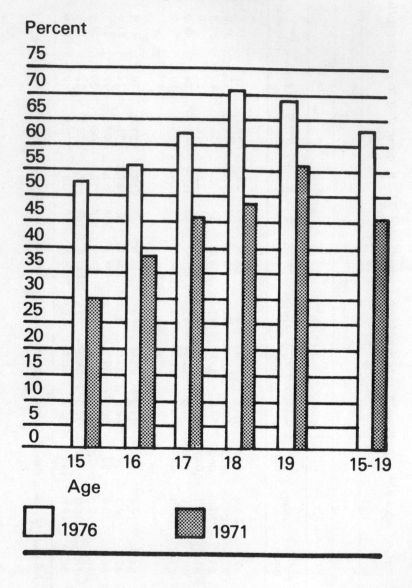

whom the use or nonuse of contraception is essentially a chance matter,[g] the proportion who have never used contraception is only slightly diminished. Some suggestion of what may be going on comes from a comparison of the methods of contraception that were being used in these two periods.

METHODS OF CONTRACEPTION

A change in the prevalence of contraceptive use would be expected if there were a shift in the mix of contraceptive methods toward more use of such noncoitally related methods as the IUD or birth control pills. These methods, with reasonable continuity of use, would tend to increase the amount of regular use and, thus, the extent of contraceptive use on any given occasion. That appears to be what happened. Table 3–10 shows that among contraceptors, use of the pill more than doubled between 1971 and 1976. Use of the IUD, still a relatively unimportant method of contraception in 1976, increased substantially also. The condom, douche, and withdrawal, the big three in 1971, all suffered great losses in popularity among contraceptors. There was also a relatively large increase in the use of rhythm, due in part perhaps to more specific questioning about this method in 1976 than in 1971. Although rhythm is not highly regarded as an effective method of contraception, particularly when its use is combined with incorrect information about the timing of ovulation, rhythm users are much better informed on the time of greatest pregnancy risk than those using other methods or those who have never used contraception, as shown in the following table:

Percent Having Correct Idea of
Period of Greatest Risk, 1976

Method ever used	Total	White	Black
Rhythm	77.3	75.6	36.8[a]
Other	47.6	55.3	24.5
None	37.3	40.4	20.8

[a] $N < 20$

The data in table 3–10 refer to ever-use, which is a montage of experience over time with various methods. Table 3–11 shows current contraceptive practice as measured by most recent use of

Table 3-10.--Percent of ever-contracepting never-married women aged 15-19, according to methods ever used, by age and race, 1976 and 1971

Methods ever used	All			White			Black		
	15-19	15-17	18-19	15-19	15-17	18-19	15-19	15-17	18-19
1976				(N=288)	(N=142)	(N=146)	(N=307)	(N=147)	(N=160)
Pill	58.8	45.1	72.9	55.6	43.7	67.1	72.3	63.3	80.6
Foam, jelly, cream. . . .	9.5	4.4	14.8	10.1	5.6	14.4	6.8	4.8	8.8
IUD	5.1	2.5	7.8	5.6	3.5	7.5	6.8	3.4	10.0
Diaphragm .	1.8	1.3	2.4	2.4	2.1	2.7	0.3	0.7	0.0
Condom . .	39.3	41.2	37.4	42.7	44.4	41.1	28.7	34.0	23.8
Douche . .	9.1	6.8	11.4	7.3	4.9	9.6	17.9	14.3	21.2
Withdrawal.	30.0	39.1	20.7	35.8	43.7	28.1	12.4	15.0	10.0
Rhythm . .	14.4	14.3	14.5	15.3	15.5	15.1	6.2	6.1	6.2
Other	0.3	0.1	0.5	0.0	0.0	0.0	1.0	0.7	1.2
1971				(N=451)	(N=248)	(N=203)	(N=565)	(N=342)	(N=223)
Pill	26.9	17.4	36.3	23.1	13.7	34.5	32.0	25.2	42.6
Foam, jelly, cream. . . .	10.2	7.7	12.7	10.0	8.1	12.3	12.4	9.6	16.6
IUD	2.8	1.7	3.8	1.8	0.8	3.0	7.3	5.8	9.4
Diaphragm .	3.2	2.6	3.8	3.1	3.2	3.0	4.1	3.2	5.4
Condom . .	60.6	61.6	59.7	59.4	61.3	57.1	65.3	64.6	66.4
Douche . .	32.0	32.0	32.0	24.8	25.0	24.6	54.5	53.8	55.6
Withdrawal.	64.3	62.9	65.6	74.1	75.0	72.9	45.8	45.0	47.1
Rhythm . .	5.5	5.6	5.5	6.4	6.8	5.9	1.1	0.3	2.2
Other	0.1	0.2	0.0	0.2	0.4	0.0	0.0	0.0	0.0

Table 3-11.—*Percent distribution of ever-contracepting never-married women aged 15-19, according to method most recently used, by age and race, 1976 and 1971*

Method	Age and race								
	All			White			Black		
	15-19	15-17	18-19	15-19	15-17	18-19	15-19	15-17	18-19
1976				(N=287)	(N=141)	(N=146)	(N=306)	(N=146)	(N=160)
Pill	47.3	36.4	58.5	43.6	35.5	51.4	59.8	52.8	66.2
IUD	3.4	2.4	4.3	4.2	3.5	4.8	4.9	2.7	6.9
Condom	20.9	27.6	14.2	22.6	27.7	17.8	17.0	25.3	9.4
Douche	3.5	3.8	3.2	1.7	2.8	0.7	7.2	6.9	7.5
Withdrawal	16.9	24.7	9.0	18.5	25.5	11.6	5.9	8.2	3.8
Other	8.0	5.1	10.8	9.4	5.0	13.7	5.2	4.1	6.2
Total	100.0	100.0	100.0	100.0	100.0	100.0	100.0	100.0	100.0
1971				(N=448)	(N=247)	(N=201)	(N=560)	(N=339)	(N=221)
Pill	23.8	15.4	32.1	20.1	11.7	30.3	27.5	21.8	36.2
IUD	1.5	0.6	2.3	0.7	0.0	1.5	3.9	2.7	5.9
Condom	32.1	40.6	23.7	30.8	38.1	21.9	37.9	43.1	29.8
Douche	5.8	6.6	5.0	2.9	2.4	3.5	12.3	13.9	10.0
Withdrawal	30.7	31.8	29.7	39.5	42.1	36.3	13.2	15.3	10.0
Other	6.1	5.0	7.2	6.0	5.7	6.5	5.2	3.2	8.1
Total	100.0	100.0	100.0	100.0	100.0	100.0	100.0	100.0	100.0

any method. The sharp decline in use of conventional contraception and the growth in use of oral contraception is even more clearly brought out in this table. Between 1971 and 1976, pill use doubled, while use of the condom declined by 27 percent among whites and by 55 percent among blacks. Condom and withdrawal, which used to account for more than half of contraceptive use among blacks and 70 percent among whites, now together capture 23 percent of black and 41 percent of white contraceptive use. Only in the youngest ages do these two methods account for as much or more use than orals. Both lose popularity rapidly among older women.

Table 3–12 and figure 3–4 show the same trend in choice of method at last intercourse. Only 45 percent of teenagers used any method at last intercourse in 1971, and just 16 percent used the pill and IUD. In 1976, on the other hand, 63 percent used a method at last intercourse and one-third used the pill and IUD. This amount is greater than pill and IUD use in 1973 among *married* women of reproductive age, and two-thirds the level of such use among married women aged 15–24.[5] The decline in condom, douche, and withdrawal for ever-use and most recent use among contraceptors is not apparent for most recent intercourse when all sexually active teenagers are considered. This is because there is a smaller proportion using these methods in 1976, but using them with greater regularity.

Many sexually experienced teenagers are relatively inactive sexually. Although oral contraception is generally considered to be best-suited to women who have regular and frequent intercourse, it is very popular among teenage women generally—including those who have sex only occasionally. It might be asked whether those who have used pills but are not currently sexually active tend to discontinue oral contraception to a greater extent than those who continue to be active. That is, does infrequent intercourse discourage continued use? The answer is yes—to some extent. About one-third of those whose most recent method was the pill and who did not have intercourse in the 4 weeks before the interview stopped using the pill, but only about one-sixth of the women who were sexually active during that period discontinued use. However, two-thirds of the sexually experienced but inactive women *did* continue to take their pills.

FIRST USE OF CONTRACEPTIVE

The older the teenager at the time of first intercourse, the more likely it is that she will commence contraception at the same time she begins to have sex (see figure 3–5). Comparisons between 1971 and 1976 are complicated by the proportionately greater number of cases in the earlier year for which the data on age at first use were deficient. Nevertheless, there is no evidence that the gap

Table 3-12.—Percent distribution of sexually experienced never-married women aged 15-19, according to method used at last intercourse, by age and race, 1976 and 1971

Method	All			Age and race					
				White			Black		
	15-19	15-17	18-19	15-19	15-17	18-19	15-19	15-17	18-19
1976				(N=378)	(N=205)	(N=173)	(N=408)	(N=215)	(N=193)
Pill	31.2	21.6	42.9	30.4	21.9	40.5	35.3	30.7	40.4
IUD	2.2	1.3	3.4	2.9	2.0	4.0	2.5	0.9	4.1
Condom	12.6	15.2	9.3	13.2	14.2	12.1	9.8	13.5	5.7
Douche	2.3	2.4	2.3	1.1	1.5	0.6	5.1	4.6	5.7
Withdrawal	10.6	14.9	5.4	12.2	15.6	8.1	3.4	4.7	2.1
Other	4.5	3.0	6.3	5.0	2.9	7.5	2.2	1.4	3.1
None	36.6	41.6	30.4	35.2	41.9	27.2	41.7	44.2	38.9
Total	100.0	100.0	100.0	100.0	100.0	100.0	100.0	100.0	100.0
1971				(N=551)	(N=314)	(N=237)	(N=674)	(N=420)	(N=254)
Pill	15.1	7.7	23.0	13.4	6.0	23.2	13.6	9.5	20.5
IUD	0.8	0.2	1.4	0.4	0.0	0.9	2.1	1.2	3.5
Condom	14.4	17.3	11.2	14.7	18.2	10.1	16.0	16.0	16.1
Douche	1.7	2.1	1.3	0.5	0.6	0.4	3.1	3.8	2.0
Withdrawal	10.3	9.4	11.3	12.9	12.4	13.5	3.9	4.8	2.4
Other	2.9	2.4	3.4	2.9	2.6	3.4	2.5	2.1	3.1
None	54.8	60.9	48.4	55.2	60.2	48.5	58.8	62.6	52.4
Total	100.0	100.0	100.0	100.0	100.0	100.0	100.0	100.0	100.0

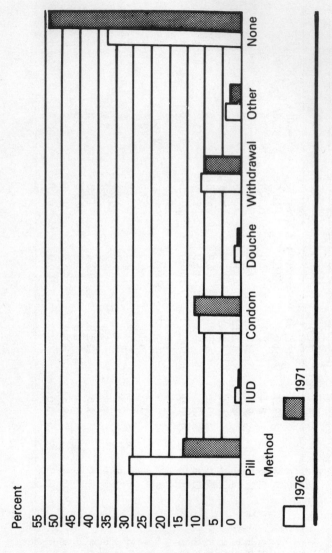

Figure 3-4.— *Percent of sexually experienced never-married women
aged 15–19, according to method used at last intercourse,
1976 and 1971*

between age at first intercourse and age at first use of contraception has narrowed in the last 5 years. The proportion of teens of each race who delay use (including those who have yet to start use) appears to be about as great as or greater today at each age of sexual initiation than it was in 1971. The only compensatory factor at work (as we shall see) is that delayed contraception is often better contraception.

FIRST METHOD OF CONTRACEPTION

The theory which holds that an upgrading of contraceptive practice, i.e., a progression from nonuse to conventional to medical methods, follows increasing commitment to sex[6] would predict that the distribution by method last used would differ from the distribution by first method used. Theory aside, it is simply easier for more knowledgeable and older girls to negotiate the institutional obstacles that regulate access to the most effective modes of contraception.

Another factor in adoption of effective methods is pregnancy. The 1971 survey showed that teenagers often adopted the most effective methods of contraception following pregnancy. The effect of pregnancy on contraceptive use would, in those cases where it occurs, tend to augment the aggregate effect of increased sexual commitment. In some cases, of course, pregnancy may destroy or prevent the development of a sense of commitment.

In view of these considerations, it is surprising to observe that although most recent use[h] is characterized by somewhat more pill and IUD use and less condom use than is first use, the difference is not as great as might be expected (see table 3–13, cols. 3 and 6).[i] Moreover, the difference is due to those who used contraception the first time they had intercourse. On that occasion, this group put major reliance on the condom and withdrawal. Even at that, a surprisingly large proportion of those who used contraception at first intercourse used either the pill or the IUD. This statement is especially true of blacks (see table 3–13, col. 13), among whom 48 percent used these methods—more than twice the percentage for comparable whites.

The contrasting first method profiles, depending on whether or not contraception was used at first intercourse (cols. 1 and 2), are puzzling. One might argue that those who fail to use at first intercourse would be those with less interest in contraception; of

---

[h]Those who had intercourse only once are excluded from this discussion since their contraceptive practice, whatever it was, could not change.

[i]Most recent use occurred at a somewhat older age on average. There is little overlap between the two groups, i.e., cases in which most recent use could be the same event as first use.

Table 3-13.—Percent distribution of ever-contracepting never-married women aged 15-19,* according to first and most recently used method, by race and use at first and last intercourse, 1976

	Race and timing of use																	
	All						White						Black					
	First method			Most recent method			First method			Most recent method			First method			Most recent method		
Method	(1) Used first time	(2) Not used first time	(3) Total	(4) Used last time	(5) Not used last time	(6) Total	(7) Used first time	(8) Not used first time	(9) Total	(10) Used last time	(11) Not used last time	(12) Total	(13) Used first time	(14) Not used first time	(15) Total	(16) Used last time	(17) Not used last time	(18) Total
							(N= 130)	(N= 134)	(N= 264)	(N= 223)	(N= 42)	(N= 265)	(N= 119)	(N= 156)	(N= 275)	(N= 211)	(N= 68)	(N= 279)
Pill	21.5	57.2	39.7	53.9	36.6	51.1	20.0	50.8	35.6	50.7	23.8	46.4	46.2	73.7	61.8	65.9	57.3	63.8
IUD	0.1	2.5	1.3	4.0	2.4	3.7	0.0	3.0	1.5	4.9	2.4	4.6	1.7	3.9	2.9	4.7	7.4	5.4
Condom ...	40.6	18.4	29.3	14.8	27.6	16.9	42.3	24.6	33.3	16.6	35.7	19.6	27.7	10.3	17.8	13.3	17.6	14.3
Douche ...	3.6	0.7	2.1	3.6	2.5	3.5	0.0	0.7	0.4	1.4	2.4	1.5	13.5	1.9	6.9	8.1	1.5	6.5
Withdrawal .	21.1	13.4	17.2	16.7	18.0	16.9	26.9	11.9	19.3	18.8	16.7	18.5	6.7	5.8	6.2	4.7	5.9	5.0
Other	13.1	7.8	10.4	7.0	12.9	7.9	10.8	9.0	9.9	7.6	19.0	9.4	4.2	4.5	4.4	3.3	10.3	5.0
Total ..	100.0	100.0	100.0	100.0	100.0	100.0	100.0	100.0	100.0	100.0	100.0	100.0	100.0	100.0	100.0	100.0	100.0	100.0

*Excludes those who had intercourse only once.

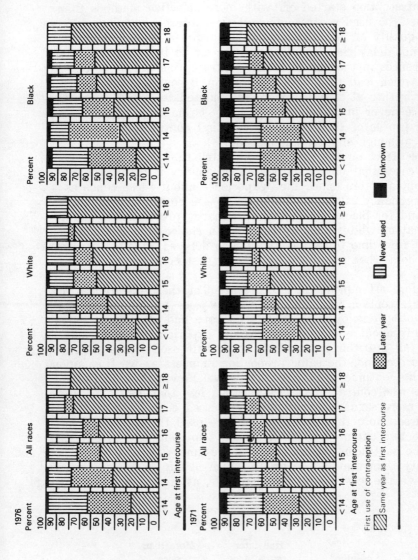

Figure 3-5.—Percent distribution of sexually experienced never-married women aged 15-19, by age at first intercourse and timing of first use of contraception, according to race, 1976 and 1971

this group, about one-third do in fact remain never-users. However, those who fail to use the first time, but do so subsequently, reveal a remarkably sophisticated initial methods profile. In fact, the group that had had some sexual experience by the time they first used contraception started off with more effective methods than did those who used contraception at first intercourse. This difference in quality of initial contraception between those who do and do not delay first use does not appear to be solely a matter of differences in the age at which contraception begins or of pregnancies which lead to adoption of improved contraception. The method profiles at first use were retabulated to include only those who were never pregnant (not shown). The superior quality of the first-use profile of those who delayed first contraception is still evident, although slightly diminished.

The effect on the first-method distribution produced by removing cases that have experienced pregnancy is greatest for delayed contraceptors (since they experience about three times as much pregnancy as those who begin to use contraception right away) and for blacks (since their pregnancy prevalence is about twice that of whites). The differences in choice of a first method between first-time users and those who delayed adoption of contraception hold when examined by age at first contraception (not shown).

Before attempting an interpretation of these differences in first contraception, let us add one more piece to the puzzle—the contraception employed by those who have had intercourse only once. Only about one in seven sexually experienced unmarried women fall into this group. Just under half used contraception on that one occasion, the same proportion of users as we find among those who continue to be sexually active. Fewer than 10 percent of those who contracepted used the pill, less than half the figure for the more sexually experienced who used contraception at first intercourse. More than three out of five used the condom, compared to two out of five among those who continued to have sex. Thus, the contraceptive practice of "one-timers" is of a much poorer quality than that of the group which in our discussion thus far has shown the least sophisticated profile, as shown in the following table:

Percent Who Used Contraception
at First Intercourse, 1976

Method	Had intercourse once	More than once
Pill	9.7	21.5
Condom	61.7	40.6
Douche	4.0	3.6
Withdrawal	16.4	21.1
Other	8.2	13.2
Total	100.0	100.0

The one-timers presumably are the least sexually committed among those who have had intercourse. Next to them, the least sexually committed teens, at least at the time of adoption of a contraceptive method, are those who used contraception at first intercourse. By definition, those who did not begin to use contraception right away were sexually experienced by the time they did; those who began contraception at their first intercourse were sexually inexperienced at that time.

It would appear that the facts conform rather well to Lindemann's theory that the less committed a young woman is to sex, the less likely she is to use contraception and the more likely, if contraception is used, that it will be a method such as the condom that does not involve much positive action or acknowledgment on her part.[7] It appears, therefore, that the greater the presumed sexual commitment, the greater the efficacy of initial contraceptive practice. Those most inclined to rely initially on male methods, particularly the condom, are those who have had the least sexual involvement, i.e., who have had sex only once. About half this group used no contraception the first time. Also reliant on conventional contraception as their first method, but to a lesser extent, are those who have had intercourse more than once and contracepted the first time they had intercourse. However, when contraception is delayed, the first method used is much more likely to be a medical method. This difference in the quality of contraception between those who delay first use and those who do not is not a matter of age at the time contraception is adopted or of experience with pregnancy, although pregnancy is frequently a stimulus to more effective contraception. What the theory does not account for is the never-users who have had intercourse more than once.

SOURCES OF CONTRACEPTION

The major change since 1971 in contraceptive practice is the massive shift to oral contraception. The shift can be observed among both races and is substantial to all ages. Table 3-14 shows the source from which prescriptions for the pill were first obtained. Whereas there is a wide diversity of outlets for conventional contraceptives, prescriptions for orals in almost all cases were obtained either from private physicians in their offices or from a clinic or other medical facility. Not surprisingly, both sources figure prominently, with blacks showing somewhat greater resort to clinic facilities and whites to private physicians.

Table 3-14.—Percent distribution of sexually experienced never-married women aged 15-19 who ever used oral contraception, according to first source of prescription, by age and race, 1976

Source	All			White			Black		
	15-19	15-17	18-19	15-19 (N=160)	15-17 (N=62)	18-19 (N=98)	15-19 (N=222)	15-17 (N=93)	18-19 (N=129)
Doctor	54.1	52.9	54.8	55.6	53.2	57.1	42.3	43.0	41.9
Clinic	45.2	45.3	45.2	43.8	45.2	42.9	57.7	57.0	58.1
Other	0.7	1.8	0.0	0.6	1.6	0.0	0.0	0.0	0.0
Total..	100.0	100.0	100.0	100.0	100.0	100.0	100.0	100.0	100.0

If the respondent went for her prescription to a doctor in his private office, it is likely that she would give "private physician" as her source. If she saw a doctor in a clinic or hospital, she may have been confused as to her proper response. Since we did not probe this matter deeply, we cannot resolve the possible ambiguity.

This extraordinary reliance by unmarried teenage women on organized clinics for oral contraception contrasts with the preference for the private doctor shown by most married women.[j] It is their unmarried status rather than age that accounts for the popularity of the clinic among unmarried teenage women. Although the numbers are small in some instances, there is no apparent trend by age in the percentages reporting the clinic as the source from which they got their prescription.

The large-scale utilization of clinics by teenagers may help to account for the increase in the use of oral contraception by teens in recent years, since it has been documented that enrollment in clinics by teenagers rose from 453,000 in 1971 to 1.1 million in 1975.[8] Unfortunately, the 1971 and 1976 surveys cannot be compared, since in the earlier survey the source question referred to all methods and asked about source *ever* used.

Since passage of the Family Planning Services and Population Research Act of 1970, Federal funds supporting the provision of family planning services have more than doubled.[9] During this period, there has also been a significant liberalization of laws and policies affecting teenagers' access to contraceptive services.[10]

Differences in contraceptive practice among teenage pill users bear little relation to the source from which they first obtained their prescriptions. Among whites, slightly more than 70 percent of those who had ever used the pill had used it at last intercourse, regardless of source. This lack of difference by source was true for blacks also, among whom 65 percent who had ever used the pill had used it at last intercourse.

SUMMARY

Data gathered in two nationwide surveys made in 1971 and 1976 provide an opportunity to examine recent changes in preva-

---

[j]Married women in the present survey who have used pills obtained their first prescription overwhelmingly from a private physician. Some of them, of course, may have been unmarried at the time. The married woman's preference for the private physician over the clinic is found in other studies also. See, for example: J. E. Anderson, L. Morris, and M. Gesche, "Planned and Unplanned Fertility in Upstate New York," *Fam. Plann. Perspec.* 9:4, 1977. The data from their study are not strictly comparable with the figures in table 3–14, since "source" is more broadly defined and refers to a wider array of methods. To have focused on the first "prescription" for "orals" presumably would have given even greater prominence to the role of the physician.

lence of sexual experience and in contraceptive use among unmarried women aged 15 to 19. Confining the analysis to unmarried (i.e., never-married) women is a data processing expedient that introduces minor distortions into the findings without, it is believed, altering major conclusions. To have included ever-married women in this analysis[k] would have increased the level of estimated premarital sexual activity, because the vast majority of the married had had intercourse before marriage. The effect on contraceptive practice is harder to judge. Many marriages are precipitated by pregnancy which results either from the failure to use contraception at all, or from ineffective use. On the other hand, the stable courtship arrangements which often precede marriage are associated, or were in 1971, with better than average contraception.

With respect to sex and contraception, the following findings are most salient:

- Between 1971 and 1976, there was, for both races and at all ages, an increase among unmarried teenage women in the prevalence of premarital intercourse. The validity of the prevalence estimate for 1976 is confirmed by the use of an indirect estimating procedure which is believed to elicit true responses to sensitive questions.
- Knowledge of the time of greatest risk of contraception during the menstrual cycle (which is relevant to the use of coitally related methods of contraception) was relatively poor in both 1971 and 1976. Sex education courses helped somewhat; however, among whites (but not blacks) experience and maturity were the better teachers. It is possible that sex education had other, and for this study, unmeasured effects on the use of contraception, the management of pregnancy, and other aspects of sex and reproduction.
- Most sexual encounters take place in the home of the girl or her male partner. The older the girl, the more likely it is to be the partner's home.
- Along with increased prevalence of sexual experience, there has been a fairly substantial increase in the number of partners with whom teenage women have ever been involved. This result is not a necessary consequence of more sex, and may be related to some stretching of the premarital period by a reduction in the age at first intercourse, as well as by greater postponement of marriage.
- At first intercourse, male partners tend to be teenagers themselves. The most recent partner, on the other hand, tends to be out of his teens and thus, presumably, some-

---

[k]They were included in the survey and will be analyzed subsequently.

what harder to reach through programs that are based on some form of institutional catchment.

- The median age at first intercourse, which declined by a few months for both blacks and whites, bears some relationship to the age of menarche among blacks, but not among whites.
- First intercourse among unmarried teenage women is seasonal—summer being the time, apparently, when temptation and opportunity peak together.
- Contraceptive practice among unmarried teenage women improved significantly between 1971 and 1976. The proportions of sexually active unmarried women who always used contraception and who used it at the time of last intercourse increased. This improvement was moderated to some extent by a concurrent though smaller growth in the proportion who never used contraception. These changes appear to have been fostered by changes in the types of contraceptives being used.
- Many more young women used the pill and IUD in 1976 than in 1971. Along with this increase in use of the most effective medical methods, there has been a substantial decline in the use of the three methods—condom, douche, and withdrawal—which were most prominent in 1971. Only among very young teenagers are these the methods of choice.
- Oral contraception is more popular among blacks at every age than among whites. It is, however, for both races, the most popular method.
- The gap between first intercourse and first use of contraception that was observed in 1971 has not narrowed significantly. Those who delay the use of contraception are much more likely than those who do not to have had a pregnancy.
- Seemingly, the more committed to sex a young woman is, the more sophisticated is her initial use of contraception. There are striking differences in the first-use profiles of those who have sex only once, those who continue to have sex but use contraception from the start and those who delay the use of contraception. For these three groups, pill use as the first method goes from less than 10 percent, to over 20 percent, to over 50 percent, respectively; while condom use declines from 62, to 41, to 18 percent, respectively. Experience with pregnancy and age at first use of contraception cannot explain these differences.
- About half of the unmarried teenage women who have used oral contraception got their original prescription from a clinic rather than from a private physician. This fact

contrasts with the practice of older, married women, who
rely much more on the private physician for contraception.
- Whether the first prescription for pills is obtained from a
private physician or from a clinic makes little difference in
continuation or effectiveness of subsequent use. The importance of the clinic for contraception among unmarried teenage women therefore seems to lie in increasing access to
oral contraception by unmarried teens.

Data from two national surveys indicate that the prevalence
of sexual intercourse is on the rise among young unmarried wom-
en in the United States. Although the majority of female teenagers have not had intercourse, the magnitude of that majority appears to be diminishing, so that more than one-half of those aged
19 in 1976 have had intercourse. The surveys also reveal that more
of the sexually active are using contraception, they are using the
more effective methods, and they are using all methods with
greater regularity. Although the increasing use of the pill and the
IUD among teenagers should help prevent undesired pregnancy,
questions may also be raised about the desirability\of early and
continued use of these contraceptives because of known and suspected increased risk of serious side effects, such as thromboembol-
ic disease with use of orals, as well as delay and possible impairment of fertility following discontinuation of pill use.

Some will see in these data cause to lament the passing of
the old ways; other will see the beginning stages of a happier,
better adjusted society. Some will argue that changes are inevita-
ble and will propose various ways of dealing with them; others
will advocate one scheme or another for turning the tide. Exhorta-
tions or simplistic tinkerings, however, can be expected to have
little if any effect. In Japan and the People's Republic of China,
there appears to be little premarital intercourse, at least among
those under age 20. However, both societies are very different
from the United States, and in ways presumably related to behavior of young people. The methods of contraception that are growing in popularity among American teenagers generally accompany
an established pattern of sexual activity. Furthermore, it is of no
little sociological significance that most sexually active young unmarried women in the United States are engaging in that behavior
either in their own homes or in the homes of their partners. This
fact, perhaps, is more telling evidence of the establishment of sexual activity than any number of statistics.

ACKNOWLEDGMENTS

This chapter is adapted from an article that appeared in
Family Planning Perspectives, 9(2), 55–71, 1977.

REFERENCES

1. For the major findings of the 1971 study, see: Zelnik, M. and Kantner, J.F., "Sexuality, Contraception and Pregnancy Among Young Unwed Females in the United States," *in* Commission on Population Growth and the American Future, *Demographic and Social Aspects of Population Growth,* Westoff, C.F. and Parke, R., Jr., eds., Vol. 1 of Commission Research Reports, U.S. Government Printing Office, Washington, D.C., 1972, p. 355; "Probability of Premarital Intercourse." *Social Sci. Res.* 1:335, 1972; "Sex and Contraception Among Unmarried Teenagers," in Westoff, C. F., *Toward the End of Growth,* Prentice-Hall, Englewood Cliffs, N.J., 1973, p. 7; "The Resolution of Teenage First Pregnancies," *Fam. Plann. Perspec.* 6:74, 1974; "Attitudes of American Teenagers Toward Abortion," *Fam. Plann. Perspec.* 7:89, 1975; Kantner, J. F., and Zelnik, M., "Sexual Experience of Young Unmarried Women in the United States," *Fam. Plann. Perspec.* 4(4), 1972, p. 9; "Contraception and Pregnancy: Experience of Young Unmarried Women in the United States," *Fam. Plann. Perspec.* 5:21, 1973; and Shah, F., Zelnik, M., and Kantner, J. F., "Unprotected Intercourse Among Unwed Teenagers," *Fam. Plann. Perspec.* 7:39, 1975.
2. Chilman, C. S. "Possible Factors Associated with High Rates of Out-of-Marriage Births Among Adolescents," University of Wisconsin-Milwaukee, School of Social Welfare, 1976.
3. Zelnik, M. and Kantner, J. F., "Probability of Premarital Intercourse," 1972, op. cit.
4. Kantner, J. F. and Zelnik, M., "Contraception and Pregnancy . . .," 1973, op. cit.
5. Westoff, C. F. "Trends in Contraceptive Practice: 1965–1973," *Fam. Plann. Perspec.* 8:54, 1976.
6. Lindemann, C. *Birth Control and Unmarried Young Women.* Springer, N.Y., 1975.
7. Ibid.
8. The Alan Guttmacher Institute. *Data and Analyses for 1976 Revision of DHEW Five-Year Plan for Family Planning Services.* New York: AGI, 1976.
9. AGI. *11 Million Teenagers.* New York: Planned Parenthood Federation of America, 1976, p. 46.
10. Paul, E. W., Pilpel, H. F., and Wechsler, N. F. "Pregnancy, Teenagers and the Law, 1976," Table 1. *Fam. Plann. Perspec.* 8:16, 1976.

Chapter 4

The Teenager and the Family Planning Experience

Virginia Ktsanes

Tulane University

In the span of little more than a decade (1963 to 1974) marked changes have occurred in the birth rate of women under age 20 and the number of women in that age group who have been served in organized family planning programs. As shown in figure 4–1, the birth rate has declined markedly since 1970, not only for the young group (ages 15 to 19), but for the next 5–year age group as well (ages 20 to 24). The rate for first-order births began to take a sharp decline after that year, a result that is more striking for women in the older group than the younger. The decline in the rate for second- and third-order births had begun earlier.

In the early 1970's, a movement began to make eligibility requirements less stringent for teenagers seeking birth control information and to provide services and facilities more appropriate to their needs and concerns. A model for appropriate service delivery had been implemented in 1969 in the San Francisco Teen Clinic, San Francisco, Calif. Started by Sadja Goldsmith, the clinic was simulated in other cities across the Nation.[2,3] In many States the legal rights of minors, including the right to obtain contraceptive care on their own consent, were being expanded.[4,5] The publication of the report of the President's Commission on Population Growth and the American Future containing recommendations addressing both these points provided impetus to the movement.

The coincidence in timing does not necessarily imply a causal connection between the provision of contraceptive services to young people in family planning clinics and the decline in the birth rate. Many other changes have been occurring concurrently. Birth control is no longer a "private" topic. Teenager pregnancy risk awareness has increased along with knowledge of prevention and may have resulted in a more effective practice of "natural" methods. The utilization of "drugstore" methods of contraception also has

Figure 4–1.—*Fertility rates (live births per 1,000 females in specified age groups for first-, second-, and third-order births, age groups 15 to 19 and 20 to 24, all races, U.S., 1964 to 1974 (Source: Reference 1)*

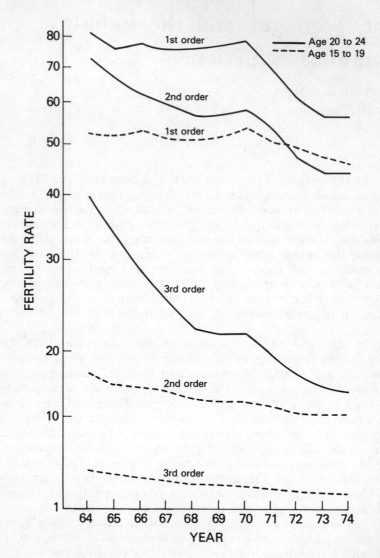

increased. Furthermore, there has been liberalization of the attitudes of many physicians to provide contraception on a private care basis. Legalized abortion has certainly had an impact. A decrease in sexual activity, however, is not an explanation. Increasing numbers of young people are sexually active and have become so at an earlier age.[6]

Whatever its weight in this complicated equation, contraceptive service provided through family planning clinics is one variable that lends itself to measurement. Many agencies have kept systematic records that disclose something about who and how many have come for service, how they were referred, how long they stayed, and whether they were effective birth preventers. Analysis of this information contributes to understanding the differential decline in birth rates of subgroups in the total population. An example is the differential rate of decline in the white and nonwhite age-specific birth rates for those aged 15 to 19, as shown in figure 4-2.

Begun in 1967, the Louisiana Family Planning Program is one such agency that has kept records. Perhaps the teenagers served by this program represent a select population. They mostly came from homes below the poverty level, and most of them are black. Perhaps, however, their program behavior is not radically different from teenagers living under similar conditions in other parts of the Nation. These young users of the program were the foci of three distinct studies. The purpose of this paper is to summarize those findings.

FAMILY PLANNING FOLLOWUP ON
PRENATAL PATIENTS: 1970 to 1971

In 1969, Dr. Ann K. Fischer began an indepth study of teenagers who came for prenatal service to the New Orleans Family Planning Clinic, New Orleans, La.[a] All girls were less than 18 years old, pregnant for the first time, and residents of one economically deprived neighborhood of the city. During the intake period, December 1969 until January 1971, white girls who enrolled did not fulfill all the sampling criteria; thus, only black girls were studied. As minors, they had not been eligible for family planning service prior to conception.

The purpose of the study, growing out of Dr. Fischer's interest in comparative family organization and structure, was to explore determinants of teenage pregnancy and to examine outcomes for family formation. She was particularly interested in obtaining information on girls who delivered in-wedlock as well as those who

---

[a]This study has not been previously published. Dr. Fischer died in April 1971, before all the data were collected. The author and two interviewers, Harriet Curole and Ruby Sumler, completed data collection and many preliminary analyses.

Figure 4–2.—*Fertility rates (live births per 1,000 females in the specified age and race groups) for first-, second-, and third-order births, age group 15 to 19, white and nonwhite, U.S., 1964 to 1974 (Source: Reference 1)*

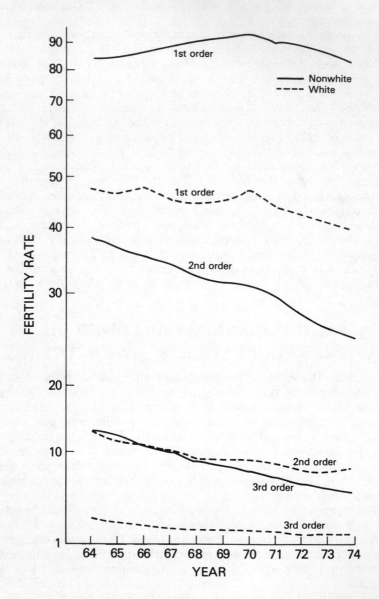

delivered out-of-wedlock. The aim was to get complete information on 30 girls in each of the two wedlock categories. This step involved three in-clinic interviews prior to delivery. The interviews covered family background; school and social participation; family planning knowledge, attitudes, and practice; feelings about pregnancy; and plans for the baby. One interview was conducted at home after delivery. A fifth interview was obtained later from the girl's mother or mother surrogate.

All girls fulfilling the study criteria were interviewed at admission. Many initiated too late in their pregnancy to make three prenatal visits. More single girls were studied because it was anticipated that some would marry before delivery. Complete information was obtained for 69 girls, 45 single and 24 married. For control, some information was obtained from 30 never-married, never-pregnant girls aged 18 or 19 and from the same neighborhood—girls who had passed through the crucial years without pregnancy.

One approach to finding out what "caused" the pregnancy was to ask, "Why do you think this (pregnancy) happened to you?" The never-pregnant girls (only five of whom indicated they had ever been sexually active) were asked, "Why do you think it did not happen to you?" The wide range of answers given by the pregnant girls is presented in the appendix. For the most part, the never-pregnant girls answered, "I don't want to get that involved with any boy." These responses were elicited from a few teenagers in 1970; there is little reason to doubt that similar answers would be forthcoming from others today.

After delivery, 67 of the 69 girls kept their postpartum appointment in the family planning clinic. The rapport developed with the nurse interviewer during pregnancy and at the postdelivery home visit may have contributed to this high initial clinic return rate. No such effect was apparent on clinic continuation, however. At the end of 1 year, 30 percent of the cases had been closed. This result is consistent with figures found for all initiates under age 20 in the Louisiana program.

At the end of 2 years, 25 of the original 67 clinic initiates (37 percent) experienced a second pregnancy. This finding is consistent with that on a similar sample of young black women in New Haven, Conn., who had participated in a Young Mothers Program between 1967 and 1969.[7,8]

At the end of 3 years, seven girls (about 10 percent) experienced a third pregnancy, and seven others (about 10 percent) had been effective contraceptors, keeping their appointment to the clinic throughout the period. Review of the data on the latter group revealed nothing that would have predicted their continuation at the clinic. All but one had delivered out-of-wedlock 3 years before. Educationally, two of the girls had been school dropouts prior to the first pregnancy, two finished high school after delivery, and the remaining three had returned to school, but it is not known if they finished. They differed in that they were older, i.e., their average age at conception was higher than that for total study group.

It would have been equally difficult to predict the seven who had had three pregnancies. With respect to educational level prior to pregnancy, and school reentry after delivery, these girls were markedly the same as the contraceptive continuers.

TEEN CLINIC EXPERIENCE

Teen clinics around the Nation report a high success rate in terms of the number of teenagers seen. Some information is available on the type of service teenagers receive, but limited data are available on the characteristics of those who receive the services or on the followup. Perhaps this situation is as it should be, in keeping with the confidentiality that is a part of teen service.

For a 1-year period, however, an opportunity was opened to set up teen clinics in three control sites in Louisiana to test recruitment techniques and to monitor the clinics in a way that is unusual in a service setting. The contract, under which this research was organized, specified that the target group be young women aged 12 to 21 who have low incomes or come from low-income families.[b]

The cities in which the clinics were placed were small (under 80,000 population) and similar in sociodemographic characteristics. The three recruitment techniques were radio, home visit outreach, and advertising the special service in the adult clinic. The service, using the teen clinic model of a "rap session" with option for family planning clinic service following the session, was the same in the three sites. For the experimental period teenage girls who were post-partum were excluded. Abortion referral for those found to be pregnant was not an option in Louisiana at that time.

Because recruitment for each clinic was limited by the experimental design to one technique, startup was particularly slow. At the end of 12 months from the time the clinics first opened, 461 new girls attended the clinics for some part of the service, and 34 who were already adult clinic patients attended, perhaps to see what they had missed. Of the new girls, approximately three-fourths (352) initiated family planning service. Comparison with

[b]This research was carried out under Contract No. HSM 110–72–394 awarded to The Family Health Foundation in June 1972 by the Health Services and Mental Health Administration of the U.S. Department of Health, Education, and Welfare. The author became Project Director in June 1973, and completed the work under the auspices of the Louisiana Family Planning Program in December 1974.

those who only attended the rap session at first visit (109) reveal-ed that a higher proportion of white girls initiated clinic service than black (84 percent compared to 72 percent). Rap session only attenders were younger and less advanced in school (median age 14.4 compared to 17.4 for initiates, and median last grade com-pleted 8.3 compared to 11.2 for initiates). A very small proportion of both groups had ever been pregnant (3 percent compared with 6 percent).

Among these girls, pregnancy experience was more evident for white girls. Of the 39 girls who reported on a pregnancy (22 prior to entry, 9 at entry, and 8 sometime after entry), 20 were white or 11.6 percent of all white girls. The 19 black girls who reported represented 6.4 percent of all black girls initiated. This result was the reverse of what would be expected from the fertili-ty rates in the area from which the girls were recruited. The fertility rates tend to follow the national average of being slightly less than half as high for whites as for blacks. The implication is that young white girls, as a whole, are more inclined than black girls to postpone use of a family planning service until it is too late, or to come to the clinic when they think they might be pregnant or are pregnant. This tendency is typified by one white girl who replied when asked if she wanted a method, "Yes, if I am not pregnant," and by another who said she had made an appointment months earlier but did not keep it when she found out she was not pregnant.

Perhaps for black girls the risk of early pregnancy is more real (as the birth statistics document), and they are more inclined to use a preventive program once it is made available, especially if their mothers, as family planning clinic patients themselves, are advocates of the program. If this hypothesis is true, it may ex-plain, in part, the faster decline in the birth rate since 1972 for nonwhites aged 15 to 19, as was shown in figure 4–2.

Parental or family support was noted in the study. The very young girls (those under age 16), who came to the clinic, were most likely to have heard about the clinic from a family member or an outreach worker in the home (58 percent). The most fre-quent information source for older teenagers (ages 16 to 18) was a friend (42 percent), but many (24 percent) were referred to the clinic by a family member. Recruitment by radio (to which older, rather than younger, girls inclined to respond) tended to require reinforcement from a friend or a family member to be effective.

The data from this study suggest that girls know what they want when they come to a program with option for contraception. No "group effect" at first visit was needed to push girls into clinic service. Girls were asked before each session began what services they were seeking. About 89 percent knew and received what they had specified. Of these, 27 percent wanted and attended

only the rap session. Only 5 percent who thought they solely wanted the rap session requested same day clinic service after this
session. Of the 6 percent who did not know what they wanted,
one-third elected only the rap session. At the end of the period of
observation, about 13 percent who had come to the rap session
earlier, initiated clinic services later.

The study documented that girls in this age group are not
good appointment keepers for a service of this type. Less than 40
percent kept appointments for initial clinic visits, that is, called or
made an appointment but never came. A little over one-half (53
percent) kept appointments for scheduled medical revisits. The continuation rate noted in other studies reported previously was the
same for this group. The 1-year continuation rate was estimated to
be between 0.54 and 0.63. At the end of the 1-year study period,
only 65 percent were still in the program. A higher proportion of
white girls than black girls had stopped going to the clinic, and
the majority of the whites who stopped were those who were in
college at initiation, very likely changing to private sector service.

The principal reason for termination was that girls did not
show up for appointments and were not heard from subsequently.
The missed appointment followup procedures used in the adult
program were less feasible for the teen service because the requests of those girls who wanted no telephone or home contact
were honored.

NULLIPAROUS COMPARED WITH PRIMIPAROUS TEENAGE INITIATES INTO ADULT CLINICS

The third and final study overcomes the limitation of a small
sample and short followup, and adds another dimension: parity at
entry. The study involved some who entered the program 1 year
before 1972 and some who came the following year. The inclusion
of equal numbers of white and black patients by parity permitted
testing of some hypotheses suggested earlier with respect to usage
by race, as well as some additional hypotheses with respect to
parity.

In the first 7 years of operation (June 1967 through June
1974), 22,890 girls under age 18 entered the Louisiana program.
More than half (53 percent) entered in the last 2 years of the
7–year period. Most had been pregnant previously: 58 percent had
been pregnant one time, and 5 percent had been pregnant more
than once. A radical change in the proportion never pregnant occurred after June 1972, when the percentage of never pregnant
increased from 28 percent in 1971 to 59 percent in 1974.

Table 4–1 provides a description of the nulliparous and primiparous initiates by race for three time periods—the early period of
restrictive eligibility (through mid-1972) and 2 single years since

that time. Table 4–2 shows some characteristics of those who had
two or more pregnancies. The number and percentage of young
initiates with higher order pregnancies decreased steadily over the
time period. In the first year (1967), 20 percent of all young initiates had experienced two or more pregnancies; by the 7th year
(1974), only 97 girls were in the category, and they represented
less than 2 percent of young girls seen for the first time. That
result does not mean that the rate of higher order pregnancies
was necessarily decreasing in this population but, as the program
was being put into place, service was available for girls after a
first, rather than a later, pregnancy.

Table 4–1 shows that for both races the proportion of teenagers entering the program before their 16th birthday increased. As
a group, the whites have been older; more than half were 17 at
entry throughout the time period. In the period preceding the 7th
year (beginning July 1973), a higher proportion (approximately
two-thirds) of black girls than white had finished at least 1 year
of high school. In the 7th year, the proportion of white girls at
this educational level began to exceed the proportion of black girls
who had attained the same level.

The descriptive summary provided in table 4–1 demonstrates
that as services became available, never-pregnant girls began to
use them. Implicit in the argument for the provision of such services is the importance of preventing a first conception. It is assumed that all persons who use a family planning service are
motivated at some level to prevent or postpone pregnancy. For
teenagers, the question is whether that motivation is a function of
pregnancy. Are teenagers who have been pregnant more motivated
to prevent pregnancy now (that is, are they more effective contraceptors) than those who have never been pregnant?

In an attempt to find the answer to this question, a stratified
random sample of black and white nulliparous and primiparous
girls under age 18 who were initiated into the Louisiana program
between July 1, 1971 and June 30, 1973 was drawn. Approximately
600 were in each of the four groups. Their records were followed
through June 30, 1975. All girls had a potential program time of 2
years and about half had a potential of 3 or more years. Indicators of motivation were continuation rates, retention without pregnancy, reasons for dropout, and pregnancy intervals for those who
did get pregnant.[c]

[c]This research, A Comparative Study of Family Planning Clinic Users, was funded by the U.S. Department of Health, Education, and Welfare, Behavioral Sciences
Branch, National Institute of Child Health and Human Development, Center for
Population Research, under contract No. NO 1–HD–52833, June 1975 to October
1976.

Table 4-1.—*Selected characteristics of nulliparous and primiparous family planning initiates under age 18 by race and program year of entry, Louisiana Family Planning Program*
[Percent]

Characteristics	Program year of entry[a]					
	Black			White		
	1 to 5	6	7	1 to 5	6	7
Age at initiation						
Less than 15	6.6	9.4	14.2	2.4	5.0	6.7
15	14.9	19.7	19.3	8.4	13.1	12.7
16	31.5	31.0	29.3	31.2	31.5	30.1
17	47.0	39.9	37.2	58.0	50.4	50.6
Last grade completed						
Less than 7	5.2	5.3	6.6	5.2	7.0	4.4
7 to 8	26.6	25.1	27.3	35.5	34.4	25.7
9 to 11	66.8	67.9	64.1	57.8	57.5	66.6
12	1.5	1.6	2.0	1.4	1.2	3.2
Marital status						
Never married	72.7	85.7	89.4	28.1	55.6	65.6
Currently married	25.0	13.6	9.7	67.9	40.9	32.2
Previously married	2.3	0.7	0.9	4.1	3.5	2.2
Adopted contraception	94.3	85.0	88.4	89.8	81.9	84.5
Ever pregnant	86.2	43.4	42.1	71.7	40.1	30.8
Age at first pregnancy						
Less than 14	8.4	7.5	8.1	2.9	4.2	5.7
14	21.4	16.7	19.7	15.6	16.9	16.5
15	39.2	38.8	35.6	44.2	39.6	43.8
16	29.8	33.3	32.7	36.1	38.0	31.7
17	1.1	3.7	3.8	1.2	1.3	2.2
Total number initiated ..	8,904	5,332	4,503	1,058	946	1,034

[a]Years 1 to 5, June 1967 to June 1972; year 6, July 1972 to June 1973; and year 7, July 1973 to June 1974.

Figure 4–3 shows the continuation rates to first closure for the four groups. Nulliparous whites are the most divergent, tending to drop out earlier and in greater proportion over the whole time period. At 6 months, almost one-third had dropped out, and at 12 months more than half (54 percent) had done so. At the end of 24 months, more than half of the other three groups had been terminated. At 36 months, the same pattern held. Except for the primiparous blacks, more than three-fourths of all groups had been terminated at some time.

Table 4-2.—*Selected characteristics, by race, of family planning initiates under age 18 with two or more pregnancies at time of entry, June 1967 to June 1974, Louisiana Family Planning Program*

Characteristic	Black		White	
	Number	Percent	Number	Percent
Age at initiation				
14	14	1.5	0	0
15	47	4.9	5	3.3
16	224	23.3	22	14.6
17	677	70.3	124	82.1
Marital status				
Never	516	53.6	15	9.9
Currently	380	39.5	111	73.5
Previously	65	6.8	25	16.6
Number of pregnancies				
2	855	88.9	134	88.7
3	99	10.3	13	8.6
4	7	0.7	4	2.6
5	1	0.1	0	0
Number of live births				
0	27	2.8	10	6.6
1	164	17.0	32	21.2
2	686	71.3	104	68.9
3	80	8.3	4	2.6
4	5	0.5	1	0.7
Outcome of last pregnancy				
Full-term live birth	730	75.9	115	76.2
Premature birth	154	16.0	15	9.9
Stillbirth	19	2.0	3	2.0
Miscarriage	53	5.5	16	10.6
Multiple birth	6	0.6	1	0.7
Age at first pregnancy				
11	6	0.6	1	0.7
12	41	4.3	4	2.6
13	170	17.7	21	13.9
14	362	37.6	58	38.4
15	312	32.4	57	37.7
16	61	6.3	8	5.3
17	2	0.2	1	0.7
Unknown	8	0.8	1	0.7
Postpartum referral	602	62.6	91	60.3
Previously used contraception	302	31.4	55	36.4
Adopted contraception	942	97.9	142	94.0
AFDC[a] recipient	195	20.3	18	11.9
Last grade completed				
Less than 7	55	5.7	21	13.9
7 to 8	303	31.5	75	49.7
9 to 11	590	61.3	54	35.8
12	12	1.2	1	0.7
Total number initiated	962	86.4	151	13.6

[a] Aid to families with dependent children.

Figure 4–3.—*Cumulative probability of continuation for patients under age 18 at specified intervals after initiation into the Louisiana Family Planning Program, by race and parity based on samples (approximately 600 in each race/parity group) of girls initiated between July 1, 1971 and July 30, 1973 (Source: Reference 9)*

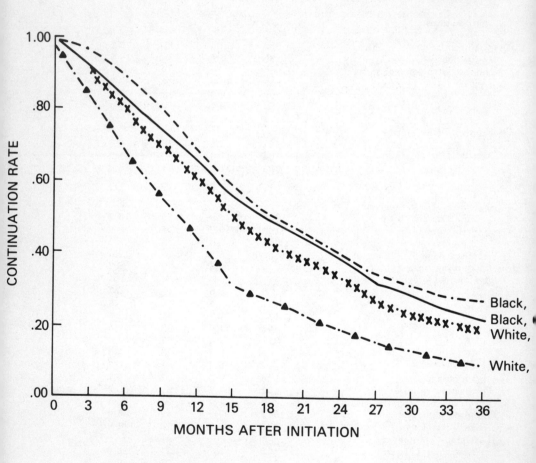

Retention rates, calculated as the number and percent active at designated time intervals and reflecting discontinuous program usage, show the same pattern but are higher than the continuation rates (table 4-3). At 24 months, more than half of the blacks were still in the program, as were close to half of the primiparous whites. Only slightly more than one-third of the nulliparous whites remained. At 36 months, the retention rates were double the continuation rates, but only the primiparous blacks showed retention above 0.50.

The most frequent reasons for first terminations for all four groups were classified as personal: patient moving away, going to a private doctor, refusing other suggested appointments, medical or surgical problems, and death (of which there were two, one was shot by her husband). The terminations were grouped together on the basis of personally stated reasons. Within this group, twice as many white girls as black indicated they were transferring to a private doctor (approximately 7.5 percent compared with 3.5 percent). Also the proportion desiring pregnancy, although generally

Table 4-3.—*Continuation and retention rates for patients under age 18 at specified intervals after initiation into the Louisiana Family Planning Program, by race and parity*[a]

Race and Parity	Months after initiation		
	12	24	36
Black, 0			
Continuation	0.663	0.400	0.226
Retention	0.740	0.587	0.425
White, 0			
Continuation	0.460	0.196	0.103
Retention	0.515	0.367	0.301
Black, 1			
Continuation	0.689	0.403	0.276
Retention	0.718	0.585	0.525
White, 1			
Continuation	0.623	0.337	0.195
Retention	0.663	0.466	0.348
Total Sample			
Continuation	0.611	0.336	0.202
Retention	0.662	0.504	0.342

[a]Based on samples (approximately 600 in each race/parity group) of girls initiated between July 1, 1971 and June 30, 1973.

Source: Reference 7.

very low, was higher for whites (5 percent compared with 2 percent).

The second most frequent reason for first closure for three groups (all blacks and the nulliparous whites) was failure to keep an appointment made on a followup home visit after a missed appointment. The situation is understandable. The young girls could not say "No" to the adult outreach worker who came to their homes even though the girls had no intention of keeping the appointment.

The third most frequent reason is a variation of the second. The girls had missed an appointment and were not located on followup. Combined with this reason were the "reason unknown" codes. These included girls who came back after an intervening pregnancy whose records should have been closed for missed appointments prior to conception and the records of cases overdue for closure that were found by the researchers during the updating.

Pregnancy, as a reason for first closure, occurred for a very small proportion in each group. It was highest (17 percent) for primiparous blacks. However, primiparous blacks had the highest continuation rate. More of this group perhaps had stayed until they were ready for a second pregnancy. Pregnancy rates could not be determined because of the high dropout rate due to followup loss. However, estimates derived by using the life table technique suggested that within 2 years, nulliparous whites had a higher probability (0.40) of pregnancy than the other race/parity groups. For those known to have become pregnant during the study period, there was a decrease in unplanned pregnancy, from 84 percent at entry to 64 percent subsequent to program use.

SUMMARY AND CONCLUSIONS

Many aspects of the teenage family planning clinic experience have been touched on in this chapter. A quick summary includes the following points:

- Availability of family planning services to teenagers has been worthwhile. Teenagers are at least initiating service and the unmarried and never-pregnant girls are doing so increasingly.
- Teenagers do not remain active participants for long. This fact is undoubtedly a function of why they went to the clinic in the first place. Some arrive at the clinic when they are pregnant and seek counsel. An estimated 20 percent of patients seek this service initially. Some come when they think they are pregnant and, "breathing a sigh of relief," either remain as clinic patients or leave with various vows about avoiding the next crisis situation. A few teenagers come with differing levels of motivation after a

pregnancy and vow that it will not happen again. Others come with determination to prevent pregnancy. This determination may be the strongest motivator when the decision has the support of a family member or a boyfriend. Some may come out of curiosity to see what contraception is about or to initiate practice of birth control first in the anonymity of a free clinic.

- There are indications that many girls think about trying the program, but do not follow through. About 6 percent of the initial appointments made to the teen clinics in Louisiana were not kept. This occurrence is probably associated with the difficulty of the decision to define oneself as "sexually active" and in need of contraceptive service.
- Preliminary findings suggest that girls who have had one pregnancy continue longer in an organized family planning program than never pregnant girls. Blacks, as a whole, continue longer without interruption than whites. Perhaps this finding is a biased "view from Louisiana," and needs more general testing. Also, the question of whether primiparous girls are more effective contraceptors than those who have never conceived needs further exploration.
- Finally, the suggestion is made that being 17 years old and near the end of high school is a crucial time for teenagers to use family planning service. Those who did not get pregnant until this age still had a chance to achieve other things. Perhaps the greatest unmet need is education in the early teen years to develop awareness of the true potentiality of early pregnancy.

APPENDIX

Classification of Teenagers' Reasons for Their Pregnancies

(1) Direct motivations[10]
   (a) Wanted to get married, pregnancy would expedite marriage.
   (b) Was planning marriage.
   (c) Wanted to leave home, which pregnancy precipitating marriage would expedite.
   (d) "To keep my boyfriend."
   (e) "My mother never loved me . . . wanted somebody to love me."
   (f) "Thought my father wouldn't beat me (anymore) if I got pregnant."

(2) Social facilitation
  (a) "My friends are doing the same thing but they are not pregnant."
  (b) "My friends must take some birth control stuff. I'm scared of that stuff."
  (c) "We be talking about everybody else having sex and being pregnant."
(3) Longterm courtship
  (a) "Been going steady for a year."
  (b) "Been knowing boyfriend for two years . . . just got too serious."
  (c) ". . . was having an affair about nine months."
(4) False ideas of protection
  (a) Method:
    (i) practiced withdrawal
    (ii) "Heard you could get caught only 7 days before your period and 7 days after."
    (iii) "Only get pregnant during your period."
  (b) Physical
    (i) "A doctor told me I probably couldn't get pregnant."
    (ii) "I thought I was too young to have a baby (age 15). I thought you had to be older."
    (iii) "Figured I wasn't developed enough to get pregnant."
(5) Self-blame
  (a) "I let it happen."
  (b) "I think deep down inside I wanted to get pregnant."
  (c) "I didn't use no protection."
  (d) ". . . because I am not as good as other people. I guess I'm bad."
(6) Fatalistic
  (a) "It didn't make no difference if I did or didn't get pregnant."
  (b) "I guess God just wanted it to happen. Everybody's got their time to go."
(7) Raped
(8) No explanation
  (a) "Just happened."
  (b) "Don't know."
  (c) "Don't like to think about it."

REFERENCES

1. National Center for Health Statistics. *Vital Statistics of the United States.* (by year) 1964–1974, Vol. I, *Natality,* Washington: U.S. Government Printing Office, (by year) 1966–1976.

2. Goldsmith, S. "San Francisco's Teen Clinic." *Fam. Plann. Perspect.* 1(2):23–26, 1969.
3. Hambridge, W. R. "Teen Clinics." *J. Obstet. Gynecol.* 43:458–460, 1974.
4. Paul, E. W., Pilpel, H., and Wechsler, N. F. "Pregnancy, Teenagers, and the Law, 1974." *Fam. Plann. Perspect.* 6:142–147, 1974.
5. Paul, E. W., Pilpel, H., and Wechsler, N. F. "Pregnancy, Teenagers, and the Law, 1976." *Fam. Plann. Perspect.* 8:16–32, 1976.
6. Zelnik, M. and Kantner, J. F. "Sexual and Contraceptive Experience of Young Unmarried Women in the United States, 1976 and 1971," *Fam. Plann. Perspect.* 9:55–71, 1977.
7. Currie, J. B., Jekel, J. F., and Klerman, L. "Subsequent Pregnancies among Teenage Mothers Enrolled in a Special Program." *Am. J. Public Health.* 62:1606–12, 1972.
8. Jekel, J. F., Klerman, L. V., and Bancroft, D. R. E. "Factors Associated with Rapid Subsequent Pregnancies among School-Age Mothers." *Am. J. Public Health.* 63:769–73, 1973.
9. Ktsanes, V. "The Teenager and the Family Planning Experience." Paper presented at the Conference on Determinants of Adolescent Pregnancy and Childbearing, Elkridge, Md., May 3–5, 1976. Washington: U.S. Government Printing Office, 1978.
10. Fischer, A. and Ktsanes, V. "Pregnant Teenagers: A Study of Some Who Marry and Some Who Do Not." Unpublished paper. Louisiana Family Planning Program, New Orleans, La., 1971.

DISCUSSION

The following people were the major participants in the discussion: R. Lincoln, F. Furstenberg, and K. Davis.

The main topics of discussion were the nature of the special teen clinics discussed and the reasons for the discontinuation of clinic attendance and contraceptive use.

Most family planning clinics for adolescents have rap sessions. However, little systematic information about the nature, content, and effects of these sessions is available. The special clinics in Louisiana offered sessions that girls could attend simply to learn more about sexuality and to discuss their concerns about it, while learning about reproduction and contraceptives. The girls could choose whether they would proceed from the discussion to actually obtaining contraceptives. A film "Twosome Blues," was shown, depicting a young couple who became sexually active and then were afraid the girl was pregnant. The film dealt with the couple's subsequent conversations and the girl's fears that she did not have anybody she could relate her problem to and obtain help. Various attitudes toward premarital coitus also were explored.

Sex education has to be extended to younger teenagers. In the Louisiana experience, black girls were more aware of the sequential reality of intercourse and pregnancy than white girls. Possibly, more of the black girls knew friends who had become pregnant. Although premarital pregnancy is not desired by most black teenagers, they appear to be more accepting of it and less likely to seek an abortion.

It is desirable to reach teenagers with contraceptive help before they become sexually active. Studies show teenagers tend to come for contraceptive help after being sexually active for a year or more. There is a high teenage rate of terminating clinic services. Many who terminate return after they have had a pregnancy. The tendency is to discontinue clinic attendance when the girl has ended a relationship and thinks she will not start another. There also is a high rate of failure to keep initial clinic appointments. Perhaps the girl has been pressured into accepting an appointment from an outreach worker, but actually does not wish to attend the clinic. Followup on missed appointments is difficult because most girls do not want letters or telephone calls from the clinic, in the fear that their parents will learn they are sexually active. Teenagers who have experienced a pregnancy seem to continue with the program longer than those who have not.

It was emphasized that family planning programs should particularly try to reach and hold sexually active younger adolescents who seem to have a less clear recognition than older ones that their risk of pregnancy is high.

Chapter 5

Toward a Reconceptualization of Adolescent Sexuality

Catherine S. Chilman
University of Wisconsin-Milwaukee

It is important to seek a broader than usual conceptualization of adolescent sexuality as related to both short- and long-range objectives. These objectives depend on the growth of knowledge and theory and the transformation of this knowledge and theory into effective policies and programs for young people.

What are the policy and program goals? Why should young people be served at all? It is useful to think of these questions in the broadest possible terms, rather than in the more specialized, population-planning frame of reference. For in the long run, population research, policies, and programs should be directed toward the enhancement of the quality of life.

Promotion of the quality of life, as it affects the individual and society, involves the physical, psychological, social, and economic welfare of all people. This welfare relates to all aspects of life, not only childbearing and childrearing, but to the way people feel and behave as sexual persons, male or female, and the way society thinks and behaves toward them.

ADOLESCENT SEXUALITY

Adolescent sexuality, like all human sexuality, is often described as the physical characteristics and capacities for specific sex behaviors, together with psychosocial learning, values, norms, and attitudes toward these behaviors. This description is broadened to include a sense of gender identity and related concepts, behavior, and attitudes about the self and others. Thus, sexuality pervades virtually every aspect of a person's life. It is affected by the totality of what it means to be a male or female: by one's past and present experiences and anticipations of the future, one's stage of development and life situation, one's physical and constitutional capacities and characteristics, and the type of society and period of time in which one lives.

This broad view of human sexuality has been adopted because it facilitates a more humane and dynamic understanding of males and females as they strive throughout their lives for growth, integration or homeostasis. Part of this understanding may be the recognition that all specific sex behaviors affect, and are affected by, one's sense of gender identity, motivations, values, and capacities.

The past few centuries have been characterized by a proliferation of specialized knowledge, social organizations, roles, and functions. This specialization has brought with it an awesome blooming of information and the enrichment of many human lives. It also has brought with it deeply disturbing fragmentations of self and society.

This fragmentation has occurred in the field of sexuality and in other aspects of the human condition. Specialized knowledge has made magnificent contributions to our understandings of genetics, human reproduction, the childbirth process, birth control techniques, the nature of sex responses, specific aspects of sex behavior, the developing of gender identity, and the sexual behavior of various species and of different human societies.[a] This knowledge has been tremendously useful in helping people lead rewarding, healthy lives, and has provided the means for controlling conception and childbirth.

This knowledge, however, has tended to create an overly technical view of sexuality focused on intercourse, reproduction, and contraception rather than on the needs and feelings of the total masculine or feminine person in relationship with the larger society. This knowledge has also had a part in the breakdown of previous traditional values that provide a certain stability and wholeness to life for people in western industrialized societies. The stability and wholeness has exacted its price: repression and denial of sexual interests, limited sexual fulfillment for many (especially females, who often also were objects of male sexual exploitation), difficulties in family size control, and high infant and maternal death rates. Now that these prices are sharply reduced, other costs are appearing. These costs involve a specialized, rational, value-free approach to human sexual behavior and functioning. Basically, this approach is largely genital and fails to include the total person as a male or female.

Males and females have particular vulnerabilities that are social and psychological in nature, especially in a culture that stresses the importance of the person as an individual. The sense of personhood of individual significance, is primarily derived from interpersonal relations. Being considered valuable, competent,

---

[a] The outstanding researchers in this field are listed, along with article titles and dates of publication, in the Bibliography.

uniquely important, and desirable by other people—especially people
who are of central importance to one's basic well-being—is how a
positive sense of self is derived. In childhood, these people may be
parents or parent substitutes and, to a lesser extent, other members of the extended kinship network and the child's community of
neighbors, peers, or teachers. In adult life, these people are apt to
be one's mate, children, relatives, peers, employers, and people in
the larger community.

The reaction of one person to another is greatly influenced by
gender. A sense of gender adequacy is central to a sense of self-
adequacy and is derived not only from specific sexual performance,
but from all interpersonal interactions, especially intimate ones.

In adolescence, the "significant others" are particularly variable and tenuous as young people move from immersion in the
family and simpler social systems toward greater independence,
distinctive self-identity, and an involvement in complex social systems. Although gaining and keeping self-assurance is difficult at
many life stages, it is particularly difficult at adolescence. The
adolescent is in the process of becoming a separate entity, and
lacks the support of intimately related, accepting, and acceptable
individuals who can provide assurance of the adolescent's value,
competence, and significance. The adolescent is vulnerable in virtually all aspects of life, and especially so in respect to his or her
sexuality.

When gender expectations are added to other sexual considerations, it becomes clear that being a female or male adolescent is
a sensitive human enterprise involving the total self in its most
intimate personal and interpersonal aspects.

The interpersonal aspects of sexuality are worthy of serious
consideration. Unlike other basic human functions, such as breathing, eating, sleeping, or less fundamental functions like working
and playing, sexual behavior (aside from masturbation) inevitably
involves the maximum exposure of the self to another. This exposure can be intensely reassuring to a sense of self-worth or, at the
other end of the continuum, intensely destructive.

The only other equally intimate interpersonal relationship is
that of pregnancy, childbirth, and breast feeding, functions that, of
course, are much more intense for females and more potentially
self-assuring in terms of gender and individual identity. Now that
present necessity makes reproduction control imperative, and technology makes it more readily possible, intercourse may become
"reproduction independent." The popular slogan, "Sex for recreation, not procreation," often is proclaimed.[1]

Pleasant as the slogan's prescription may be, it contributes
little to the sense of individual significance. It advocates a superficial "fun and games" approach to male and female personhood and

further removes the individual's sense of connection with basic life principles.

This is not to suggest that all people should become parents or have an unlimited number of children, but interpersonal sexual relations should be regarded as significant (as well as fun) and as involving important human vulnerabilities, despite the fact that reproductive outcomes can be controlled. The question is not simply, "Will a baby be the result of the human sexual encounter?" The point is that responsibility, commitment, and compassion for the self and others are not only required when parenthood is involved, but are needed for fulfilling intimate human relations whether or not a pregnancy may occur. Adults, as well as adolescents, are partly children and partly parents (in the psychological sense). Nurturance, trust, intimacy, and protection from and for each other in relationships are required if individuals are to be fully human. The need is greater for these qualities in an age when fewer children can be afforded by society and when society itself becomes increasingly impersonal and bureaucratic.

The dictum that some people propose, "Have any sex experiences you want, but don't get pregnant or become infected with a venereal disease," is essentially dehumanizing. It implies that society does not care what happens to the psychological or social person as long as his or her physical problems do not burden society.

To fully humanize sexuality, further knowledge should be obtained with respect to its social-psychological aspects. The power of sexuality to help or hurt the human personality needs to be more fully recognized. New values, appropriate to our times, have to be evolved to provide the protection of constraints as well as the exhilaration of freedom as guidelines for young males and females.

Hendin, particularly, calls attention to the loneliness and depersonalization of a group of (primarily) Columbia University students psychoanalytically studied. Most were sexually active but afraid of intimate committed interpersonal relationships.[2] In an attempt to take an unemotional approach to sex, they seemed to find little release or self-confirmation in their activities.

The current enchantment with nostalgia, the resurgent popularity of romantic novels that emphasize love rather than sex may be a search for ways to find rewarding male-female relationships beyond specific sexuality.

In an attempt to conceptualize adolescent sexuality as it affects the total person in the context of today's society, an effort is made here to synthesize a number of related research areas.

Adolescence is a period during which young people are moving from childhood, when they are incapable of reproduction, toward adulthood, when they are able to reproduce and when society expects and needs them to be competent to care for them-

selves and others, including children, if they should become
parents.

Of course, teenagers can become parents before they reach
adulthood. This significant fact is basic to what adolescence is all
about. Our society demands physical, social, and psychological
strengths of its adult members, especially of its parents, so that
they may cope effectively with life's opportunities and constraints
and, as parents, raise their children to do so.

Adolescent development tends to elicit heightened concern
about how well youngsters are "shaping up." As they emerge from
childhood it may become increasingly clear that some of their
problems and deficits probably are not something they will simply
outgrow. It becomes much more serious, for instance, when such
behavioral patterns as extreme shyness and withdrawal continue
and the adolescent norms of peer group membership and heterosexual "dating" are difficult to fulfill. Aggressive, explosive behavior
is usually viewed even more critically, particularly since the adolescent's increasing physical capacities can make him/her (more usually him) a direct threat to the family and society. In the case of
girls the fear of sexual "acting out" and a possible illegitimate
pregnancy is strong. Problems in learning and school adjustment
loom larger: will the youngster ever be able to "make it" in the
larger world?

PHYSICAL DEVELOPMENT

An increased release of hormones from the endocrine glands
stimulates the onset of puberty. These hormones include testoster-
one for males and estrogen for females. Endocrine action triggers
the growth spurt and secondary sex characteristics.

A wide variation within the sexes in rates of physical maturation tends to cause a good deal of anxiety among adolescents.[3]
Girls generally reach menarche at any time between the ages of
10 and 17, with an average age of 13. No such clear-cut distinction
occurs for males. On the average, the male growth spurt is
reached at age 14 and voice change at age 15.

The fact that girls mature earlier than boys sharpens conflicts
between the sexes. It creates insecurities for those males whose
socialization has led them to believe they should be stronger, big-
ger, and "sexier" than females. A number of studies suggest that
early maturing girls tend to suffer a social handicap at ages 11 or
12. Later, these handicaps are reversed. Early maturing boys apparently have consistent social advantages, at least through high
school.

Probably the male's ability to impregnate, and the female's
ability to conceive, generally does not develop until a year or so

after adolescence is reached. (This fact may be why some sexually active girls think they will "luckily not get pregnant.")

There is considerable argument as to whether a biologically determined sex drive exists. Simon and Gagnon,[1] for instance, contend that the desire for sexual gratification is largely learned and culturally determined. It appears that the motivation for masturbation, petting, intercourse, and other forms of sexual expression (voyeurism or exhibitionism) have a biological and a social base. The gratification potential is sharply increased by endocrine changes associated with adolescence. Behavior that achieves that potential promotes learned motivation for repetition of the behavior. The behavior is positively reinforced and, in this sense, is learned. Culture, of course, heavily affects sex-related values, perceived needs, and behaviors.

Kinsey's studies[6] indicated that the male sex drive and orgasmic capacity rise rapidly with the onset of adolescence and reaches a peak at about age 16 with variations in related sexual behavior occurring in association with the religiosity, educational, and occupational levels of the subject. The females studied by Kinsey reportedly experienced less specific sex needs, on the average, and perceived sex in more ambiguous and diffuse terms. Their orgasmic response is slower to develop and reaches its average peak at age 29.[7] Possibly, the differences between the sexes would be far less extreme today in association with societal changes that are far more permissive regarding female sexual behavior. Kinsey also found differences in female sexual behaviors in relation to their education, occupation, and religiosity.

COGNITIVE DEVELOPMENT

Cognitive development is related to sexuality in terms of the ability to understand and deal with sexual and gender capacities and behavior. The adolescent must foster verbal and interpersonal communications skills to perform effectively in school, work, and society. The development of these attributes is essential to the eventual formation of stable and secure relationships between mates and between parents and children.

These aspects of cognitive development in adolescents probably have a close association with the failure of many young sexually active teenagers to use contraceptives. Kantner and Zelnik [9] reported the reason given by adolescent girls: "I thought I wouldn't get pregnant." This reasoning shows not only a failure to understand the basic causes of pregnancy, but also reflects a poor capacity to project future possibilities from the realities of the moment.

Adelson,[10] in a study of the development of adolescent ideology from the end of grade school to completion of high school;

reports similar shifts of thinking. He concludes that childish perceptions are concrete and narrow and are swept away as the child advances through adolescence.

> He is ever more able to transcend the sheer particularity of an act, to place behavior within a web of circumstances . . . by expanding and commanding time, linking past to present and present to future; the act has a history and its effects extend forward in time. . . . The young adolescent is locked into the present. His view of the future is constricted; he may grasp the effect of today on tomorrow, but not on the day after tomorrow.

Apparently, young (and intellectually limited) adolescents would be unlikely to grasp the future significance of giving birth to a child, either within or outside of marriage. Another relevant finding reported by Adelson is that younger adolescents rarely reason logically a course of action in cost/benefit terms. They are more likely to make an arbitrary choice, based largely on impulse.

Moral development is linked closely to cognitive development and has implications for sex-related values and behavior. Moral development, like cognitive development, proceeds sequentially from simplistic, present-oriented concepts of rights and wrongs to more abstract, complex principles. According to the research of Kohlberg[11] (criticized by some for its limited samples and subjective methods of measurement), the formal operation stages of moral development, often starting at about age 12, includes these two steps:

1. The orientation to interpersonal mutuality ("I'll help you, you help me," or, the sexual giving as a path to sexual fulfillment as proposed by Masters and Johnson).[12]
2. The maintenance of social order through fixed rules and authority and on through several stages to the eventual highest order of stage 6, an orientation toward universal ethical principles chosen by the individual as having personal meaning rather than a mere adjustment to convention.

At more childish levels of moral development, Kohlberg[11] proposed stage 0: "The good is what I want and what I like," an attitude similar to a current proposed sex-related value, "If it feels good, do it." Stage 1 is a punishment-obedience orientation: "You're wrong if you get caught," or, perhaps, "Premarital coitus is all right as long as you don't get pregnant or a venereal disease." Stage 3 is instrumental hedonism and concrete reciprocity, somewhat similar to the Masters and Johnson[12] formulation, or, "What can I gain from having sex with him (her)?" This idea is similar to the exchange theory in Homan's[13] concept of human relations or the Skinner concept of programed learning and the specific reward structure.

Few adolescents (or even adults) proceed to stage 6, which requires an individual search for moral and ethical principles to which the individual can subscribe and to which he/she can hold in spite of pressures for opportunistic or conventional behavior.

It seems likely that, in the current period of general upheaval in moral values, adolescents would have a difficult time in defining even conventional values, not to mention universal principles to which they personally can subscribe. The inner pressures brought on by adolescent growth, the confusion of parents caught up in the maelstrom of current changes, and the opportunities and temptations for hedonistic behavior (including sexual expression) must conspire to create special problems for today's youth. However, the breakdown of old traditions can clear the way for less conventional, more individually developed moral values. A search for such values is evidenced by the growing beliefs in sincerity, honesty, egalitarianism, and interpersonal commitment.

THE SEARCH FOR PERSONAL IDENTITY

Erikson[14] has advanced the theory that late adolescence is marked by the search for personal identity, and the search for individually held moral values. He advocates allowing young people a period of "psychosocial moratorium." Young people are given the freedom to try many routes to personhood to enable them to integrate past identities and to find what patterns best suit their individual tastes, abilities, traits, and interests.

Personal identity and gender identity are, of course, closely allied. Even though sex role differentiations are becoming blurred, it still matters enormously to individuals whether they are males or females. Gender identity, like personal identity, is developed, for the most part, in the first few years of life. A person's view of self and of others, of goals and values, and of ways of being and feeling grow out of the earliest family experiences and are modified by other childhood experiences in the school, neighborhood, and community. All of these experiences are colored by whether one is male or female.

According to the findings of Douvan and Adelson[15] in a 1958 national study, girls find it more difficult than boys to obtain a separate identity. The tendency has been to seek self-identity first through their families, then through their boyfriends and, eventually through their husbands. Perhaps in today's society, with the push for equal sex roles and with less training for passivity and dependence, females will be more able to work independently toward their own sense of individual identity. Because marriage and motherhood no longer constitute the prescribed pattern of their lives, females should be able to establish an autonomous identity. Although this should be possible, it is not certain that it will occur.

It is dubious whether the majority of adolescents actually go through an intensive identity seeking process. This process requires a large cushion of affluence, cultural values that support individual development, a high order of intelligence, a wide range of environmental opportunities, and freedom from responsibilities such as marriage or parenthood. Douvan and Adelson[15] found that an early foreclosure of personal identity development was the more frequent pattern. Although Erikson and others have regarded this as a serious problem in terms of wasted individual potentialities and denial of parts of the self, this perception may not be accurate in respect to most young people. Offer and Offer[16] found that their sample of middle-class, urban, white boys revealed considerable life satisfaction and little rebellion (or identity crisis upheavals) during their high school years. A smaller subject group showed considerable, but not extreme, disturbance, and a few appeared to be deeply troubled.

Almost no recent studies exist on the development of gender identity during adolescence. The clinical work of John Money and his associates[17,18] reveals that severe psychological disturbance is found among their patients when this issue is in doubt. Although theirs is a special clinic population of people suffering from physical sex and gender anomalies, their findings are suggestive for the larger population.

In these days of confusion over sex roles and appropriate sexual behavior for males and females, it must be exceptionally difficult to establish a clear sense of gender identity. A reflection of this problem may be the increasing incidence (or at least emergence) of homosexuals in the population, rising rates of premarital and extramarital coitus among males and females (especially females), rising divorce rates, lower rates of marriage among the young, rising rates of teenage illegitimacy, and a birth rate that continues to decline.

Not enough attention has been given in research to the sociocultural development of youngsters, nor to the impact on them of the socioeconomic, racial, ethnic, regional, religious, or particular age group to which they belong. Space limitations prevent an adequate treatment of this subject, but considerable variation in adolescent development and behavior (including its sexuality aspects) does occur.

Subcultures within U.S. society tend to take different views of adolescent sexuality. For instance, related values and attitudes among low-income black people in urban ghettos (where the few available studies have been performed) tend, for the most part, to be fairly accepting of premarital intercourse for male and female teenagers. The double standard is less strong, and virginity at marriage is less highly valued. In general, when one attempts to seek causes of adolescent sex behavior and early childbearing, it is important to recognize that these causes are multiple and relate differentially to different subgroups within the population.

MALE-FEMALE DIFFERENCES

Most research and survey data about people are presented in terms of gender. This division recognizes that, indeed, males and females are different. Yet, the usual conception of sexuality is, in this author's opinion, a masculine one. This appears to be the reason that it is usually specifically genital and coital.

Males and females are different biologically, and no matter how one may attempt to equalize sex roles and change socialization, biology affects, though it does not determine, destiny. Females have a more dual conception of their sexuality than do males. Males have a specifically genital-coital approach to sexuality, and females have a coital and a reproductive orientation. Women are the ones who can become pregnant, go through the long gestation period, give birth, and lactate. Even if modern contraceptive techniques, including abortion, are available, generally it is the female who uses the contraceptives and always the female who has the abortion. Biologically, the male has to be involved for a few minutes to impregnate the female. From that time onward, the male can more or less decide on his degree of involvement with the female and the child.

Moreover, the male is physically stronger than the female. He can usually force coitus upon her if he chooses. Thus, the female must take a self-protective stance toward the male. She must be wary of his strength, his penetration of her, and his ability to impregnate her. If she becomes pregnant, she needs him to remain involved to protect and support her and the child. Thus females, more than males, tend to be impressed by personal stability and earning potential of their possible mates.

Maccoby and Jacklyn's[19] recent analytic review and summary of related research concludes that no systematic psychological differences can be found between males and females except that, on the average, males are fundamentally more aggressive than females and more competent in their discrimination of spatial relations. The latter does not directly concern us but the former certainly does. If males tend to be inherently more aggressive than females, the females clearly need to defend themselves against uncontrolled masculine aggression.

Although some researchers claim that females are inherently more nurturant than males, Maccoby and Jacklyn[19] fail to find clear evidence to support this contention. Newton,[20] however, showed that the female orgasmic release during intercourse and reactions during childbirth have strikingly physical similarities, thus linking her dual sexual function as mate and mother.

Also, breastfeeding is erotically stimulating to women, and its stimulative effects cause uterine contractions. The eroticism involved in breast stimulation, both in sex play and in breastfeeding, further underlines the complexity of the mating and mothering functions.

Unlike males, females generally need considerable foreplay and body caressing to become sexually aroused and ready for intercourse. They are more psychologically sensitive to the total relationship than are males and find it difficult to be sexually responsive if there are psychological barriers between them and their partners. Then, too, females (more than males) can be easily distracted during lovemaking by outside stimuli, especially perhaps, the cry of their children.

For the foregoing reasons, each related to the mate-mother connection, females are especially apt to be deeply involved in psychosocial and physical ways with their mate. Research studies reveal that most adolescent girls say they can accept premarital intercourse only in the context of a close, loving relationship.[21, 22] In the past few years, these expressed attitudes are changing somewhat, with many females espousing the value of premarital coitus simply because it is enjoyable, regardless of the closeness of the relationship.[23] Self-reported rates of premarital intercourse are rising and becoming equal or almost equal for both sexes, according to recent studies of some high school and college populations. Perhaps the so-called double standard is disappearing.[24]

The population explosion, along with the need to control the birth rate, has devalued the female mother role. Teenage girls (as well as older women) are, therefore, appearing to develop a more specifically genital-coital view of sex, irrespective of its reproductive and maternal aspects. This finding may suggest that women may be denying some basic biological aspects of their fertility. Much of civilization, however, rests on a control of human biological tendencies, so this development is not necessarily unique.

In fact, Sherfey[25] argues that the female has a stronger orgasmic capacity than the male (often interpreted as sex drive) and that, for this reason, the female, over the centuries, has been socialized toward inhibition and denial of her sexual self. Otherwise, she would totally exhaust her male partner and destroy civilization with her sexual appetite. If Sherfey is right, these developments should occur in the near future.

Sherfey's observations can be viewed as being speculative. Masters and Johnson,[12] however, offer evidence that females are more capable of multiple orgasms than males. Females also can fake sexual excitement and orgasmic response whereas males cannot.

Males are much more "on the spot" for competent sexual performance than females (perhaps one of the reasons that some male psychologists equate a sense of competence with positive mental health).

The male focus on genital-coital sex and his need to prove his virility is probably closely related to the findings of Money and Tucker.[18] Male fetal development is far more likely to go astray than female. As Sherfey[25] pointed out in her 1966 literature review, the human embryo is basically female until 6 weeks of age, at which time endocrine action within the genetic male promotes development of male biological characteristics. This action has to be strong enough to counteract the endocrine influence present in the maternal placenta. As Money and Tucker[18] put it, "Nature's original intent is to make a female." Hence, sexual anomalies at birth are much more common for males than females. The male fetus is more vulnerable than the female. It has been estimated that conceptions number 140 male to 100 female; at birth, male babies outnumber female babies about 112 to 100; by age 30, females in the population outnumber males.

Hence, considerable evidence indicates that the male, on the average, is biologically more vulnerable than the female, including his genital equipment and coital functioning. While the female is vulnerable to impregnation, the male is more vulnerable in terms of his ability to impregnate. The male can never be absolutely sure that his reproductive mission has been accomplished. Although the female can be sure that she has mothered a child, the male can never have this absolute confidence in his fathering role.

Furthermore, culture has put heavy pressures on males for heroic and virile accomplishments. As the former hunters and defenders of the tribe, they are still expected to be strong achieving protectors and supporters of themselves and their families. This concept has been fading of late.

Males formerly achieved a good deal of automatic physical superiority over females because the latter were frequently pregnant, consumed with child care, often in ill health, and often died in childbirth. Now that most women in our society can control the reproductive outcomes of coitus (although often with some discomfort or personal hardship), their possible innate superiority for physical survival and endurance under stress becomes more evident and threatening.

Another threat for the beleaguered male is the fact that girls, on the average, mature physically earlier than boys. This earlier maturation and an earlier socialization along with lower aggressive responses tend to promote earlier acquisition of interpersonal social skills in girls. Thus, boys between the ages of 12 and 18 or so are apt to feel socially inferior to girls in mating relationships. This attitude, coupled with extremely high genital and coital response capacities, can create an agonizing impasse for adolescent boys.

If we accept that females have a dual view of their sexuality as potential or actual mates and mothers, if we recall the original female component in the male embryo and the biological struggle to become and remain a male, and if we add to this that most males are predominantly reared by females, we can understand that males may basically wish only a direct, coital penetrative contact with females (and a quick one at that). They may resist, or even fear, further involvement with them. Thus, the anxiety of most males about their virility and their need to prove themselves sexually, especially when they lack other sources of self-esteem, can be more clearly understood. (An example of this may be the machismo orientation of many low-income, especially minority group, males.)

The previous speculative comments about male and female sexuality apply with particular cogency to young men and women, including adolescents. As, and if, males and females gain greater self-security, increased interpersonal skills, and a surer sense of their own gender and personal identities during their middle and later years, they can, perhaps, rejoice in their differences as men and women and take pleasure in their basic similarities as people. The more adults are able to understand, accept, and support psychosocial and biological aspects of adolescent sexuality, the more they may be able to come to terms with their own sexuality, including its adolescent aspects that still affect adult lives to some degree.

A positive sense of gender identity does not relate exclusively to mate relationships or reproductive abilities, but to many gender roles (daughter or son, sister or brother, aunt or uncle, and membership in same sex groups). Apparently, the more assurance and satisfaction adolescents find in these gender roles, the less they will need the reassurance of gender adequacy that mate relationships can bring. For instance, Kantner and Zelnik[26] found that girls who do not confide much in their parents are especially apt to have premarital coitus (Chilman obtained the same finding in an as yet unpublished 1974 investigation of University of Wisconsin freshmen).[27] Ladner's[28] anthropological study of inner city black girls indicates similar findings.

CHANGING MORES

At present, the rules for adolescents as sexual beings are not as clear as they once were. Not too long ago there were many sanctions against premarital intercourse for teenagers. Adolescence was seen by the mainstream culture as a period of sexual frustration, guilt, and fears. Much was written about unhappy adolescents who matured physically at ages 12 or 13 but who were supposed to refrain from coitus until they married at about age 20. They were to keep themselves pure until Mr. or Mrs. Right came along. After a prolonged courtship, engagement, and marriage, they were to form a family that Mr. Right supported by making a living. Mrs. Right stayed home with the kids. They were to keep their sexuality purely within marital boundaries so they could bring up pure children who would repeat the pure process.

Purity as an ideal was particularly cherished for girls. Boys were expected to be boys, after all, but express their so called carnal drives with "bad girls" whom one never loved or married. With "good girls," sexual interests were to be restrained and romanticized. Hence, the double standard.

Sex roles also were fairly clear. Adolescent males were to prepare themselves arduously for steady jobs to enable them to protect and support their helpless little wives and dependent children. Teenage females also worked arduously to attract and hold worthy males who would love and take care of them forever. Women were to develop homemaking and mothering skills and minor occupational abilities to contribute to the family purse before the children were born, and, perhaps, contribute again after the children were grown.

If a "good girl" should become "bad" and, even worse, become pregnant, a major crisis ensued. Families and schools expelled the culprit. She often left town, it was whispered, to get an illegal abortion or have the baby and place it for adoption. If she kept the baby, her chances for finishing school, getting a job, and finding a respectable husband were considered ruined. Her child was branded a bastard and was often an outcast. Social agencies were set up to deal with what was considered to be a problem of nearly overwhelming proportions. Psychiatric consultations were sought to determine the deep personality disturbance that led the girl into such outrageous behavior.

Those of us who grew up in those days still carry a sense of deep concern about the sexual activities of the young (particularly the female young and most particularly if they should have children out of marriage). We tend to be sure that this attitude creates serious lifelong problems for these girls and their children.

On the other hand, reason and logic lead to the understanding that times have changed. The bitter controls of youth, the frustrated longings, the guilty adventures across moral barriers rise to memory and we cannot be sure these earlier guidelines are relevant to contemporary conditions. Virginity originally emerged as a value when there was property for males to inherit and hold. It was important to men to be certain that their heirs were really their sons. The inheritance tax, disappearance of land as a major source of wealth, jobs for women, the equal rights movement, and the availability of modern contraceptives and abortion leaves virginity with virtually no rationale.

These developments, and other major changes in society, have led to a general questioning about what controls, if any, should be applied to sexual behavior, and what distinctions, if any, should be made between male and female sex roles. Now that effective contraceptives are readily available, and marriage/parenthood is considered one of many lifestyle options, what are the sex and gender issues and goals for adolescent youth?

ADOLESCENT SEXUALITY AND CONTEMPORARY SOCIETY

These questions are related to the kind of society in which adolescents find themselves and the kind of society they anticipate for the future. The major characteristics of contemporary American society include a highly developed technology, enormous public and private bureaucracies that operate on national and international levels, almost instantaneous worldwide communication, mechanization of virtually all aspects of life, a high degree of urbanization (though limited countertrends are now visible), a huge quantity of mass-produced consumer goods, and rapid social and economic change.

Outgrowths of this kind of society include a high standard of living for over half of the population (dangerously higher than that of the rest of the world); international tensions; the ever-present threat of nuclear global destruction; widespread materialism; increased demands for females as workers; an increased involvement of women in the work force; a decrease in craft skills and work that requires the superior physical strength of men; a resultant shift toward equal roles between the sexes; overpopulation; air and water pollution; threats to the supply of the world's natural resources; economic crises of inflation, depression, and unemployment; a breakdown of neighborhoods, communities, and previously held cultural values; a growing instability of families; a lack of family formation; the concentration of power in industry, military, and mass communication systems; and the polarization of racial, ethnic, and socioeconomic groups within the population.

There is a belief that the United States, as a society, is falling apart. The 1960's historically may be viewed as a profoundly revolutionary decade. The first 5 years of that decade represented an attempt to resuscitate a dying social and economic period. President Kennedy's slogan was, "Get America moving again." There were those famous words, "Ask not what your country can do for you, but what you can do for your country." The early Johnson years almost countered the tragic shock of President Kennedy's assassination with the exhilarating push for "the Great Soci-

ety," the "war against poverty," support for the rising aspirations
for "equal opportunity" on the part of many minority groups. The
high point may have come in 1965, with the romantic fervor to
resuscitate the American dream of "liberty and justice for all" and
a "government of the people, by the people, for the people." The
dream dissolved for the most part, in this author's opinion, because
of the United States' vast national economic and political power
operations in many parts of the world. Some believe that the
United States was corrupted by that power, with its most apparent
manifestations being the involvement in Vietnam and the related
withdrawal from commitment to domestic reforms. The assassina-
tions of Robert Kennedy and Martin Luther King (symbols to
many Americans of the best national hopes) were dramatic expres-
sions of growing corruption and societal dissolution.

What of the young people born in the 1950's (often called the
"Age of Apathy") and growing up in this period? The lives of
most of us were shaken by the 1957 launching of Sputnik. Sudden-
ly, the Soviet Communist "menace" was escalated. Soviet scientists
were better than America's! Drastic action was required, including
a strong national push for more rigorous scientific education of the
young. Away with fun, games, and humanistic concerns on the
part of the educational system. Up with science, intellectual
achievement, scholastic competition! The national anxiety even pervaded the nursery school. Youngsters were pushed for excellence in
mathematics and the hard sciences at all levels of their schooling.
The soft fields (social sciences and humanities) could not survive
unless they, too, became scientifically rigorous. Girls, as well as
boys, were pushed into the academic race, because the national
peril seemed to require the heretofore "dubious" intellectual talents
of females as well as the more "respected" talents of males.

Anxiety for academic achievement pervaded many homes and
the young people in them. Hordes of youngsters were converted to
the rational scientific approach and the potential miracles of science were glorified throughout society. Economic recession during
the same years increased the anxieties of the populace as did the
growing racial tensions related to the rising tide of urban inmigra-
tion of black people, displaced by the industrialization of agricul-
ture in the rural south.[3] (These developments, among others of the
late 1950's, may well have led to the decline in the birth rate that
started at that time.)

The early 1960's constituted a period of rising hope and idealism for many American adults, young people, and children. When
the directions of society shifted radically in the mid-1960's, this
hope and idealism were replaced by a growing despair and cynicism, a sense of personal powerlessness and disillusionment with
social institutions, the government, education, organized religion,
the intellectual and professional establishment, and the family. Sci-

ence delivered more problems (biochemical warfare, air and water pollution, tear gas and mace to quell domestic riots and demonstrations, and invasion of private lives through the computer) than it resolved.

These developments gave a strong push to the "counterculture"—widely perceived as a revolutionary youth culture. (It is recognized that the so-called youth revolution occurred in many other parts of the world at the same time. Developments in the United States simply had their own particular versions of this movement.) Many young people saw themselves harassed by an authoritarian, hypocritical society. Owing to the 1948–1958 baby boom, almost half of the population was under age 25, and their numbers alone appeared to constitute a threat.

The huge group of dissident youth were particularly viewed by the Nixon administration and its supporters as a danger to the entire Nation. Increasingly repressive measures were used to "keep youth in line." Youth resistance escalated in response to these measures and to the continued involvement in Vietnam. A high point in the overt youth rebellion was reached in the early 1970's. Many young people became increasingly politicized and active in antiwar demonstrations. There was the involvement in the 1972 political campaign in which liberal and radical youth gave strong support to Senator McGovern, President Nixon's opponent. The overwhelming defeat of their candidate left many young people feeling hopeless. The ending of the Vietnamese war left many without a central cause. Reforms on the campuses toward less academic pressure and rigidities and more opportunities for student participation in academic affairs reduced the student drive for educational reform. A growing economic recession and rising unemployment among youths created anxieties about individual economic security. Affluent youth, who had railed against security preoccupations of the older generation, developed similar concerns as material success was no longer easily at hand.

Earlier movements for equal rights between the races, increased opportunities for the poor, and sweeping social and economic reform were replaced by the push for sexual liberation (equal rights for women, homosexuals, and for those who chose alternative life styles). Although these movements clearly call for equal employment and educational rights, they also are concerned with equal personal and familial rights.

A central aspect of these movements is an insistence on freedom for self-expression and self-actualization. A major preoccupation of the 1970's has been a turning inward from the larger society, that frequently has been regarded as hopeless and a threat to personal freedoms, to liberation and fulfillment through individual and interpersonal expression. It might be termed a psychological, rather than a sociopolitical age. In some respects, it is like the

1950's, although the women's movement for equality is a radical difference.

One aspect of this movement is a heightened awareness by women that they are no longer willing to be the only ones to perform the nurturant, caretaking, self-abnegating service functions of a society. Women are seeing themselves as being able to do virtually anything done by men. They are freed by opportunities for employment outside the home, by increased access to higher education, by the "intercourse independent" contraceptives, by anti-natalist attitudes, by technologies that make housework and child-care comparatively simple, and by better medical care.

The population explosion, together with the widespread recognition that it must be controlled through smaller family size (or nonparenthood), releases and traps women. They are released from the social obligation of bearing children. They are trapped, in a sense, by their recognition that their reproductive capacities are no longer valued—in fact, they are disvalued. An earlier basic rationale of the major mission of feminity has been severely shaken if not swept away. Motherhood and altruism are closely linked. Since motherhood has been denigrated as a central feminine function, women see little point in behaving altruistically. Moreover, fewer women have training in altruism through the mothering process. Motherly, altruistic attitudes are a positive handicap in the competitive employment arena.

As women become less altruistically, humanistically oriented, louder and louder cries are heard, especially from the males for a rebirth of altruism in our society. Male liberation groups are being formed to find ways of liberating males from their competitive, achievement-oriented, power-driven attitudes and behavior. Perhaps they are finding the need to be more giving and nurturant as women refuse to assume these roles automatically.

These shifts are related to current trends toward antiscientism. Many of today's young people, pushed for intellectual achievement in the late 1950's and early 1960's, are reacting against these pressures, especially because they can see few gains and many losses through such an approach. The scientific wonders of the intrauterine device and oral contraceptives produce adverse side effects in some cases.

The "retreat inward," the disenchantment with rationality, science, and constituted authority has led, for some, to fascination with drugs, mysticism, new religious cults, various forms of encounter groups, astrology, rural living, communes and cooperatives, worship of the primitive, naturalism (as in the case of organic foods, crafts, and having babies outside of marriage), and many forms of sexual experimentation.

More recently, a reaction to these developments resulted in a reemphasis on the family, the potential of a rising birth rate, perhaps a greater interest in romantic love, growing antiabortion sentiment, and a greater academic seriousness on the part of students. Whether this reaction is a temporary response to current trends remains to be seen.

The drastic change toward far more permissive egalitarian sexual and sex role attitudes and behaviors is true not only of college youths but also of the so-called blue collar youth.[30] It also is true, though to a lesser extent, of older people in the population. These attitudes increasingly permeate younger adolescents (and, for all we know, children).

Among the symptoms are higher rates of premarital coitus among those at the high school and college levels (with a sharp increase from about 20 percent of females under age 19 or 20, from the late 1920's to early 1960's, to 40 percent by the late 1960's and, perhaps, 70 percent or higher of college groups by the mid-1970's).[24]

A similar increase, though not so marked, has occurred for adolescent males. The comparatively sparse available data suggest that the rates have risen from about 25 to 40 percent from the late 1920's to the early 1960's, to about 65 percent in the late 1960's, and 80 percent for those of college age in the mid-1970's.[24] Rather expectedly, these increased rates of premarital coitus in the past decade are similar to increased rates of illegitimate births. However, the coital rates far exceed those for out-of-wedlock births by about five to six times in a given year. Apparently, the rates for the two sexes have become increasingly similar during the past 10 years. Participation in premarital intercourse is becoming the norm, rather than deviant behavior as previously believed, for males and females over age 18.

There seems to be relatively little promiscuity among sexually active adolescents. Commitment to a loving, nonexploitative, temporary monogamous relationship is a strongly held value by the majority. Numerous simultaneous or promiscuous sexual relationships tend to be associated, in at least one study[31] with such personality characteristics as anxiety, low self-esteem, narcissism, and poor parent-child relationships.

In previous decades when so much emphasis was placed on premarital virginity or premarital coitus only within a loving, marriage-oriented relationship, petting was used as a substitute for intercourse. With the advent of "intercourse-dependent" contraceptives for females, along with other changing attitudes and values consonant with a changed society, coitus is replacing premarital petting. Apparently for the majority of today's older adolescents, premarital virginity is no longer an important value.

Turning to a consideration of sex role behaviors by today's adolescents, one can observe far more equality between males and females than was seen 10 or 15 years ago. Along with the decline in the double standard, attitudes are shifting toward a virtual interchangeability of roles in interpersonal relationships, and in home life, employment, and recreation. It is clearly appropriate to rid society of sex role steroetypes that belong to earlier days and life situations. Currrently, arguments abound as to whether equality between the sexes can be, or should result in, complete sameness between them. Biological differences, at least, argue that sameness is an impossibility. These puzzles must be solved by society, particularly by its young members who have their lives ahead of them.

SOCIAL STRATIFICATION AND ADOLESCENT SEXUALITY

The social class system in the United States is considerably less rigid than in many other countries. Individuals move up and down the socioeconomic ladder (as defined by occupation, education, and income), but movement on a large scale is relatively rare, especially for minority group members (blacks, native Americans, and Spanish speaking Americans). Although the average per capita income has risen markedly in the past 20 years, inflation has consumed much of this rise. Income distribution has not changed at all. Among the Nation's poorest are the young, the old, members of families headed by females, residents of inner cities and decaying rural areas, members of minority groups, and people with little education and few employment skills. Several recent large-scale studies[32,33] show that further education and job-training for long-term victims of poverty and discrimination generally fail to provide the anticipated effects of helping these groups move to a higher socioeconomic status. Most are locked into a societal system that blocks their life chances from early infancy.

The resulting life experiences strongly affect all aspects of their functioning, behavior, attitudes, and goals, including those in the broad area of sexuality. Illegitimacy, premarital and extramarital coitus, family breakdown, and large family size tend to be higher for these groups.

SOME SUGGESTIONS FOR FUTURE PROGRAMS AND POLICIES

The issues that have been discussed have many program and policy implications. The questions raised suggest that family planning programs need a reorganization to make them more human. These programs need to work with the total person in the context of his or her stage of development, values and goals, feelings about the self, and present life situation. Greater efforts are needed to reach males and females to provide service supports for them in their interpersonal and sexual relationships. Beyond the specific family planning program, a need exists for increased attention to the needs of adolescents in respect to their family relationships, their physical and mental health, income, and educational and vocational development.

SOME SUGGESTIONS FOR FUTURE RESEARCH

There is a need for comprehensive, multidisciplinary longitudinal studies that seek to learn more about the development of adolescents, as males and females, in the broad context of sexuality. Such research should provide a valuable understanding of the causes and consequences of a wide range of adolescent behavior that include premarital sexual activities, contraceptive use, abortion, and early childbearing, within and outside of marriage.

SUMMARY

Adolescent sexuality, like all sexuality, includes the physical, social, psychological, and economic aspects (not only specifically sexual aspects, but also those related to gender identity and sex role behavior). This broader view of sexuality is needed if society is to arrive at a humane, integrated understanding of adolescent males and females as thinking, feeling people interacting with peers and society.

The essential nature of adolescence is sexual maturation, a movement from a dependent, sexually immature child to an independent, sexually mature adult. Because adolescents may become parents in the near or distant future, both the adolescent and society have a stake in their physical health, socialization, intellectual competence, and emotional development.

Although adolescence is not necessarily a period of extreme stress, it is accompanied by pervasive sex-related physical changes that require numerous adjustments, increased sexual behavior and interest, new issues with respect to personal and gender identity, and increased pressures from the outer society.

Adolescents grow and change intellectually, cognitively, ideologically, and physically during the years of maturation. These changes are likely to increase, over time, their understanding of themselves as sexual beings, their abilities to handle interpersonal relationships effectively, and their capacity to plan their behavior with an eye to future outcomes and present pleasures. A concern is that they may make important life choices such as parenthood before they are developmentally ready for such roles.

Present societal and cultural developments are important factors in promoting current trends for adolescents: A marked decline in the double standard, earlier sexual behaviors, higher rates of premarital coitus and increased acceptance of sexual expression, rising illegitimacy rates, rising rates of venereal disease, and lower rates of early marriage.

Earlier scripts for adolescents have almost disappeared. They emphasized a clear and different sex role for the male and female and a control of sexual desires in anticipation of a happy, permanent marriage and parenthood. What the life script for today's teenager may be is decidedly murky. Emerging values, such as love, freedom, interpersonal honesty, open communication, self-actualization, short-term commitments, and nonexploitation, have an appealing ring of sincerity. How workable they are remains to be seen.

Biological differences between the sexes cannot readily be denied, although biology is not a sole determinant of sexual behavior. Now that the reproductive capacities of males and females are largely disvalued as a result of the population explosion, new ways need to be found to confirm one's sense of gender worth and significance. This statement is especially true for females and it is among females that the most marked changes in sex-related attitudes and behavior are seen.

Large-scale trends and data from research findings about adolescent sexual behavior can be misleading. Fallacies in understanding the nature, causes, and consequences of adolescent sexuality may result unless subgroup characteristics within the larger population and a wide range of variables from many disciplines are considered. A broader conceptualization of adolescent sexuality in programs, policies, and research can lead to such an understanding.

ACKNOWLEDGMENTS

This paper is based, in large part, on a much more extensive report prepared by the author under contract with the Behavioral Sciences Branch, Center for Population Research, National Institute of Child Health and Human Development. (Contract No. NO1–HD–52821). The report title is *Social and Psychological Aspects of Adolescent Sexuality: An Analytic Review of Related Research Together With Implications for Further Research, Programs and Policies.*

REFERENCES

1. Simon W. and Gagnon, J. *The Sexual Scene.* Chicago: Aldine Publishing Co., 1973.
2. Hendin, H. *The Age of Sensation.* New York: Norton and Co., 1975.
3. Conger, J. *Adolescence and Growth.* New York: Harper and Row, 1973.

4. Faust, M. "Developmental Maturity as a Determinant in Prestige of Adolescent Girls." *Child Dev.* 31:173–184, 1960.
5. Clausen, J. "The Social Meaning of Differential Physical and Sexual Maturation." *In* Dragastin, Sidney, and Elder, Glenn, Eds., *Adolescence and the Life Cycle.* New York: Hemisphere Press, 1975.
6. Kinsey, A. C., Pomeroy, W., and Martin, C. *Sexual Behavior in the Human Male.* Philadelphia: W. B. Saunders Co., 1948.
7. Kinsey, A. C., Pomeroy, W., Martin, C., and Gebhard, P. H. *Sexual Behavior in the Human Female.* Philadelphia: W. B. Saunders, Co., 1953.
8. Piaget, J. "Intellectual Evaluation from Adolescence to Adulthood." *Hum. Dev.* 15:1–12, 1972.
9. Kantner, J. and Zelnik, M. "Contraception and Pregnancy: Experience of Young Married Women in the U.S." *Fam. Plann. Perspect.* 5(1):21–35, 1972.
10. Adelson, E. *Sexuality and Psychoanalysis.* New York: Brunner-Mazel, 1975, pp. 67–68.
11. Kohlberg, L. "Development of Moral Character and Moral Ideology." *In* Hoffman, L., and Hoffman, M., Eds., *Child Development Research.* Vol. 1. New York: Russell Sage Foundation.
12. Masters, W. and Johnson, V. *Human Sexual Response.* Boston: Little, Brown and Co., 1966.
13. Homans, G. *The Human Group.* New York: Harcourt Brace, 1950.
14. Erickson, E. *Identity: Youth and Crisis.* New York: Norton and Co., 1968.
15. Douvan, E. and Adelson, J. *The Adolescent Experience.* New York: John Wiley and Sons, 1966.
16. Offer, D. and Offer, J. *The Psychological World of the Teenager.* New York: Basic Books, 1969.
17. Money, J. and Ehrhardt, A. *Man and Woman, Boy and Girl.* Baltimore: The Johns Hopkins University Press, 1972.
18. Money, J. and Tucker, P. *Sexual Signatures.* Boston: Little, Brown and Co., 1975.
19. Maccoby, E. and Jacklin, C. *The Psychology of Sex Differences.* Stanford: Stanford University Press, 1974.
20. Newton, N. and Newton, M. "Psychological Aspects of Lactation." *N. Engl. J. Med.* 277(22):1179–1188, 1967.
21. Ehrmann, W. *Premarital Dating Behavior.* New York: Holt, Rinehart and Winston, 1959.
22. Reiss, I. *The Social Context of Sexual Permissiveness.* New York: Holt, Rinehart and Winston, 1967.
23. Bell, R. and Chaskes, J. "Premarital Sexual Experiences Among Coeds, 1958 and 1968." *J. Marr. Fam.* 32(1):81–84, 1970.

24. Chilman, C. *Adolescent Sexuality in a Changing American Society: Social and Psychological Perspectives.* Washington: U.S. Government Printing Office, 1978.
25. Sherfey, M. J. "The Evaluation and Nature of Female Sexuality in Relation to Psychoanalytic Theory." *J. Am. Psychoanal. Assoc.* 14(1):28–128, 1966.
26. Kantner, J. and Zelnik, M. J. "Sexual Experiences of Young Unmarried Women in the U.S." *Fam. Plann. Perspect.* 4(4):9–17, 1972.
27. Chilman, C. Unpublished paper. University of Wisconsin-Milwaukee, 1974.
28. Ladner, J. A. *Tomorrow's Tomorrow: The Black Women.* Garden City: Doubleday and Co., 1971.
29. Campbell, D. "New Directions in Psychology." *Am. Psychol.* Nov., 1975.
30. Yankelovich, D. *The New Morality.* New York: McGraw-Hill, 1974.
31. Sorenson, R. *Adolescent Sexuality in Contemporary America.* New York: World Publishers, 1973.
32. Jencks, C., Smith, M., Acland, H., Bane, M. J., Cohen, D., Gintis, H., Heyns, B., and Michelson, S. *Inequality: A Reassessment of the Effects of Family and Schooling in America.* New York: Basic Books, 1972.
33. Kenniston, K. *All Our Children.* Carnegie Council on Children. New York: Harcourt Brace Jovanovich, 1977.

BIBLIOGRAPHY

Benedek, T. *Psychosexual Functions in Women.* New York: Ronald Press, 1952.

Ford, S. and Beach, F. *Patterns of Sexual Behavior.* New York: Harper Bros., 1951.

Kantner, J. and Zelnik, M. "Sexual Experiences of Young Unmarried Women in the U.S." *Fam. Plann. Perspect.* 4(4):9–17, 1972.

Kantner, J. and Zelnik, M. "Contraception and Pregnancy: Experience of Young Unmarried Women in the U.S." *Fam. Plann. Perspect.* (1):21–35, 1973.

Kinsey, A. C., Pomeroy, W., and Martin, C. *Sexual Behavior in the Human Male.* Philadelphia: W. B. Saunders Co., 1948.

Kinsey, A. C., Pomeroy, W., Martin, C., and Gebhard, P. H. *Sexual Behavior in the Human Female.* Philadelphia: W. B. Saunders Co., 1953.

Masters, W. and Johnson, V. *Human Sexual Response.* Boston: Little, Brown and Co., 1966.

Masters, W. and Johnson, V. *Human Sexual Inadequacy*. Boston: Little, Brown and Co., 1969.

Mead, M. *Male and Female*. New York: William Morrow and Co., 1939.

Money, J. and Ehrhardt, A. *Man and Woman, Boy and Girl*. Baltimore: The Johns Hopkins University Press, 1972.

Rainwater, L. *And the Poor Get Children*. Chicago: Aldine Publishing Co., 1959.

Rainwater, L. *Family Design*. Chicago: Aldine Publishing Co., 1965.

Reiss, I. *The Social Context of Sexual Permissiveness*. New York: Holt, Rinehart and Winston, 1967.

DISCUSSION

The following people were the major participants in the discussion: A. Rossi, K. Davis, and F. Jaffe.

At the request of Dr. Chilman, Dr. Rossi presented some of her material about differences in male-female sexuality. Dr. Rossi pointed out that sex identity and gender identity should not be thought of as synonymous. Gender identity, the sense of being a male or female, is established at a very young age. The sense of the self as a sexual being evolves primarily during adolescence. Dr. Rossi notes a considerable flux at present about a sense of sex identity. Adult discussions of homosexuality, bisexuality, and heterosexuality are picked up by young adolescents. Dr. Rossi feels that, unfortunately, young adolescents now tend to see chum relationships as having homosexual overtones. The tendency is to label youngsters who have best friends as being homosexual or bisexual. This labeling may adversely affect their sense of sexual identity.

Dr. Rossi expressed doubt that males and females actually do accept the same standard of sex behavior. Although both sexes are becoming more accepting of casual sex relationships, more males than females accept these relationships, according to trend data from the American Council on Education.[1] An increasing tendency is to emphasize the physical aspect of the sex relationship. This trend also is growing for young adolescents.

Dr. Rossi discussed the recent critical review by Block (as yet unpublished) of the Maccoby and Jacklyn book on sex differences.[2] Block points out that most of the research reviewed by Maccoby and Jacklyn refers to the sexual differences found between infants or young children. Such studies are important because they attempt to understand inherent differences before differences resulting primarily from socialization become paramount. However, their finding of almost no intersex differences overlooks the possibility that some biologically based differences may occur by adolescence, because of endocrine changes during that period.

Dr. Rossi commented further that the current push toward male-female equality has tended to downgrade the female role in the family. Thus, the conception of parenting is moving more toward male standards. The current culture is split between sexuality and maternity and is causing great confusion, especially among young people. It does damage to a sense of kinship structure. "Mary used to be in and Eve, out. Now it is the other way around."

It was remarked by a participant that concern about adolescent pregnancies is justified because pregnancies tend to have adverse consequences for many teenagers, although a lack of agreement as to how adverse these consequences are is apparent. Social policies aimed at preventing these pregnancies should have positive effects. Policymaking can be paralyzed if the major consideration is the occasional adverse effect.

It was agreed that the availability of family planning services for teenagers is very important, but such availability should not be the only concern regarding the overall adolescent well-being. Family planning services, that focus on contraceptive education and acceptance, may further depersonalize sexuality and the meaning of relationships to young people. Rap sessions, which are held in many family planning clinics, often provide an opportunity for adolescents to express a wide range of social, psychological and physical concerns about sexuality. Teenagers are concerned about their male-female relationships and their relationships to their parents. They need a chance to discuss their concerns and, one may hope, gain some guidance from the group leader and other group members.

One discussant received the impression that Dr. Chilman was saying that the act of providing family planning services for teenagers would increase the levels of premarital sex activity among them. Dr. Chilman replied that this was not her point. Rates of adolescent premarital coitus are rising because of basic socioeconomic changes in the society and the resultant value shifts. The point is to attempt to provide humane, integrative family planning and other services, rather than to think of adolescent sexuality as a mechanical, isolated aspect of teenage behavior. Evaluative research concerning the effect of various program models is needed.

A verbal report by Dr. Simon regarding needed research and studies he had been doing was discussed. He particularly emphasized the heterogeneity of cultures in the United States. In his studies of blue collar youth, he found little of the social change in attitudes and values about sexuality expressed in earlier discussions. The concepts are less sophisticated, more traditional.

Ms. Ktsanes commented that of the teenagers she had worked with in Louisiana clinics, most were not future- or planned-oriented or independent in making decisions. Many girls had not yet come to terms with the fact that they have begun menstruating and could get pregnant. If they did get pregnant, they passively accepted it as a fact of life. Often, the possible pains of childbirth were their major concern.

Other discussants emphasized the need to recognize cultural and developmental differences among adolescents to provide appropriate services. Some objected to this more complex approach. To prevent pregnancies among adolescents under age 17, a simple, direct, and specific family planning service is needed. A large number of unwanted babies are born to teenagers, and a more readily available service is needed to provide necessary help with contraceptives and abortion.

The discussion was more or less polarized between those who were concerned about adolescent development, including adolescent sexuality, and those who were primarily concerned with providing specific contraceptive and abortion education and services for teenagers.

REFERENCES

1. American Council on Education. Trend Data.
2. Maccoby, E. and Jacklyn, C. *The Psychology of Sex Differences.* Stanford: Stanford University Press, 1974.

Chapter 6

Fertility Control Services For Adolescents: Access and Utilization

Frederick S. Jaffe and Joy G. Dryfoos
The Alan Guttmacher Institute

With the overall decline in fertility in the United States, concern has shifted from numbers of births to insuring that those children being born have fewer physical, social, and economic handicaps. From this perspective adolescent childbearing is of major importance. The consequences of too early maternal age are often adverse for both the young mother and her child. Yet the patterns of teenage nonmarital fertility (out-of-wedlock births) have not followed the overall trends: 1 out of every 10 young women below the age of 20 is pregnant each year including more than one-fifth of all sexually active unmarried adolescents.

The incidence of adolescent pregnancy, which could be described as "epidemic," poses one of the most difficult challenges remaining in a society that has otherwise brought fertility under a high degree of control. The Conference on the Consequences of Adolescent Pregnancy and Childbearing sponsored by the Center for Population Research offered a useful corrective to the conventional wisdom on the subject. Its conclusions could be summarized as follows: Although the consequences of adolescent childbearing are not always bad, sufficient adverse health, economic, social, and emotional outcomes have been documented to warrant greater attention to the prevention of unintended adolescent pregnancies.

Accordingly, it has become increasingly important to examine the determinants of adolescent sexuality, pregnancy, and childbearing. This examination would not only add to knowledge of human behavior, but also guide policy formation and development of effective programs of prevention. The steps an adolescent must go through to bear a child are easily conceptualized. The literature contains numerous models usually depicting a pathway of decisions dividing adolescents into those who do or those who do not follow a particular branch leading to each outcome. Whether deliberately or not, the models tend to imply that each branching represents a genuine choice between alternatives, primarily reflecting the personal characteristics of the adolescent involved. The models also tend to ignore exogenous factors over which the adolescent has little control, factors that may be more powerful in determining the outcome than any personal characteristics.

If conceptualization of the steps leading to early childbearing is relatively easy, the measurement of them is extraordinarily difficult. Only in recent years have major elements in the picture at least begun to fall into place. At the outcome end, vital statistics provide reliable data on total and out-of-wedlock births to women below age 20. Recently, better information has become available on the proportion of premarital pregnancies legitimated by marriage (data on adoption are still inadequate). At the initiation end, the 1971 Johns Hopkins Study of Adolescent Sexuality, Contraception, and Pregnancy[1] provides the first information for a national cross section of adolescents on the age of initiation of sexual activity and intended and unintended pregnancy rates.

Other papers presented at this conference dealt with the determinants of the processes at the beginning and end of the cycle. The available data on use of contraceptive and abortion services by adolescents have been assembled in this chapter. Special attention has been given to trends of use since 1969 and to policy and program changes during the same period that have affected access by adolescents to the services. This review leads to suggestions for the emphasis of future research and to fundamental questions about the underlying assumptions of many current investigations.

At the outset, certain attributes of current contraceptive technology and of adolescent sexual patterns need to be mentioned. Although it remains true that any method of contraception is more effective in preventing pregnancy than not using any method at all, it is also true that there are sharp differences in efficacy among methods. Ryder's[2] analysis of the 1970 National Fertility Study (NFS) data on use/effectiveness among married couples shows the following standardized 12-month failure rates for various methods.

Method	Percent Failing
Pill	6
IUD	12
Condom	18
Diaphragm	23
Foam	31
Rhythm	33
Douche	39

Both the pill and the IUD presently require medical supervision, and their distribution is controlled by physicians and health institutions. The methods used most frequently by adolescent contraceptors, according to the 1971 Johns Hopkins study, are withdrawal or condom (by whites) and condom or douche (by blacks).[3] None require medical intervention, but each is less reliable than the medically administered methods. The pill and the IUD, however, are methods designed to fit the well-established sexual patterns, such as those thought to prevail among married couples, and are not well suited to the more sporadic and irregular sexual patterns of adolescents.

Because present contraceptive technology is generally not well adapted to the needs of the adolescent, adequate fertility control may be limited until the technology is modified. Within the current situation, the health system serves as gatekeeper for the most effective existing medical methods. As a result, the system's policies and practices regarding access to services for adolescents are important factors affecting whether adolescent sexuality leads to pregnancy and childbearing. The condom is inherently better adapted to sporadic sexual patterns and presumably is available in most drug stores (though not always to young adolescents). Nevertheless, the condom has never achieved more than a limited degree of acceptance among Americans. Some adolescents use the condom with great effectiveness, but its failure rate is three times that of the pill, even among married couples who are generally older and more experienced than adolescents. Similarly, other conventional methods are used effectively by some contraceptors. In the aggregate, however, their efficacy is considerably less than the modern methods.

USE OF CONTRACEPTIVE SERVICES

The 1971 Johns Hopkins study provides a baseline picture of the contraceptive practices of unmarried adolescents. Less than one-fifth of never-married sexually active teenagers reported that they always used contraception of some kind, and an additional three out of five used contraceptives sometimes. Of those who used contraception always or sometimes, nearly three out of four used nonmedical methods with high failure rates. The distribution of methods used by sexually active adolescents the last time they

used any method at all prior to the interview in 1971 is as
follows:

Percent Distribution of Methods Used Most Recently by Ever Contracepting Never Married Women 15–19, 1970–71

Pill	25.5
IUD	1.4
Condom	32.5
Withdrawal	28.7
Douche	5.4
Other	6.5

Data from the 1971 Johns Hopkins study, the annual Current
Population Surveys, and local studies can be used to develop reasonable estimates of the number of adolescent women who are,
over a 12-month period, at risk of unintended pregnancy. Table 6–1
presents such an estimate for 1975. It indicates that about 4 million women below age 20, or about 4 out of 10 in this age group,
were at risk during the year—700,000 currently married and 3.3
million unmarried.[a] In examining data on utilization of contraceptive services, it will be useful to view this estimate as an approximation of the size of the market for fertility control services
among adolescents.

Table 6-1.—*Estimated number of women aged 15 to 19 at risk of unintended pregnancy over a 12-month period, in thousands, 1975*

| Risk status | Marital status | | |
	All marital statuses	Currently married	Unmarried
All adolescent women	10,205	972	9,234
Sexually active	4,295	972	3,323
Pregnant or seeking pregnancy	272	272	0
At risk of unintended pregnancy	4,023	700	3,323

Source: Reference 4.

[a]These estimates are derived by the procedures described in reference 4. The
estimates assume that none of the unmarried adolescents wanted to have children
while they remained unmarried. This assumption is arguable, but the overall estimate would not decrease by much if some proportion of those not currently married were assumed to want to become pregnant. The estimates derived by Dryfoos
(ref. 4) are quite similar to those using slightly different assumptions by L. G.
Morris (ref. 5).

There are four available data bases from which to estimate the use of contraceptive services by young women—the National Reporting System for Family Planning Services (NRSFPS), which is an ongoing census of about 80 percent of the caseload of organized family planning clinics; the National Ambulatory Medical Care Study (NAMCS), which monitored visits to private physicians' offices in 1973; the National Survey of Family Growth (NSFG), which has data on contraceptive practices and sources of care for married teenagers in 1973; and the 1971 Johns Hopkins study, which has similar data for all teenagers in 1971. Each of these sources sheds light on part of the picture, although differences in definitions and survey universes create problems of comparability. When their findings are juxtaposed and reasonable inferences are added, a more complete, albeit still approximate, picture emerges.

Inasmuch as the norm for health care delivery in the United States is the physician in private practice, the limited data available on use of private physicians by adolescents for family planning services is studied first. Tables 6–2 through 6–4 present selected findings of the NAMCS, a survey conducted by the National Center for Health Statistics in 1973 among a representative sample of private physicians. In that year, women of childbearing age (and presumably of all marital statuses) made 8.3 million visits to private physicians for contraceptive counseling and prescription. This figure represents less than 5 percent of all medical visits by women in this age group. Nearly one-fifth (19 percent) of the visits were by women below age 20, who constitute 22 percent of women aged 15 to 44.

The distributions in tables 6–2 through 6–4 are subject to considerable error because of sample size; nonetheless, they suggest that the adolescent patterns are different from those of older women. Three-quarters of all visits for family planning by women over 20 were to obstetrician-gynecologists (Ob-Gyn's), compared to only half among adolescents, who used general practitioners (GP's) twice as frequently. Within the adolescent group, the reversal in pattern (if it is not an artifact of sampling variability) is striking between those aged 15 to 17, most of whom use GP's, and those aged 18 to 19, who use Ob-Gyns in almost the same proportion as older women.

Regional variations are also suggested. The proportion of all family planning visits made by adolescents in the West and South is substantially greater than that in the Northeast and North Central States. This disparity cannot be accounted for by the relatively small differences in the proportions of women of childbearing age in the different regions who are below age 20. It may be related to sampling error, to differentials in sexual activity rates among adolescents (although the 1971 Johns Hopkins study showed little regional variation in sexual activity), or perhaps to regional differ-

Table 6-2.—*Visits to private physicians for family planning service, 1973*

Type of physician	Visits for family planning (percent distribution)				
	All women 15 to 44 (8,299,000 visits)	Women over age 20 (6,698,000 visits)	Women aged 15 to 19[a]		
			Total (1,601,000 visits)	15 to 17 (548,000 visits)	18 to 19 (1,053,000 visits)
General practitioner	20.1	16.9	33.3	63.7	19.4
Obstetrician-gynecologist	70.2	74.6	52.0	31.0	63.0
Other	9.7	8.5	14.7	5.3	17.6
U.S. Total	100.0	100.0	100.0	100.0	100.0

[a] Any estimate of 1.5 million or less has a relative standard error of 25 percent or more.

Source: National Center for Health Statistics: Special Tabulations of the National Ambulatory Medical Care Survey, 1973. Unpublished.

Table 6-3.—*Visits to private physicians for family planning services, by region, 1973*

	Visits for family planning (percent distribution)		
Region	All women 15 to 44 (8,299,000 visits)	Women over age 20 (6,698,000 visits)	Women aged 15 to 19[a] (1,601,000 visits)
Northeast	36.1	38.9	24.5
North Central	22.3	23.3	18.1
South	26.4	25.0	32.2
West	15.2	12.8	25.2
U.S. Total	100.0	100.0	100.0

[a] Any estimate of 1.5 million or less has a relative standard error of 25 percent or more.

Source: Same as table 6-2.

Table 6-4.—*Visits to private physicians for family planning services, by age, 1973*

	Visits for family planning (percent distribution)		
Region	All women 15 to 44 (8,299,000 visits)	Women over age 20 (6,698,000 visits)	Women aged 15 to 19[a] (1,601,000 visits)
Northeast	100.0	86.9	13.1
North Central	100.0	84.3	15.7
South	100.0	76.5	23.5
West	100.0	68.0	32.0
U.S. Total	100.0	80.7	19.3

[a] Any estimate of 1.5 million or less has a relative standard error of 25 percent or more.

Source: Same as table 6-2.

ences in policies, laws, and attitudes affecting the willingness of physicians to treat adolescents.

A different perspective is provided by the 1973 NSFG. Table 6–5 shows that nearly three-quarters of the white, but less than one-half of the black, married adolescents made at least one family planning visit. More than half of the whites went to their own doctors, and less than one-fifth went to organized clinics. The small sample size among blacks yields results of limited reliability, but a reverse pattern is suggested, in that most black married adolescents went to clinics. The racial difference is congruent with other studies showing that a larger proportion of blacks of various ages must rely on clinics for health care, partly because of the scarcity of private physicians practicing in black neighborhoods.

Table 6-5.—*Percent of currently married women aged 15 to 19 with family planning visits, 1973*

Place of visit	Race		
	White	Black	Total
Percent with one or more family planning visit	73.1	47.4	70.8
Percent with visit to private physician	55.4	[a]16.1	51.6
Percent with visit to organized clinic	17.7	[a]31.3	19.2

[a]Not statistically reliable because of small sample size.

Source: Reference 6.

Some information on the sources of contraceptive services for unmarried sexually active adolescents is provided by the Hopkins study, summarized in table 6–6. As would be expected from adolescent reliance on nonmedical methods, drug stores were the primary source of contraceptives for teenagers. Less than one-fourth of all sexually active adolescents saw a doctor or attended a clinic in 1970 and 1971. Although the combined proportions using both sources are similar for whites and blacks (22.1 against 23.1 percent, respectively), the pattern is quite different. More than three times as many white teenagers consulted private physicians as attended clinics (17.0 against 5.1 percent), while more blacks attended clinics than saw a private physician (12.3 against 10.8 percent). About one-quarter did not specify the source of their contraceptive services.

These statistics more or less exhaust the limited information available on the use of private physicians by adolescents for contraceptive care. More information is available about adolescents who obtain their contraceptive care from organized clinics. In fiscal

Table 6-6.—*Percent of never-married sexually active women below age 20, 1970 to 1971*

Use status and source	Race		
	White	Black	Total
Never contracepted	16.0	14.9	15.7
Ever contracepted	84.0	85.1	84.3
Source of care			
Private physician	17.0	10.8	15.3
Clinic	5.1	12.3	7.0
Drugstore	31.2	39.5	33.4
Other	3.2	0.5	2.5
Not specified	27.5	22.0	26.1

Source: Reference 1.

year 1975, more than 1.1 million women under age 20 attended organized clinics: 739,000 whites and 404,000 blacks and others. Together they were 30 percent of the total caseload of 3.8 million clinic patients.

Table 6–7 presents detailed data on selected characteristics of more than half a million new adolescent patients. Almost 10 percent were aged 15 or younger, one third were aged 16 to 17, and the remainder were aged 18 to 19.

Although two-thirds of all adolescent patients were white, more than half of those aged 15 or younger were nonwhite. The proportion of whites increased with each single year of age to 73 percent of 19-year-olds. Nearly half had never used a contraceptive prior to enrollment, a proportion that, as would be expected, declined with age. At their first clinic visit, five out of six chose pills or IUD's, the two most effective reversible methods. Nearly three-quarters of the patients were nulliparous, with only 9 percentage points differentiating those aged 15 from those aged 19.

In contrast, in each age group, the proportion reporting no pregnancies was about 10 percentage points lower than those reporting no live births. If abortion accounted for the difference, it would follow that more than 10 percent of adolescent patients had had an abortion before attending a family planning clinic.

The data can be used, with appropriate assumptions, to develop a point-in-time approximation of the proportion of sexually active adolescents who received medical contraceptive services in 1975. The uncertain element in such an estimate is the use of private physicians. The proportion of unmarried sexually active adolescents at risk of unintended pregnancy, who obtained contraceptive care from private physicians in the mid-1970's, is estimated to be as low as 15 percent or as high as 19 percent, as shown in the

Table 6-7.—Selected characteristics of new female patients below age 20 in organized family planning programs, fiscal year 1975

Age	Percent white	Percent never used a method prior to enrollment	Percent choosing pills or IUDs[a] after first visit	Characteristics				Total number (thousands)	Total percent
				Percent with no live births	Percent with no prior pregnancies	Percent with one live birth	Percent with two or more live births		
15 or under	45.7	63.2	76.9	78.7	68.8	13.1	8.3	49.4	9.6
16	62.0	56.0	79.3	76.3	65.8	16.3	7.4	65.6	13.5
17	68.6	50.8	81.3	74.0	63.0	18.4	7.6	100.3	20.7
18	72.1	44.7	82.0	72.7	61.5	18.8	8.5	143.3	27.9
19	72.8	37.5	87.2	69.2	59.7	20.7	10.1	145.1	28.2
15 to 19	67.7	47.2	82.4	73.1	62.6	18.3	8.6	513.8	100.0

[a]Intrauterine device.

Source: Reference 7.

appendix. These proportions are applied in table 6–8 and yield an estimate that 50 to 54 percent of the 4 million adolescents at risk in 1975 received contraceptive care from either clinics or private physicians. Under either assumption, the number served by clinics was greater than the number served by private physicians, a virtually unprecedented pattern of health services delivery in the United States. Whereas adult clinic patients are almost entirely marginal- and low-income women, the socioeconomic classification of adolescent patients is more uncertain. Presumably family planning clinics serve a relatively larger proportion of adolescents than older women from higher income families, but many or perhaps most adolescent clinic patients probably are from marginal- or low-income strata. In any case, their access to disposable income for purchasing birth control is generally limited.

TRENDS IN THE LAST DECADE

The foregoing analysis suggests that by 1975, about half of the sexually active adolescents at risk of unintended pregnancy either had seen a physician in private practice or had attended a clinic for contraceptive services. The indicator is a limited one. It does not, for example, convey any information regarding how long the women continued to attend the clinic, see a doctor, or use the methods they chose or regarding the effectiveness with which they used the methods.

These variables, important for determining success in the regulation of fertility, can only be examined with other kinds of studies, and little of the required information is available for the Nation as a whole. Yet the information available should not for that reason be ignored. It measures a critical step on the path toward fertility control, provides an indicator of adolescent interest in avoiding unintended conception, and reveals the extent to which the health system has accorded young persons access to services. A closer study of the data could yield significant insights into important social processes that are undergoing rapid change. Therefore, an examination of these indicators for the data they contain on trends during the last decade may be useful.

Trends in adolescent use of private physicians for contraceptive care are difficult to monitor. The source of care has rarely been studied and, when it has, there have been differences in design and definition that limit comparability. Among all married women of reproductive age, the proportion who saw a private physician for contraceptive services changed little between the 1970 NFS sample and the 1973 NSFG sample. These data sets are not available by age, so it is not known if the pattern for adolescent wives also showed no change. Among unmarried adolescents, the 1971 Johns Hopkins proportion (15 percent) can be compared, more

Table 6-8.—*Estimated number of sexually active adolescents at risk of unintended pregnancy receiving contraceptive services from an organized clinic and private physician, 1975*

[Thousands]

Sexually active adolescents	Unmarried		Currently married	Total	
	Assuming 15 percent see private physician	Assuming 19 percent see private physician		Assuming 15 percent see private physician	Assuming 19 percent see private physician
Estimate at risk of unintended pregnancy	4,023	4,023	700	3,323	3,323
Estimate receiving services from					
Organized clinic	1,143	1,143	[a]NA	NA	NA
Private physician	883	1,016	385	498	631
Total	2,026	2,159	NA	NA	NA
Percent of those at risk served (total receiving services divided by estimate of those at risk)	50.4	53.6	NA	NA	NA

[a]Clinic data not available by marital status.

Source: Table 7-5, appendix, and reference 8.

or less, to the approximation derived from the 1973 NAMCS and NSFG data (19 percent—see the appendix). This comparison suggests a trend toward increased adolescent use of private physicians in the early 1970's that may have continued in recent years.

Much more detail is available on trends in the organized clinic system as a result of the NRSFPS, a computerized record system that provides year-to-year information on the number and characteristics of clinic patients and the services they receive. In 1969, organized family planning clinics served a total of 1.1 million patients, of whom 20 percent (220,000) were estimated on the basis of fragmentary characteristics data, as having been under age 20. Table 6-9 shows the distributions from 1970 through 1975, the period in which more detailed information on the age and race of patients became available. The proportion of clinic patients from the adolescent age group increased each year in both racial groups, reaching 30 percent in 1975. At the same time, the total number of patients more than tripled between 1969 and 1975. As a result, the number of adolescents receiving services increased more than five times from an estimated 220,000 in 1969 to 1.143 million in 1975.

A more concrete notion of what being "served" by a family planning clinic means is presented in table 6-10. It shows the distribution of contraceptive methods used by adolescent clinic patients before and after enrollment in the program in the last 3 years for which data are available. In each year, about half of the clinic patients used no method prior to enrollment, and in 1974 and 1975 an additional one-sixth used nonmedical methods. At their last clinic visit, approximately five-sixths reported the use of pills or IUD's, the most effective reversible methods. In contrast, less than one-fifth of patients aged 20 to 29 in fiscal year 1975 used no method prior to clinic enrollment and 14 percent used the least effective methods (not shown). The clinics clearly carry out two primary functions for adolescent patients. They introduce contraception to large numbers who have never practiced it, and they upgrade the practices of others from less to more effective methods.

Adolescent Use of Abortion Services

From 1972 through 1974—the 3 years for which the Center for Disease Control (CDC)[11] has been able to collect and analyze legal abortion data—the proportion of all reported legal abortions performed on women under age 20 has remained constant at about one-third. The total number of abortions, however, has increased rapidly, so that the number obtained by adolescents has also increased.

Table 6-9.—*Estimated number of patients and patients under 20 years old in family planning clinic programs, fiscal year 1970 to fiscal year 1975*

[Thousands]

Fiscal year	Total patients			Patients under 20 years					
				All races		White		Black and other	
	All races	White	Black and other	Number	Percent of total all races	Number	Percent of total white	Number	Percent of total black
1970	1,410	887	523	330	23.4	209	23.6	121	23.1
1971	1,889	1,200	689	518	27.4	344	28.7	174	25.3
1972	2,612	1,627	985	718	27.5	463	28.5	255	25.9
1973	3,089	1,974	1,115	894	28.9	587	29.7	307	27.5
1974	3,282	2,120	1,162	982	29.9	640	30.2	342	29.4
1975	3,813	2,463	1,350	1,143	30.0	739	30.0	404	29.9

Source: Derived from National Reporting System for Family Planning Services for 1971 to 1975; racial distribution estimated for 1970.

Table 6-10.—*Percent distribution of methods used by female patients aged 15 to 19 prior to clinic enrollment and at last clinic visit, fiscal year 1973 to fiscal year 1975*

Fiscal year	Methods			
	No method	Condom	Other methods	Oral; IUD[a]
1975				
Before clinic enrollment. .	50.4	7.3	9.1	33.3
At last visit	8.0	1.0	7.2	83.8
1974				
Before clinic enrollment. .	56.2	9.0	7.0	27.9
At last visit	6.6	0.6	6.6	86.0
1973				
Before clinic enrollment. .	49.0	[b]NA	NA	NA
At last visit	6 to 8	1 to 2	4 to 6	86 to 88

[a] Intrauterine device.
[b] Not available.

Source: References 8 to 10.

Tables 6–11 through 6–13 combine CDC age distributions with survey data collected by the Alan Guttmacher Institute (AGI). The number of abortions obtained by adolescents increased dramatically from 191,000 in 1972 to 342,000 in 1975. Abortion rates (abortions per 1,000 adolescents) and abortion ratios (abortions per 1,000 teenage births) also rose rapidly so that by 1975, 36 percent of all pregnancies among adolescents (excluding miscarriages) were terminated by abortion compared to 22 percent among women aged 20 to 24.

Implications

Available information (table 6–14), based on the 1974 to 1975 data, provides an approximation of the overall adolescent experience with sexual activity, contraceptive services, pregnancy, abortion, and childbearing. To begin with, there are almost 7 million male adolescents who are estimated to be sexually active. Obviously they must be included in any considerations about adolescent fertility along with their 4 million female peers.

Indications are that 4 out of 10 women under age 20 are sexually active and at risk of unintended pregnancy. Half of them have access to medical contraceptive services and choose the most effective available methods leaving close to 2 million sexually ac-

Table 6-11.—*Reported legal abortions, number and percent performed on women under age 20, 1972 to 1975*

| Year | Abortions | | |
	Percent performed on women under age 20	Number performed on women under age 20 (in thousands)	Total reported
1972	32.6	191.2	586.6
1973	32.7	243.4	745.4
1974	32.6	293.4	899.9
1975	33.1	342.3	1,034.2

Source: References 11 to 13.

Table 6-12.—*Reported legal abortions, selected rates, 1972 to 1975*

| Year | Abortions | | |
	Women aged 20 to 24	Women aged 15 to 19	Women aged 18 to 19
1972	21.3	19.2	29.7
1973	26.0	24.0	36.3
1974	30.7	28.7	42.5
1975 (partial)	[a]NA	NA	NA

[a]Not available.

Source: References 11 to 13; rates provided by Christopher Tietze.

Table 6-13.—*Reported legal abortions, selected ratios, 1972 to 1973*

| Year | Abortions | |
	Women aged 20 to 24	Women aged 15 to 19
1972	168	250
1973	218	326
1974	256	389
1975 (partial)	[a]NA	NA

[a]Not available.

Source: References 11 to 13; ratios provided by Christopher Tietze.

Table 6-14.—*Adolescent sexuality, contraception, pregnancy, abortion, and childbearing experience: A point-in-time approximation (circa 1974 to 1975)*

Experience	Number (in thousands)
Sexually active men aged 15 to 19[a]	6,870
Sexually active women aged 15 to 19[b]	
Married	972
Unmarried	3,323
Total	4,295
Sexually active women at risk of unintended pregnancy	4,023
Adolescent women obtaining medical contraceptive services	
From clinics	1,143
From private physicians	883 to 1,016
Total	2,026 to 2,159
Sexually active women not receiving contraceptive services from clinics or private physicians	1,864 to 1,997
Pregnancies	
Births	610
Abortions	292
Miscarriages (estimated at 20 percent of births and 10 percent of abortions)	151
Total	1,054
Births	
Out-of-wedlock	221
In wedlock	389
Premartial conceptions	126
Total	610
Intended births	
Marital (estimated at 72.4 percent)	191
Premarital (estimated at 50.2 percent)	63
Out-of-wedlock (estimated at 21.4 percent)	47
Total	310
Unintended births	
Marital (estimated at 27.6 percent)	73
Premarital (estimated at 49.8 percent)	62
Out-of-wedlock (estimated at 78.6 percent)	174
Total	309
Unintended pregnancies	
Unintended births	309
Abortions	292
Unintended miscarriages (estimated in same proportions as births)	77
Total	678
Proportion	
Unintended pregnancies	64%
Unintended births	51%

[a] Total number of men, 10,570.
[b] Total number of women, 10,205.

Source: Table 6-10; references 14 to 19.

tive adolescents without an identified medical source for birth control counselling and/or services. More than 1 million pregnancies were experienced by U.S. adolescents in 1974–1975: 600,000 ended in a live birth, 300,000 were terminated by induced abortion, and 150,000 were terminated by miscarriage. One-third of the births are out-of-wedlock, an additional one-fifth are premaritally conceived, and less than half are conceived after marriage.

On the basis of responses to the 1971 Johns Hopkins study, only about half of these births and one-third of all pregnancies, are intended. Thus, almost 700,000 unintended pregnancies occurred to adolescents in one year. The magnitude of this number gives evidence to the critical problem our society must confront if adolescents are to gain adequate fertility control as practiced by older women and men.

The data suggest that the fertility control picture today is considerably improved. In 1969, when abortion was not yet legal, only one-fourth to one-third of sexually active teenagers had access to medical contraceptive services from clinics or private physicians. Although the proportion obtaining contraceptive care from private physicians has increased slightly during this period, the most dynamic aspects of the situation clearly have been the increasing number of legal abortions and the rapid growth of adolescent use of contraceptive clinic services. At the same time, more and more adolescents are initiating sexual activity. The trends in the first half of the 1970's suggest that sexually active adolescents are replicating patterns observed among older women in the United States during the 1960's and characterized elsewhere as the "modernization of U.S. contraceptive practice."[20]

The trends have occurred in association with policy changes that have significantly altered adolescents' access to fertility control services. The repeal of abortion laws in some States between 1967 and 1972 and the Supreme Court abortion decisions in 1973 perhaps were the most highly visible of the policy changes, but others also have affected the situation.

A persistent trend in the last 5 years has been for States to change laws regarding the ability of minors to give consent for their own medical care. By 1975, 12 states had affirmed the right of minors to obtain any type of medical care on their own consent; 27, had affirmed this right for contraceptive services; 37, for pregnancy-related care; 26, for abortions; and all States for venereal disease diagnosis and treatment.[21]

As a result of Federal policy and increasing appropriations (until 1973), the organized family planning clinic system expanded rapidly, more than tripling the number of patients served.[22]

Family planning clinics changed their policies regarding provision of services to adolescents. In the 1960's, services to unmarried women in many clinics were restricted to those who had borne at least one child. These policies began to change late in the decade, and many clinics initiated services to unmarried minors regardless of whether they had borne a child or had parental consent. A number of clinics established special sessions for adolescents and directed educational efforts to these groups.

These patterns emerged first in the large metropolitan areas starting in 1968, but were quickly adopted in many small cities and nonmetropolitan areas. They were reinforced by Federal legislation, such as the 1967 and 1972 Social Security Amendments, that permitted first, by inference and later explicitly, authorized contraceptive services to certain classes of sexually active unmarried adolescents.

In addition to changes in the family planning clinic system, the period witnessed the establishment of a number of free clinics and women's health centers, with large proportions of adolescent patients and with fertility control a major program focus.

All of these changes also are likely to have had indirect effects on the attitudes and practices of private physicians and on such providers as college health services. By 1973, one-fifth of the colleges reported providing family planning medical and educational services, and one-third reported referring for such services. More than half of the schools of higher education with enrollments greater than 5,000 said they provided services.[23]

If it were not for the fact that a large proportion of sexually active adolescents was ready to adopt effective fertility control practices and a large proportion of the adult population was ready at least to tolerate, if not to vocally support, the provision of such services, these changes could not have taken place so rapidly, and the number of adolescents involved could not have been so large.

In the short period under review, it is remarkable that no family planning clinics were closed down for serving minors and that few incidents of adverse community reactions were serious enough even to be reported in the newspapers, although services have been made available in communities with widely ranging cultural settings. This experience contrasts sharply with the implicit view of negative community attitudes toward fertility control services for adolescents, expressed in President Nixon's abrupt rejection of the 1972 recommendations of the Commission on Population Growth and the American Future.

Thus policy and program changes in the last 7 or 8 years have lowered the barriers to access, and a large number of sexually active teenagers have responded by using the services and choosing the most effective methods of available fertility regulation. The rapid response is even more remarkable in view of the fact that the availability of both contraceptive clinic and abortion services is still geographically uneven. The range in State and metropolitan area abortion rates is such as to make clear that

legal abortion remains almost as unavailable in some parts of the
Nation today as it was before the Supreme Court decisions.[12,13]

These developments would not have been predicted by many
social or health researchers. Much of the literature on adolescent
fertility attitudes and practices, often based on small groups of
unwed mothers, depicts sexually active adolescents as somewhat
ambivalent about pregnancy and childbearing and indifferent or
resistant to fertility control.[b] Some investigators hypothesize that
childbearing represents a rational calculation of benefits to costs
for some adolescents. In a diverse population of adolescents, no
doubt some fit the picture that emerges from these studies. It is
unlikely, however, that many do. Many researchers appear to have
ignored the evidence of a marked affirmative response to fertility
control services in the last several years, as barriers to access have
been lowered, or to have drawn any implications from the trends.

In fact, much of the current literature on the subject repli-
cates that of a decade ago on low-income attitudes and practices
toward fertility control and on black attitudes toward abortion.
Neither the rapid increase in use of clinic services by low-income
persons in the last decade nor the higher abortion rates among
blacks compared with whites in the last 5 years, were, or could
have been, predicted by many of the published articles. Both
trends could have been predicted on the basis of the evidence from
the Growth of American Families and National Fertility Studies of
a disproportionate incidence of unwanted and unintended fertility
among low-income and black women, but only if researchers had
believed that low-income and black persons would deal rationally
with the issues once effective fertility control services began to
become accessible. These findings, which formed the basis for the
affirmative Federal policy on family planning in the late 1960's,
were often ignored by social scientists whose implicit model empha-
sizes the irrational aspects of fertility behavior.

The parallels suggest that the problem is in the models underlying much current research on fertility. The dominant models
look for explanations of differential fertility practices and outcomes
in the characteristics of individuals, ignoring the differential functioning of social institutions. A decade ago, the prevailing models
assumed that all adults in the United States "could get birth control if they really wanted it" (as was often stated informally by
researchers and laymen alike). Therefore, investigators using these
models were unprepared for the massive response of low-income
persons to the initiation of family planning clinics.

Today, sexually active adolescents are described as choosing
whether to use contraception or abortion. This description assumes

---

[b]See reference 24 for a summary of these developments.

that the choice is really theirs to make and ignores the barriers to access that have been erected by social institutions in control of the distribution of fertility control services in the United States. As a result, many social scientists were equally unprepared for the rapid increase in adolescent use of contraceptive and abortion services as the barriers began to be removed. Apparently, the development of models capable of predicting reality with some degree of accuracy and relevance is overdue.

A recent study that controls for social, economic, and demographic factors known to affect fertility has shown that the most powerful factors determining the proportion of low-income women who need family planning services and who are enrolled in clinics in a given area are the program activity variables (the number of agencies and clinic locations providing the services).[25] These variables are particularly sensitive to policy change: Increased funding can induce more agencies to provide services and other agencies to establish clinics at additional locations. On the basis of the 1968 to 1975 trends, a similar policy to expand adolescent service programs probably would evoke a similar response among sexually active adolescents. Changing policies and funding levels is relatively easy and inexpensive, but very little is known about how to modify directly the fundamental values and attitudes of individuals.

NEEDED RESEARCH

The increases in adolescent use of fertility control services in the last several years have been impressive, but, clearly, further changes will be needed before all sexually active adolescents have adequate access to services. The data available are fragmentary and do not permit the total group of teenagers to be disaggregated into smaller age-race-socioeconomic status subsets to determine which groups face particular difficulties in gaining access to services.

The largest unknown in the total picture is the extent to which physicians in private practice provide contraceptive and abortion services to adolescents (as well as to older women). An important research direction, accordingly, would be to examine the sources and timing of contraceptive care and abortion services. (With respect to abortion, for example, adolescents are disproportionately represented in the second trimester abortion caseload when the risks of morbidity and mortality are greater.[26] To what extent is this situation a result of the negative attitudes and policies of physicians toward treating adolescents, and to what extent does it stem from adolescent inability to face up the fact of pregnancy, as often posited in the literature?)

A few questions on the source of contraceptive care were included in the 1970 NFS, the 1971 Johns Hopkins study, and the

1973 NSFG. Unfortunately, the same questions are not included in the NFS, Johns Hopkins and NSFG resurveys now underway.

It will not be possible to use the survey results to estimate how many women use private physicians for family planning services during the course of a year, the datum needed to compare that source of care with organized clinic care. Furthermore, in none of the fertility studies have questions been asked about payment for services so that financial arrangements for family planning services could be investigated.

The emerging social importance of adolescent pregnancy would justify a special study of the sources of care and access problems of teenagers, as it is doubtful that these subjects will ever be treated adequately in fertility studies designed for other purposes. An adequate study of the processes might well replicate the design employed by Cartwright in England.[27] She interviewed samples of consumers and providers and crosscut them between the two perspectives. Such a study could illuminate the remaining barriers to services and their effects on the practices of subgroups of adolescents. It could also dispel the prevailing misinformation that affects adolescent attitudes and practices (and that conceivably might be influenced by changes in the educational system).

Research into improved ways of delivering services to adolescents is also needed. The service system that has emerged, like other human service delivery systems, is largely unevaluated, although program personnel tend to have strong views regarding the best ways of delivering services.

The comprehensive versus categorical controversy over which family planning and health service providers have long debated has now been extended to services for teens: Must birth control be offered only along with a wide variety of other services (basketball to psychiatry) or can it continue to be offered in freestanding clinics that typify the family planning service delivery system?

How can males be involved in this delivery system—and will it make any difference if they are? What should be offered at that crucial initial visit, considering that the rate of return visits by adolescents is often very low?

Studies are needed to determine particularly if program dropouts also become contraceptive dropouts and, if that is the case, to examine program modifications that would result in higher program continuation rates.

Many unintended pregnancies are experienced by adolescents and can be attributed to problems with contraceptive methods: fear, ignorance, side effects, actual method failure, misuse, and other reasons. In reality, the current contraceptive technology has not produced a safe, efficient, and effective method adaptable to the needs of youngsters. This need demands a high research priority.

Finally, systematic work is needed on the other main potential intervention to prevent unintended adolescent pregnancy—education, whether called family life, population, or sex education. Little information is yet available on the extent to which courses are offered under any of these rubrics, and almost none on their content. As a result, it remains almost impossible to evaluate whether education has any effect on adolescent sexual patterns, fertility control practices, pregnancy experience, abortion use, or childbearing.

APPENDIX

Approximate Proportion of Sexually Active Adolescents Who Obtained Contraceptive Care From Private Physicians in 1975

From the NAMCS data (tables 6–2 through 6–4), it appears that 1.6 million private physician visits for family planning were made in 1973 by all teenagers. A high proportion of them were aged 18 or older.

From the NSFG data (table 6–5), it appears that about 514,000 married women (50 percent of 1,027,700) made one or more visits for family planning to private physicians in the last 5 years (1973 or before). Certain assumptions allow us to put these diverse findings together:

The 1.6 million NAMCS visits were made by fewer than 1.6 million women. The assumption is that married women made 2 visits and unmarried women, 1.3 within the year. The allocation is arbitrary but plausible in the light of the regular sexual activity pattern of the married and the sporadic patterns among the unmarried.

It also is assumed that approximately 75 percent of the NSFG currently married women, or 385,000, made visits in 1973, accounting for 770,000 of the total visits to private physicians. This leaves 830,000 visits among unmarried women. On the basis of the first assumption that unmarried women made 1.3 visits per year, the total figure for unmarried women was 638,000.

The estimates show that 700,000 married adolescents were at risk of unintended pregnancy during 1975. The computation in the foregoing thus implies that more than half (55 percent) consulted a private physician for contraceptive care. The estimates also show that 3,323,000 unmarried adolescents were at risk during the year, implying that less than one-fifth (19 percent) saw a private physician.

The 1971 Johns Hopkins data (table 6–6) show that 15 percent of unmarried adolescents used private physicians as a source of

care in 1970 and 1971. The proportion of unmarried teens using
private physicians ranges from 15 to 19 percent.

REFERENCES

1. The Johns Hopkins University. "Study of Adolescent Sexuality,
   Contraception and Pregnancy" conducted by John F. Kantner
   and Melvin Zelnick.
2. Ryder, N. B. "Contraceptive Failure in the U.S." *Fam. Plann.
   Perspect.* 5:133–142, 1973.
3. Kantner, J. F. and Zelnick, M. "Contraception and Pregnancy."
   Fam. Plann. Perspect. 5:21–35, 1973.
4. Dryfoos, J. G. "Women Who Need and Receive Family Planning Services: Estimates at Mid-decade." *Fam. Plann. Perspect.*
   7:172–179, 1975.
5. Morris, L. G. "Estimating the Need for Family Planning Services among Unwed Teenagers." *Fam. Plann. Perspect.* 6:91–97,
   1974.
6. National Center for Health Statistics. *Utilization of Family
   Planning Services by Currently Married Women 15–44 Years of
   Age.* Vital and Health Statistics: Series 23, No. 1, DHEW Publ.
   No. (PHS) 78–1977. Washington: U.S. Government Printing Office, 1973.
7. National Reporting System for Family Planning Services (excluding Guam, Puerto Rico, and the Virgin Islands). 1975. Special tabulations produced for 1975 unpublished.
8. The Alan Guttmacher Institute. *Data and Analyses for 1976
   Revision of U.S. Department of Health, Education, and Welfare
   Five-Year Plan for Family Planning Services.* New York: AGI,
   1976.
9. The Alan Guttmacher Institute. *Data and Analyses for 1975
   Revision of U.S. Department of Health, Education, and Welfare
   Five-Year Plan for Family Planning Services.* New York: AGI,
   1975.
10. The Alan Guttmacher Institute. *Data and Analyses for 1974
    Revision of U.S. Department of Health, Education, and Welfare
    Five-Year Plan for Family Planning Services.* New York: AGI,
    1974.
11. Center for Disease Control. *Abortion Surveillance, Annual Sum-
    mary, 1972–1975.* Atlanta: Center for Disease Control,
    1974–1977.
12. The Alan Guttmacher Institute. *Provisional Estimates of Abor-
    tion Needs and Services in the Year Following the 1973 Su-
    preme Court Decisions: United States, Each State and Metro-
    politan Area.* New York: AGI, 1975.

13. The Alan Guttmacher Institute. *Abortion 1974–1975: Needs and Services in the United States, Each State and Metropolitan Area.* New York: AGI, 1976.
14. U. S. Bureau of the Census. "Population Estimates and Projections." Current Population Reports, Series P–25, No. 601, 1974.
15. Sorenson, R. *Adolescent Sexuality on Contemporary America.* New York: World, 1973.
16. Dryfoos, J. G. "Estimating Potential Market for Male Involvement Program in South Carolina." Unpublished paper.
17. National Center for Health Statistics. "Advance Report: Final Natality Statistics, 1974." *Monthly Vital Statistics Report.* Vol. 24, No. 2, Suppl. 2, 1976.
18. Bongaarts, J. Population Council. Personal communication.
19. Zelnick, M. and Kantner, J. "The Resolution of Teenage First Pregnancies." *Fam. Plann. Perspect.* 6:74–79, 1974.
20. Westoff, C. F. "The Modernization of Contraceptive Practice." *Fam. Plann. Perspect.* 4(3):9–12, 1972.
21. Paul, E., Pilpel, H. F., and Wechsler, N. F. "Pregnancy: Teenagers and the Law, 1976." *Fam. Plann. Perspect.* 8:16–32, 1976.
22. Dryfoos, J. G. "The U.S. National Family Planning Program, 1968–1974." *Stud. Fam. Plann.* 7:80–92, 1976.
23. Hollis, G. and Lashman, K. "Family Planning Services in U.S. Colleges and Universities." *Fam. Plann. Perspect.* 6:173–175, 1974.
24. Perkins, B. B. *Adolescent Birth Planning and Sexuality—Abstracts of the Literature.* Washington: Consortium on Early Childbearing and Childrearing, 1974.
25. Hout, M. "Determinants of Family Planning Caseloads, 1969–1971." In P. Cutright and F. S. Jaffe, Eds., *Determinants and Demographic Impact of Organized Family Planning Programs in the United States, 1969–1970, Final Report.* (Pursuant to contract No. 1–HD–3–2722) Submitted to U.S. Department of Health, Education, and Welfare, National Institute of Child Health and Human Development, Center for Population Research, 1975.
26. Pakter, J., Nelson, F. and Svigir, M. "Legal Abortion: A Half-decade of Experience." *Fam. Plann. Perspect.* 7:248–255, 1975.
27. Cartwright, A. *Parents and Family Planning Services.* New York: Atherton, 1970.

DISCUSSION

The following people were the major participants in the discussion: F. Jaffe, F. Furstenberg, R. Lincoln, H. Presser, K. Luker, A. Rossi, V. Ernster, C. Westoff, C. Chilman, W. Simon, D. Kallen, and W. Baldwin.

There was considerable discussion about why younger teenagers use abortion less than older ones. It was suggested that this lower rate of use accounts for the rising illegitimacy rate. The many barriers to abortion for young adolescents were noted. In 1975, for example, no abortion services were available in many parts of the country. Young teenagers are less able than older ones to go elsewhere for an abortion. A number of States prohibit abortion for females under age 18 who do not have parental consent. In most States this prohibition is true for those age 15 and younger. The inexperience and ignorance of adolescents under age 18 also prevents them from seeking an early abortion. They are more likely to need a second trimester abortion, which subjects them to greater risk. Although young adolescents have been found to have more conservative attitudes toward abortion than older ones, this fact does not necessarily mean they behave in accordance with their expressed attitudes.

It is more difficult for sexually active teenagers under age 18 to accept their own behavior, partly because society regards premarital intercourse as deviant for their age group. Young sexually active girls can be declared delinquent because of this fact, alone.

A number of discussants thought that more efforts should be made to promote the use of condoms for males. Clinics overemphasize reaching females and usually promote the use of the pill as the most effective contraceptive method. Yet, the Kantner and Zelnik national study showed that younger adolescent females tended to rely on the male contraceptive methods of condoms and withdrawal. It was noted that efforts to get males to use condoms have never been very successful. Moreover, there are higher failure rates with the condom than with the pill.

"The Door," a New York organization was mentioned as a possible model. This agency, located in a low-income, mostly black neighborhood, offers drug counseling, vocational counseling, and health care services. It attracts many males because it serves a free lunch. This model and other programs need evaluation.

Many people may be having good success with the nonmedical methods of contraception, but little information exists. Studies from other countries show that when motivation to prevent pregnancy is high, nonmedical contraception methods work very well. The oral contraceptives are not very appropriate for teenagers who are having infrequent sex relations. Different kinds of contraceptives for people at different ages and stages should be considered.

A viewpoint, expressed by at least one discussant, was that it should be possible to encourage the female to insist that the male use a condom; otherwise she should refuse to have intercourse.

Contraceptive education for teenagers has been inadequate. Many think there is only one method, the pill, and most would not even consider the diaphragm. Diaphragm use would require better communication between partners, and adolescents usually have problems in this area.

The difficulty not only in reaching teenagers about contraceptive use, but in their high rates of contraceptive discontinuance, is a problem. The extent of risktaking that goes on among people of all ages in respect to contraceptive practice is not known. Actual pregnancy risks are affected by a host of factors, including frequency of intercourse and the person's age.

Many teenagers have historically engaged in petting to orgasm as a form of birth control. This pattern may be changing, and more of them may be having intercourse, now that contraceptives and abortion are available and less stigma is attached to illegitimate births. This reduced stigma may account, in part, for lower abortion rates among teenagers and fewer illegitimate babies being placed for adoption.

Although a number of people say they practice the rhythm method of birth control, numerous studies indicate vast confusion and ignorance about the time of ovulation and how ovulation can be calculated.

The discussants suggested that young people should receive more education about the realities of the problems associated with childbearing and childrearing. A few studies reveal that teenagers know almost nothing about this subject.

Some discussants thought that research was needed concerning the effects of daughters seeking contraceptive help on the mother-daughter relationship. To what extent can daughters discuss their contraceptive needs with their mothers? If daughters seek family planning help independently, what communication blocks develop? To what extent are daughters educating their mothers in the "new morality"?

Some discussants thought too much research emphasis was placed on the social and psychological characteristics of contraceptive users compared with nonusers. Instead, more attention should be paid to the barriers to use that result from unavailability or inadequacy of services. It was recommended that the distribution of contraceptives be seen as a marketing problem and that research address itself to the service preferences of different kinds of groups. It is important to remember the heterogeneity of the adolescent population.

Questions were raised by other discussants as to whether teenagers actually demand contraceptive services, as is often assumed. Teenagers (as well as others) have many conflicting desires to use or not use contraceptives. The use of contraceptives has a number of costs, such as an admission of an individual's sexual behavior and the possible adverse side effects of the pill or the IUD.

Some called for both marketing research and longitudinal studies that would consider the biological, social, and psychological causes and consequences of a number of sexual behaviors (premarital coitus, contraceptive use and nonuse, and out-of-wedlock births).

Program evaluation was suggested, as was the evaluation of varying models of such services as sex education, contraception, abortion, and prenatal and postnatal programs for unmarried parents and their children. Mr. Campbell pointed out that program evaluation was not in the domain of the Center for Population Research of NICHD. Rather, responsibility for these kinds of studies had been assigned to other parts of the Department of Health, Education, and Welfare.

Chapter 7

The Health and Demographic Consequences of Adolescent Pregnancy and Childbearing

Jane Menken
Princeton University

Several years ago, a report was prepared for the Commission on Population Growth and the American Future on teenage childbearing and, in particular, on the medical aspects and demographic implications of adolescent pregnancy.[1] This chapter closely follows the structure of the earlier report, bringing the material up to date, first to 1973 and then to 1975. It adds newly available data on the medical and demographic consequences of certain methods of preventing adolescent motherhood, that is, of abortion and various contraceptive methods. Because most of the relationships and views expressed in 1971 remain unchanged, this chapter should be viewed as a new edition of the earlier report.

RECENT TRENDS IN TEENAGE BIRTHS, BIRTH RATES, AND ABORTIONS

In 1975, some 595,000 women under age 20 bore children; over 240,000 of these mothers were under age 18 (table 7–1). The total number of births to teenagers has remained relatively steady over the past decade. There has been a shift, however, in the ages of teenage mothers (table 7–2). Births to 18- and 19-year-old white women declined and, up to 1973, births to teenagers age 17 and under rose, in some cases, quite precipitously. Between 1968 and 1973, the increase was over 25 percent; by comparison, during the same period, total births decreased over 10 percent. The most recent data (for 1974 and 1975) show a small decline in births to all groups of teenagers, except the youngest white women.

During the decade of the 1960's, as the overall birth rate declined, births to teenagers had become an increasingly larger proportion of all births (as shown in tables 7–1 and 7–2). Thus, in

Table 7-1.—*Births by race for all women and for teenagers, United States, selected years 1961-1975*

Race and year	Numbers of births (thousands)					Percent of births			
	All ages	Less than 15	15 to 17	18 to 19	All under 20	Less than 15	15 to 17	18 to 19	All under 20
White									
1961	3,601	2.8	125	347	475	0.1	3.5	9.6	13.2
1968	2,912	3.1	121	306	430	0.1	4.2	10.4	14.7
1973	2,551	4.9	153	271	429	0.2	6.0	10.6	16.9
1975	2,552	5.1	148	262	415	0.2	5.8	10.3	16.3
Nonwhite									
1961	667	4.7	53	77	135	0.7	7.9	11.6	20.2
1968	589	6.4	72	93	171	1.0	12.1	15.8	28.9
1973	586	8.0	85	94	187	1.4	14.5	16.0	31.9
1975	592	7.6	79	93	180	1.3	13.3	15.7	30.4
Total population									
1961	4,268	7.0	178	424	609	0.2	4.2	9.9	14.3
1968	3,502	10.0	193	398	601	0.3	5.5	11.4	17.2
1973	3,137	12.9	238	366	617	0.4	7.6	11.7	19.7
1975	3,144	12.6	227	355	595	0.4	7.2	11.3	18.9

Sources: References 2 to 6.

1973, 20 percent of all births were to teenagers, as compared to 17 percent in 1968 and 14 percent in 1961. By 1975, the percentage had declined slightly to 19. The increase was mainly the result of the increase among nonwhites. Nonwhite teenagers accounted for 32 percent of births in 1973 contrasted to 29 percent in 1968 and 20 percent in 1961. A decline to 30 percent occurred in 1975. The changes by legitimacy status are quite striking. Legitimate births to teenagers are declining. Between 1968 and 1973, there was a sharp rise in the legitimate births to white women age 17 and under, but the most recent data show declines in this age group also (tables 7–3 and 7–4). Overall, less than 15 percent of legitimate births are to teenage mothers. The concentration of illegitimacy in the young ages, however, is striking (tables 7–5 and 7–6). By the early seventies over half the illegitimate births were to teenagers. In absolute numbers, illegitimate births continued to climb, while legitimate births declined for teenagers age 15 or over.

Table 7-2.—*Percent change in births for all women and teenagers, United States, 1961-1975*

Race and year	Age of mother				
	All ages	Less than 15	15 to 17	18 to 19	All under 20
White					
1961 to 1968	−19.1	10.9	−3.2	−12.9	−9.4
1968 to 1973	−12.4	58.1	26.4	−11.4	−0.2
1973 to 1975	0.0	4.1	−3.3	−3.3	−3.3
Nonwhite					
1961 to 1968	−11.7	37.3	36.3	20.8	27.2
1968 to 1973	−0.5	25.0	18.1	1.1	9.4
1973 to 1975	1.0	−5.0	−7.1	−1.1	−3.7
Total population					
1961 to 1968	−18.0	42.9	8.5	−6.1	−1.3
1968 to 1973	−10.4	29.0	23.3	−8.0	2.7
1973 to 1975	0.2	−2.3	−4.6	−3.0	−3.6

Source: See table 7-1.

These changes in the age distribution of births are only partly a result of increasing numbers of teenagers in the population. As tables 7–7 and 7–8 show, the decline in age-specific birth rates has not been uniform. For the first two periods examined, 1961 to 1968 and 1968 to 1973, the birth rate for those aged 15 to 19 declined much more slowly than almost any other age group, with the exception of the 10- to 14-year olds whose rates have actually increased in recent years. Again, these differences are particularly noticeable for nonwhites, for whom the percentage change for those aged 15 to 19 was approximately half or less that of any older age group. Only in the last 2 years for which data are available have the declines in the 15- to 19-year-old birth rate been similar to those at older ages. Furthermore, the difference in fertility between whites and nonwhites has consistently been greatest under age 20.

Table 7–9 examines cohort experience with early childbearing. The percent of each cohort becoming mothers by the time they reached age 18 declined from 12.5 percent for the 1940 cohort to 9.4 percent for the 1949 to 1951 cohorts. In the past few years, the ogive of the age distribution of first births has risen for successive cohorts so that 10.7 percent of the 1958 cohort became mothers by 18. The total becoming mothers by age 20 declined from 34 percent for the 1940 cohort to 23 percent for girls born 16 years later. The proportion of mothers who bore at least one

Table 7-3.—*Legitimate births by race for all women and for teenagers, United States, selected years 1961-1975*

Race and year	Age of mother								
	Numbers of births (thousands)					Percent of births			
	All ages	Less than 15	15 to 17	18 to 19	All under 20	Less than 15	15 to 17	18 to 19	All under 20
White									
1961	3,510	1.4	109	327	438	0.0	3.1	9.3	12.5
1968	2,757	1.2	93	267	361	0.0	3.4	9.7	13.1
1973	2,388	1.7	111	232	345	0.1	4.6	9.7	14.4
1975	2,366	1.5	99	217	317	0.1	4.2	9.2	13.4
Nonwhite									
1961	518	0.9	23	50	74	0.2	4.4	9.7	14.3
1968	405	0.6	23	51	74	0.1	5.7	12.6	18.3
1973	342	0.2	16	39	55	0.1	4.7	11.4	16.2
1975	330	0.1	11	32	43	0.0	3.3	9.7	13.0
Total population									
1961	4,028	1.8	133	376	511	0.0	3.3	9.3	12.7
1968	3,163	2.3	115	318	435	0.1	3.6	10.1	13.8
1973	2,730	2.0	127	272	401	0.1	4.7	10.0	14.8
1975	2,696	1.6	110	249	361	0.1	4.1	9.2	13.4

Sources: References 2 to 6.

additional child before they reached age 18 or 20 declined for many years, although there has been a rise in the most recent years. These figures reflect the increasing birth rates among the youngest women capable of childbearing, the decreasing rates among older teenagers, and the tendency for women who begin childbearing early to have more babies quickly.

Illegitimacy Rates and Ratios

Table 7-10 shows that illegitimacy rates have declined substantially in all groups except the 15- to 19-year-old group for whom the rate has continued to rise. Still, teenagers are not the highest risk group with respect to illegitimacy. Single women in their twenties continue to have higher illegitimacy rates. However, a higher proportion of teenagers than any other group are unmarried. The proportion currently unmarried among 15- to 19-year-old women has increased from 85 percent in 1960 to 89 percent in 1970[21] and was estimated to be 88 percent in 1974.[22] These factors

Table 7-4.—*Percent change in legitimate births for all women and teenagers, United States, 1961-1975*

Race and year	Age of mother				
	All ages	Less than 15	15 to 17	18 to 19	All under 20
White					
1961 to 1968	−21.5	−13.3	−14.7	−18.3	−17.6
1968 to 1973	−13.4	41.7	19.4	−13.1	−4.4
1973 to 1975	−0.9	−11.8	−10.8	−6.5	−8.1
Nonwhite					
1961 to 1968	−21.8	−33.6	0.0	0.0	0.0
1968 to 1973	−15.6	−50.0	−30.4	−23.5	−25.7
1973 to 1975	−3.5	−50.0	−31.3	−18.0	−21.8
Total population					
1961 to 1968	−21.4	33.3	−13.5	−15.4	−14.9
1968 to 1973	−13.7	−13.0	10.4	−14.5	−7.8
1973 to 1975	−1.2	−20.0	−13.4	−8.5	−10.0

Source: See table 7-3.

combined to produce the situation noted above: In 1975, over half the out-of-wedlock births were to teenagers.

Illegitimate births represent a large proportion of the total births to teenagers (table 7–11). Illegitimacy ratios have increased greatly for all age groups, but are by far the highest for teenagers. Table 7–12 shows that in 1975, the illegitimacy ratio declined with each teenage year. It indicates that of births to mothers aged 15, over 70 percent were illegitimate, and of births to those aged 19, approximately 26 percent were illegitimate. For nonwhites the corresponding figures (94 and 60 percent, respectively) are considerably higher than those for whites, but the relationships are similar: The ratios are increasing over time but decreasing with age.

Standard vital statistics data do not indicate the number of out-of-wedlock conceptions that are legitimized by marriage. However, data obtained from the National Natality Study, conducted for 1964 to 1966 by the National Center for Health Statistics, included date of marriage for a sample of over 2,500 mothers of legitimate first births. If all births occurring within 8 months after marriage are assumed to have been premaritally conceived, the results shown in table 7–13 are obtained. Among women aged 15 to 19, 56 percent of primiparae conceived prior to marriage. The lower proportion among whites (49 percent) than among nonwhites (83 percent) may reflect differences in the availability of abortion. The data show a much greater probability that whites who deliver a premaritally conceived infant will marry before the birth occurs.

Table 7-5.—*Illegitimate births for all women and for teenagers, United States, selected years 1961-1975*

| Race and year | Age of mother | | | | | | | | |
| | Numbers of births (thousands) | | | | | Percent of births | | | |
	All ages	Less than 15	15 to 17	18 to 19	All under 20	Less than 15	15 to 17	18 to 19	All under 20
White									
1961	91	1.4	16	20	37	1.5	17.0	22.6	41.1
1968	155	1.9	28	39	49	1.2	18.3	25.1	44.6
1973	163	3.2	42	39	84	2.0	25.8	23.9	51.7
1975	186	3.6	49	45	98	1.9	26.3	24.2	52.7
Nonwhite									
1961	149	3.8	30	27	61	2.5	19.9	18.4	40.8
1968	184	5.8	49	42	97	3.2	26.9	22.4	52.5
1973	244	7.7	69	55	132	3.2	28.3	22.5	54.0
1975	262	7.5	68	61	137	2.9	26.0	23.3	52.3
Total population									
1961	240	5.2	45	48	98	2.2	18.8	20.0	41.2
1968	339	7.7	78	80	166	2.3	23.0	23.6	48.9
1973	407	10.9	111	94	216	2.7	27.3	23.1	53.1
1975	448	11.0	117	106	234	2.5	26.1	23.7	52.2

Sources: References 2 to 6.

Results for Detroit in 1958 that are similar, but more detailed, show that the percent of births conceived out of wedlock that were legitimized increased from age 14 to age 17.[25] Zelnik and Kantner[26] found that 8.7 percent of their 1971 sample of close to 5,000 in the 15 to 19 age group reported a premarital first pregnancy and that, of all women reporting a first pregnancy, about three-quarters were premarital. Nearly 35 percent of the premaritally pregnant married before the outcome of that pregnancy (8.5 percent of blacks and 51 percent of whites). Because over 15 percent of those ever premaritally pregnant were still pregnant and unmarried at interview and since not all terminated pregnancies ended in live births, these figures are not quite comparable to those from the Natality Survey. Data from more recent surveys will be of particular interest in view of the changes in availability of abortion.

Table 7-6.—*Percent change in illegitimate births for all women and teenagers, United States, 1961-1975*

Race and year	Age of mother				
	All ages	Less than 15	15 to 17	18 to 19	All under 20
White					
1961 to 1968	70.4	35.7	83.2	95.0	84.2
1968 to 1973	5.2	68.4	50.0	0.0	21.7
1973 to 1975	14.1	12.5	16.7	15.4	16.7
Nonwhite					
1961 to 1968	23.3	52.6	66.9	55.6	59.2
1968 to 1973	32.6	32.8	40.8	31.0	36.1
1973 to 1975	7.4	2.6	1.4	10.9	3.8
Total population					
1961 to 1968	41.2	48.1	72.7	66.7	68.7
1968 to 1973	20.1	41.6	42.3	17.5	30.0
1973 to 1975	10.1	0.9	5.4	12.8	8.3

Source: See table 7-5.

Abortions

The Center for Disease Control routinely collects and publishes data on legal abortions in the United States. In 1975, 33.1 percent of abortions in which the age of the woman was known were performed on teenagers (1.5 percent were under age 15).[27] The estimated abortion ratios were 1,193: 1,000 live births for women under 15 and 542 for those aged 15 to 19. The national data are not cross-tabulated by both age and marital status but, during the first 2 years of legalized abortion in New York, 90 percent of the teenagers whose pregnancies ended in abortion were unmarried.[28]

Several studies considered the impact of abortion on overall illegitimacy figures. Pakter and Nelson[29] reported that New York City out-of-wedlock births interrupted and temporarily reversed their previously unbroken upward trend a year after abortions were legalized. Sklar and Berkov[30,31] found a drop of 16 percent in illegitimacy rates in California a year after liberalization of abortion laws. They also found that States with moderate or nonrestrictive laws experienced a 12 percent drop in overall illegitimacy rates in 1971, and those with restrictive legislation sustained only a 2 percent decline. Illegitimacy among those aged 15 to 19 declined the least. Whether continued availability of abortion will substan-

Table 7-7.—*Birth rates by age and race, United States, selected years 1961-1975*

Race and year	All ages	Age of mother							
		10 to 14	15 to 19	20 to 24	25 to 29	30 to 34	35 to 39	40 to 44	45 to 49
White									
1961	22.2	0.4	78.8	247.9	194.4	110.1	53.2	14.8	0.9
1965	18.3	0.3	60.7	189.8	158.8	91.7	44.1	12.0	0.7
1968	16.6	0.4	55.3	162.6	139.7	72.5	33.8	8.9	0.5
1971	16.2	0.5	53.8	145.4	134.6	65.7	26.9	6.4	0.4
1973	13.9	0.6	49.3	115.4	113.7	54.9	20.7	4.9	0.3
1975	13.8	0.6	46.8	109.7	110.0	52.1	18.1	4.1	0.2
Nonwhite									
1961	31.6	4.0	152.8	292.9	221.9	136.2	74.9	22.3	1.5
1965	27.6	4.0	136.1	247.3	188.1	118.3	63.8	19.2	1.5
1968	24.2	4.4	133.3	200.8	144.8	91.2	48.6	15.0	1.2
1971	24.7	4.7	129.2	184.6	135.7	79.6	40.2	11.7	0.9
1973	21.9	5.0	119.1	153.2	133.9	63.9	31.0	8.7	0.6
1975	21.2	4.7	108.6	143.5	112.1	59.7	27.6	7.6	0.5
Total population									
1961	23.3	0.9	88.0	253.7	197.2	113.3	55.6	15.6	0.9
1965	19.4	0.8	70.4	196.8	162.5	95.0	46.4	12.8	0.8
1968	17.5	1.0	66.1	167.4	140.3	74.9	35.6	9.6	0.6
1971	17.2	1.1	64.7	150.6	134.8	67.6	28.7	7.1	0.4
1973	14.9	1.3	59.7	120.7	113.6	56.1	22.0	5.4	0.3
1975	14.8	1.3	56.3	114.7	110.3	53.1	19.4	4.6	0.3

Source: References 3 to 5 and 7.

tially reduce teenage illegitimacy remains a question for the future.

Since the characteristics of teenage childbearing vary greatly according to race and legitimacy, data will be presented separately, whenever possible, in the review of the medical aspects that follows. The illegitimacy data are included as a substitute for the preferable, but rarely available, information on out-of-wedlock conceptions. Illegitimacy is emphasized ". . . not because of the moral characteristics of the mothers and children involved, but because (a number of) indices suggest that mothers and children involved in illegitimacy are in grave difficulties."[32]

Table 7-8.—*Percent change in birth rates by age and race, United States, 1961-1975*

Race and year	All ages	Age of mother							
		10 to 14	15 to 19	20 to 24	25 to 29	30 to 34	35 to 39	40 to 44	45 to 49
White									
1961 to 1968	-25.2	0	-29.9	-34.4	-28.1	-34.2	-36.5	-39.9	-44.4
1968 to 1973	-16.3	50	-12.2	-29.0	-18.7	-24.3	-38.8	-44.9	-40.0
1973 to 1975	-0.7	0	-5.1	-4.9	-3.2	-5.1	-12.6	-16.3	-33.3
Nonwhite									
1961 to 1968	-23.4	10.0	-12.8	-31.4	-34.7	-33.0	-35.1	-32.7	-20.0
1968 to 1973	-9.5	13.6	-10.7	-23.3	-21.8	-29.9	-36.2	-42.0	-50.0
1973 to 1975	-3.2	-6.0	-8.8	-6.3	-16.3	-6.6	-11.0	-35.0	-44.4
Total population									
1961 to 1968	-24.9	11.1	-24.9	-34.0	-29.0	-33.9	-36.0	-38.5	-33.3
1968 to 1973	-14.8	30.0	-9.7	-27.9	-19.0	-25.1	-38.2	-43.8	-50.0
1973 to 1975	-0.7	0.0	-5.7	-5.0	-2.9	-5.3	-11.8	-14.8	0.0

Source: See table 7-7.

Medical Aspects

Much of the medical and statistical literature related to age at childbearing examines reproductive loss at specified stages on the continuum of development of the infant. The concern is with fetal mortality, perinatal mortality (from 28 weeks of gestation through the first week of life), neonatal mortality (first 28 days of life), and postneonatal mortality (28 days to 1 year). The latter two, of course, are components of the standard measure of infant mortality (deaths in the first year of life). These distinctions are important here in that fetal, perinatal, and, to a lesser extent, neonatal mortality appear to be caused primarily by factors related to the pregnancy itself, whereas postneonatal mortality is attributed more often to environmental causes.

The risks of reproductive loss vary with the age and parity of the mother. These two factors, although usually rising together, have quite different biological interpretations: Age is a rough indicator of whether a young pregnant woman has reached full physical maturity or of whether the reproductive effectiveness of the older woman has begun to decline. Parity, on the other hand, reflects previous experience with the reproductive process. The combination, parity at a certain age, is a result of the timing of births (the mother's age at her first birth and the rapidity with which subsequent births occur).[33]

Table 7-9.—*Percent of cohort having at least one live birth by age 18 and age 20: U.S. birth cohorts 1948-1958*

Fiscal year of birth of cohort	Percent becoming mothers by age 18 ... age 20		Percent of mothers having at least 2 live births by age 18 ... age 20	
1940	12.5	33.8	18.5	34.6
1941	12.2	33.2	18.7	34.9
1942	11.5	31.9	19.0	34.5
1943	10.9	30.0	19.2	34.0
1944	11.0	30.0	19.3	33.6
1945	10.8	29.4	19.8	32.6
1946	10.8	29.4	19.3	31.0
1947	9.1	25.8	17.8	27.5
1948	9.5	26.4	17.8	27.0
1949	9.4	25.9	17.0	25.7
1950	9.4	26.0	16.2	24.9
1951	9.4	26.0	14.8	24.1
1952	9.5	25.5	14.0	23.7
1953	10.0	24.7	13.3	23.0
1954	10.2	24.2	13.2	22.5
1955	10.5	23.9	12.2	23.8
1956	10.7	23.4	11.4	23.8
1957	10.9		13.5	
1958	10.7		13.4	

Sources: References 3 and 8 to 19.

The present discussion is not intended as an exhaustive review of the literature. It will be limited to only the most recent data, preferably for the United States. For a thorough review of worldwide literature, see Nortman.[34]

Infant Mortality in Relation to Maternal Age

Since maternal characteristics are not recorded on infant death certificates, they must be ascertained by matching a sample of death certificates to the birth certificates of the infants or by requesting information from the families. It is not surprising, therefore, that only a handful of large-scale studies exist. Those in the United States and the United Kingdom consistently have shown that infant mortality follows a U-shaped curve with respect to maternal age from 15 to 44. The rate is extremely high for very young mothers (<15), declines to a minimum in either the early or late twenties, and then increases fairly sharply

Table 7-10.—*Estimated illegitimacy rates (per 1,000 women) by age of mother, United States, selected years 1961-1975*

Year	Age of mother						
	15 to 44	15 to 19	20 to 24	25 to 29	30 to 34	35 to 39	40 to 44
1961	22.6	16.0	41.2	44.8	28.9	15.1	3.8
1965	23.4	16.7	38.8	50.4	37.1	17.0	4.4
1968	24.1	19.8	36.1	39.4	27.6	14.6	3.7
1970	26.4	22.4	38.4	37.1	27.0	13.6	3.5
1972	24.9	22.9	33.4	31.1	22.8	12.0	3.1
1973	24.5	22.9	31.8	30.0	20.5	10.8	3.0
1975	24.8	24.2	31.6	28.0	18.1	9.1	2.6
Percent change							
1968-1973	1.7	15.7	−13.6	−23.9	−25.7	−26.0	−18.9
1973-1975	1.2	5.7	−0.6	−6.7	−11.7	−15.7	−13.3

Sources: References 3 to 5, 14, and 20.

thereafter.[35,36] Figure 7–1 illustrates this standard curve with data from a matched birth certificate infant death study.[36] The investigation, carried out by the National Center for Health Statistics, succeeded in matching birth and death certificates of 94 percent of the nearly 110,000 children born in 1960 who died before reaching their first birthday.[37] Results clearly demonstrate racial differences in infant deaths. The shapes of the curves are similar; but, at all ages, the infant mortality rate is considerably higher among non-whites than among whites.

When a comparison is made of mortality among infants born to mothers under age 20 and among those whose mothers were aged 20 to 30, the differences are far greater in the first month of life (neonatal mortality) than in the remainder of the first year (postneonatal mortality) (figure 7–2). Just after birth, when biological factors related to the pregnancy are the primary determinants of survival, risks to infants of young mothers are much higher than to infants of older mothers in both racial groups.

Postneonatal death rates are high and racial differences are least in mothers under 15, suggesting large negative environmental influences for infants of the youngest mothers, regardless of race. It is well documented that postneonatal mortality rates (28 days to 1 year) have declined over the past 30 years more rapidly than neonatal mortality rates, owing mainly to declining death rates from infectious diseases.[38] For nonwhites, however, the relative im-

Table 7-11.—*Estimated illegitimacy ratios* by age and race, United States, selected years 1961-1975*

Race and year	All ages	Less than 15	15 to 19	20 to 24	25 to 29	30 to 34	35 to 39	40 and over
White								
1961	25	499	158	24	13	11	14	17
1965	40	573	114	38	19	16	19	22
1968	53	610	77	51	20	21	25	28
1970	57	579	171	52	21	21	27	33
1973	64	652	191	53	24	24	33	41
1975	73	710	229	61	26	27	39	46
Nonwhite								
1961	223	817	439	209	168	155	157	157
1965	263	864	492	230	163	149	149	140
1968	312	908	550	264	144	132	130	127
1970	349	942	614	295	181	173	169	169
1973	417	968	691	359	218	194	202	200
1975	442	991	747	400	227	195	203	211
Total population								
1961	56	697	155	51	31	29	31	32
1965	77	785	208	68	40	37	40	43
1968	97	810	267	83	39	41	47	51
1970	107	808	295	89	41	45	52	57
1973	130	848	339	108	49	50	65	79
1975	143	870	382	123	54	53	70	82

*Illegitimate births per 1,000 live births.

Sources: References 3 to 5, and 14.

provement in mortality conditions has occurred much more slowly. Shapiro et al.[38] found that in 1960, at almost all ages, postneonatal mortality accounted for approximately one-fourth of the infant deaths in each maternal age group among whites, but closer to one-third of the deaths among nonwhites. Examining postneonatal mortality, according to the infants' age (in months), they found that the rates for whites and nonwhites diverged increasingly during the first 4 months. After the first 4 months of life, nonwhite infant mortality was three times that of whites.[38]

Infant mortality by legitimacy status of the birth was derived from the period 1964 to 1966 by the National Center for Health Statistics from the National Infant Mortality Study.[39] Except for nonwhites aged 25 to 29, the rates shown in figure 7-3 follow the

Table 7-12.—*Numbers of illegitimate births and illegitimacy ratios, for ages 15 to 19, by race, United States, selected years 1971-1975*

| Race and year | Number of illegitimate births (thousands) | | | | | Illegitimacy ratio | | | | |
	15	16	17	18	19	15	16	17	18	19
White										
1971	6.5	12.4	17.3	20.0	19.9	419	282	205	154	115
1973	8.1	15.2	19.1	20.3	18.4	443	312	221	167	123
1975	9.5	17.4	22.0	23.6	21.4	519	,370	265	202	148
Other										
1971	13.9	23.2	27.6	27.9	25.6	891	818	716	595	494
1973	15.0	24.4	29.6	28.8	26.0	912	835	753	628	538
1975	14.3	24.0	29.6	31.9	28.8	943	887	807	705	601
Total population										
1971	20.4	35.3	44.9	47.8	45.4	656	491	365	271	201
1973	23.0	39.6	48.7	49.1	44.4	662	508	387	293	224
1975	23.8	41.4	51.6	55.6	50.2	712	558	431	343	261

Sources: References 4, 5, and 7.

age pattern already described. For each group, with one exception, infant mortality rates for illegitimate births exceed those for legitimate births, and the differential increases with age. The single exception is for nonwhites under 20 years, for whom the proportion of infants surviving the first year is lower for legitimate births.

No data are available for the mortality experience of U.S. infants conceived out of wedlock. In England and Wales in 1949, however, neonatal mortality among single live births was 16.4 per 1,000 for all legitimate births, 22.4 per 1,000 for births occurring in the first 9 months of marriage, and 27.0 per 1,000 for illegitimate births.[40] It is distinctly possible that these figures are, at least partially, the result of the age distribution of women conceiving premaritally; but they do suggest increased risks to infants whose conception precedes marriage.

The pattern of fetal death ratios by age (the number of fetal deaths reported for pregnancies of over 20 weeks' duration, divided by the total number of live births) is typically U-shaped (figure 7–4); that is, the ratios for women under age 15 are elevated in comparison with those for women aged 15 to 19 or 20 to 29. Women over 30, however, clearly are subject to far higher risks of not bringing their pregnancy to full term. Again, nonwhites are

Table 7-13.—*Percent of first births conceived out-of-wedlock by age and race, United States, 1964-1966*

First births	Age of mother at first birth					
	15 to 19			15 to 44		
	White	Non white	Total	White	Non white	Total
Number of first births (thousands)	348	94	442	1008	171	1180
Percentage of births that were illegitimate	15.0	57.3	24.0	9.3	45.5	14.5
occurred less than 8 months after marriage	33.9	26.0	32.2	17.7	22.6	18.5
were conceived out of wedlock	48.9	83.3	56.2	27.0	68.1	33.0
Percentage of legitimate births conceived premaritally	39.9	60.8	42.4	19.5	41.6	21.6
Percentage of out-of-wedlock conceptions leading to live births that were legitimized by marriage	69.3	31.1	57.2	65.6	33.3	55.9

Sources: References 23 and 24.

exposed to higher risks at all ages. The fetal loss ratio is greater for illegitimate pregnancies in all age and race categories except under age 15, where the ratio for legitimate pregnancies is somewhat higher than that for illegitimate. At older ages, the differential between the ratio for legitimate compared to illegitimate births is greater for whites than nonwhites. What proportion of reported fetal deaths results from abortion is, of course, a matter of conjecture, inasmuch as the most recent available data are for 1973 when liberalization of abortion laws had only recently taken place.

The preliminary results demonstrate that, at nearly all stages of pregnancy and infancy, the very young mother is exposed to greater risks of losing her baby than her slightly older counterparts.

The Influence of Parity

Risks of reproductive loss are highest for young women who have already had several births and for older women.[38] Figure 7–5 illustrates fetal death rates for 1960 to 1961 by age and parity. The patterns are obvious: At all parities, the risks for young

Figure 7-1.—*Infant mortality of white and nonwhite infants by age of mother, United States, 1960 birth cohort (Source: Reference 35)*

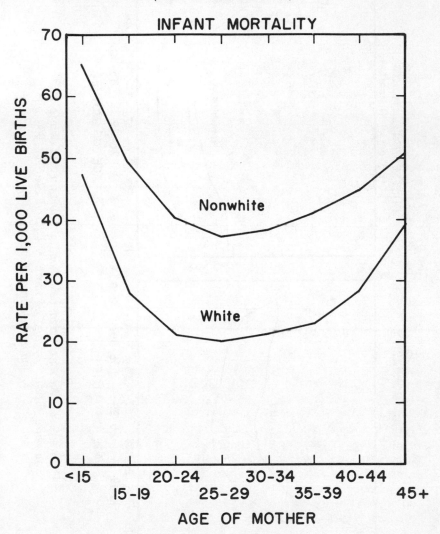

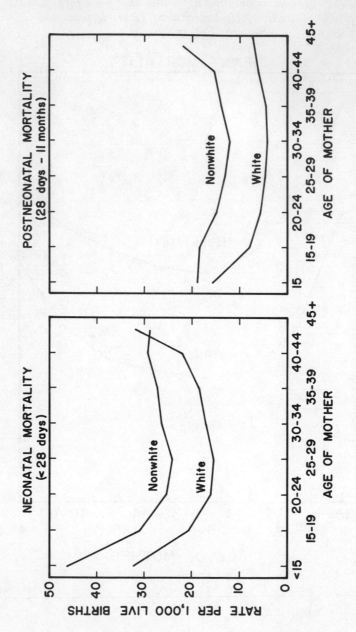

Figure 7-2.—Neonatal and postneonatal mortality of white and nonwhite infants by age of mother, United States, 1960 birth cohort (Source: Reference 35)

Figure 7–3.—*Infant mortality ratio by race of child and legitimacy status by age of mother, United States, 1964 to 1966 (Source: Reference 39)*

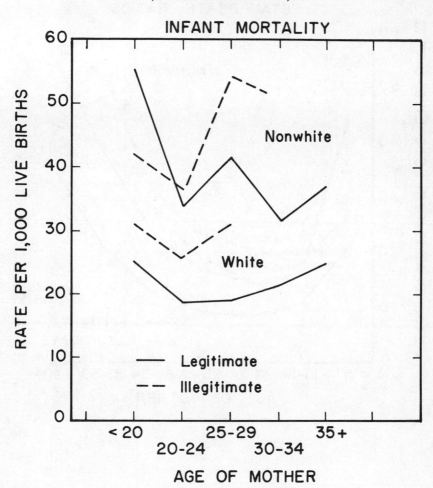

Figure 7–4.—*Fetal death ratios by race and age of mother and legitimacy status, United States, 1973 (Source: Reference 41)*

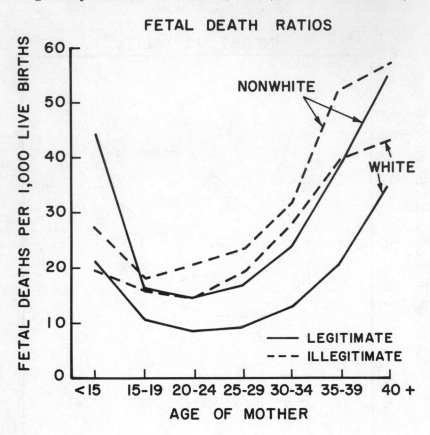

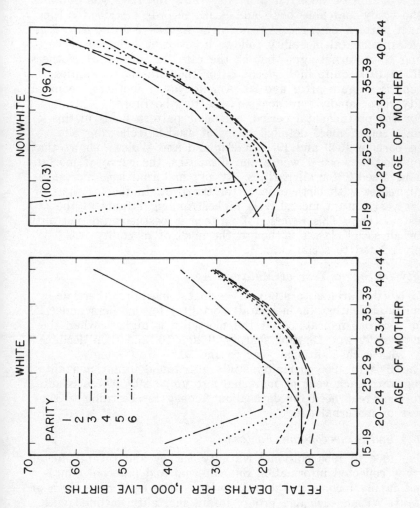

Figure 7-5.—*Fetal death rates by race, age and parity, United States, 1960 and 1961 (Source: Reference 38)*

mothers are high, and they increase rapidly with parity after the first birth.

Information on neonatal mortality rates for 1960 was obtained from the study matching birth and death records described earlier. A distinct pattern emerged. As shown in figures 7–6 and 7–7, for all parities, neonatal mortality follows a reversed J-shaped curve according to maternal age—that is, the rate for infants of mothers aged 15 to 19 is quite high, declines for those in their twenties, and then rises again after age 30. Among young mothers, neonatal mortality rises rapidly for each parity after the first.[41]

For the postneonatal period, a similar pattern holds in this same data set. A more detailed series of studies, following all children born in 1949 and 1950 in England and Wales,[40] shows that in the period between 4 weeks and 6 months, the curve of mortality is a reversed J for all parities. At any maternal age, mortality again increases with birth order after the first. In the last half of the first year, infant mortality is highest among infants of the youngest mothers. This reversed J pattern is postneonatal mortality held for all social classes, although the level of mortality was inversely related to social class.[41]

Mortality by Single Year of Maternal Age

In North Carolina, a study of perinatal mortality (here defined as fetal deaths plus neonatal mortality) for mothers under 20 years of age has indicated that the mortality is highest when the mother is under age 15, dips sharply at age 16, and then declines slightly with each additional year to age 20.[42]

The 1964 to 1966 mortality study also found infant mortality declining with each year of maternal age up to 20.[34] These results indicate the great need for data about teenagers according to single years of maternal age.

Mortality and Socioeconomic Factors

The 1964 to 1966 National Natality Survey and Infant Mortality Survey collected information on maternal and paternal education and family income in the year prior to the legitimate birth of the infant. Within each age group, infant mortality declined with education, except for college graduates. For each educational category, the J- or reversed J-shaped pattern of infant mortality according to the mother's age was preserved.[43] Less detailed findings of an inverse relationship between mortality and occupation exist for fetal and neonatal mortality in certain areas of the United States.[38,44]

The British Perinatal Mortality Survey, which studied all stillbirths and livebirths occurring in a single week in England and Wales in 1958, found similar inverse relationships between social class and the perinatal mortality rate (defined as stillbirths and

Figure 7–6.—*Neonatal mortality rates for white females by race, age, and parity of mother, United States, 1960*
(Source: Reference 42)

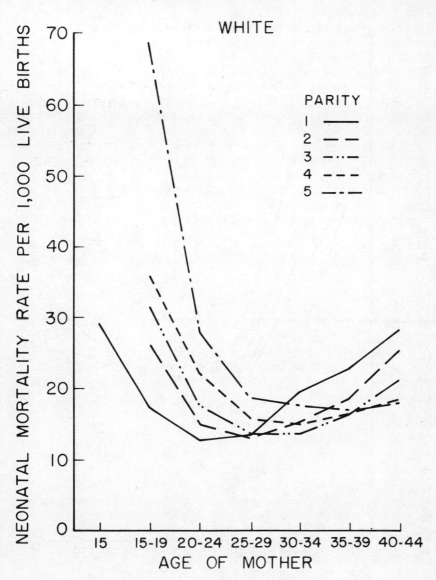

Figure 7–7.—*Neonatal mortality rates for black females by race, age, and parity of mother, United States, 1960* (Source: Reference 42)

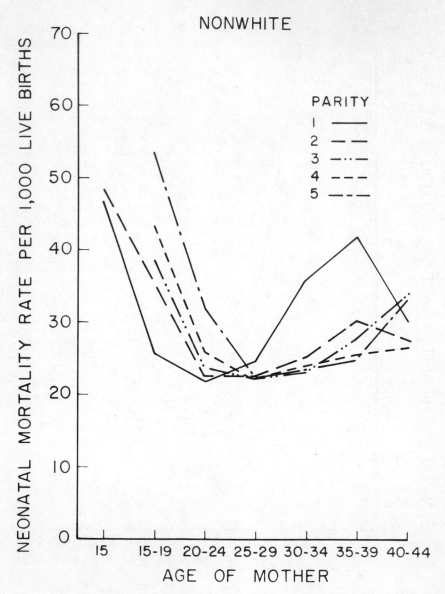

deaths in the first week). This study also found the now familiar J-shaped curve of mortality versus maternal age.[45]

Summary of Mortality Risks

The major high-risk groups according to maternal age have been identified as young women, particularly multiparous young women, and older women. Table 7–14 summarizes the evidence thus far in terms of the risk of mortality for infants of mothers in a given age group, relative to the risk to infants of mothers aged 20 to 24. The first line shows that infant mortality for white mothers under age 15 is over twice as high as when the mother is in her early twenties. For the younger mothers, the relative risk of fetal death or neonatal, postneonatal, and infant mortality climbed as parity rose to parity four, so that neonatal mortality for the infants of women under 20 years of age who already had had three births was 60 percent higher than for infants of slightly older mothers of the same parity. The reverse holds for older mothers. Apparently, a mother delivering a child after age 40 is more likely to have a liveborn child who survives the neonatal and postneonatal periods, if she has already had previous births.

These data illustrate, again, the need for additional information, at a minimum for girls under age 15, and preferably by single years of age throughout the teens, in order to assess the risks to infants of very young mothers.

Birth Intervals

Girls who marry [47,48] or have a first child at an early age also tend to bear their subsequent children at a rapid rate, so that the intervals between births are relatively short. Perhaps a selection process is operating through which girls who are more fecund, or have less access to abortion or contraception, or who use contraception less effectively tend to marry or become pregnant early in their sexual experience. Some evidence also exists that marriage at an early age is related to education and religion—two variables that have been associated with fertility in almost every study of the subject.[49]

Wray[50] reviewed the studies that link short-birth intervals to increased rates of stillbirth, prematurity, neonatal deaths, and postneonatal deaths. The findings are entirely compatible with the increase in infant mortality for higher parity very young mothers. If a girl is going to have three or four babies between the time she reaches puberty and age 18 or 20, the infants have to arrive in rapid succession and, consequently, are subject to high risks of mortality and prematurity.

Table 7-14.—*Infant mortality rate for the under-20 and over-40 age groups of mothers relative to the rate for infants of mothers aged 20 to 24, by race, United States*

| | Age of mother | | | | | |
| | White | | | Nonwhite | | |
Mortality and year	Less than 15	15 to 19	40 to 44	Less than 15	15 to 19	40 to 44
1960						
Infant mortality	2.2	1.3	1.3	1.6	1.2	1.1
Neonatal mortality	2.2	1.3	1.4	1.8	1.2	1.2
Postneonatal mortality	2.8	1.4	1.1	1.3	1.3	1.0
1964 to 1966						
Infant mortality						
Legitimate births	a—	1.3[+]	1.3[@]	—	1.7[+]	1.1[@]
Illegitimate births	—	1.2	—	—	1.2	—
1960 to 1961						
Fetal death ratios by parity						
1	—	1.0	4.8	—	0.8	3.9
2	—	1.2	3.5	—	1.2	3.9
3	—	1.3	3.0	—	1.4	3.4
4	—	1.4	2.3	—	1.5	2.6
1960						
Neonatal mortality rates by parity						
1	2.3	1.4	2.2	2.1	1.2	1.4
2	—	1.7	1.7	2.2	1.6	1.2
3	—	1.8	1.2	—	1.6	1.4
4	—	1.6	0.8	—	1.7	1.0
Postneonatal mortality rates by parity						
1	4.7	1.8	1.5	2.3	1.8	1.1
2	—	2.1	1.0	3.2	1.9	1.4
3	—	2.2	0.6	—	1.8	0.6
4	—	1.7	0.5	—	1.7	0.6

[a] Not applicable.
[+] Under 20.
[@] Over 30.

Sources: References 35, 38, 39, and 46.

Prematurity

"One of the most important themes that runs through any consideration of infant mortality is the critical role of the maturity of the infant at birth."[38] In fact, the increased risk of prematurity may be the single most important medical aspect of teenage pregnancy. Maturity is most commonly, albeit imperfectly, measured by birth weight, although it has long been realized that the same weight may represent different development levels in different populations.[38] Nonetheless, birth weight has effectively distinguished high-risk groups. In fact, in 1960, "The risk of death in the first year of life among infants who weigh 2,500 grams or less at birth is 17 times the risk among infants weighing 2,501 grams or more."[51] This finding is verified in two national studies of neonatal mortality in 1950 and mortality in the first year of life in 1960.[37,52] In 1960, as table 7-15 shows, mortality declined sharply as birth weight rose. For birth weights under 2,500 g, the risk of postneonatal mortality for a white infant was less than one-third that for a nonwhite infant.

For nonwhites and whites, the percentage of infants weighing less than 2,500 g is greatest among very young mothers; it increased for nonwhites between 1950 and 1967 (table 7-16). Unfortunately, more recent data on maternal age and birth weight group all women under age 20 in a single category.[14] For young mothers, the percent of infants with low birth weight increases greatly, as both the 1950 study[52] and the 1964 to 1966 National Natality Study[23,34] document. One theory offered as an explanation of the increasing frequency of low birth weight is based on the effort since 1950, to prolong ". . . pregnancies which gave indication of terminating prematurely."[53] This effort may have decreased fetal losses while at the same time increasing prematurity rates and tending to increase neonatal mortality. The data necessary to test this conjecture are not available.

More recent analysis of data for the 1960 U.S. birth cohort showed that the infant mortality rate for premature infants born to mothers under age 20 or over age 40 was slightly higher than when the mothers were age 20 to 39 (20.2 against 18.7 percent).[54] Therefore, the high proportion of premature births to young mothers and the mortality rates among "preemies" are determining factors in the infant mortality rates of young mothers.

The National Academy of Science,[55] in its Institute of Medicine's report on legalized abortion and the public health, speculated, "It should be possible to provide an effect of increased frequency of teenage abortions on the total proportion of newborns weighing less than 2,500 grams." Data necessary for a thorough analysis are not available, but indirect observation was made by comparing the percentage decline in infant mortality rates between

Table 7-15.—*Infant, neonatal, and postneonatal mortality rates, by birth weight and race, United States, 1960*

Birth weight	Rate per 1,000 live births						Rate per 1,000 survivors		
	Under 1 year			Under 28 days			28 days to 11 months		
	White	Nonwhite	Total	White	Nonwhite	Total	White	Nonwhite	Total
All birth weights									
2,500 g or less	191.9	185.7	190.3	177.4	154.8	171.6	17.7	36.6	22.6
2,501 g or more	9.7	20.0	11.2	5.1	7.7	5.5	4.6	12.4	5.8
1,000 g or less	929.3	893.6	919.3	924.1	883.7	912.8	67.8	84.4	74.0
1,001 to 1,500 g	575.6	478.1	548.5	555.1	434.2	521.5	46.2	77.6	56.5
1,501 to 2,000 g	219.0	171.8	206.6	198.4	130.3	180.6	25.6	47.7	31.7
2,001 to 2,500 g	58.2	59.4	58.4	45.0	30.7	41.4	13.8	29.5	17.7
2,501 to 3,000 g	17.3	25.3	19.0	10.1	9.4	9.9	7.3	16.0	9.2
3,001 to 3,500 g	8.9	17.4	10.1	4.4	6.4	4.7	4.5	11.1	5.5
3,501 to 4,000 g	6.9	17.0	8.0	3.3	6.6	3.6	3.6	10.5	4.3
4,001 to 4,500 g	7.0	21.0	8.3	3.6	10.1	4.2	3.4	11.0	4.1
4,501 g or more	11.2	28.1	13.3	7.7	16.3	8.7	3.5	11.9	4.6
All birth weights	22.2	41.4	25.1	16.9	26.7	18.4	5.4	15.1	6.9

Source: Reference 37.

Table 7-16.—*Percent of low birth weight infants by age and race of mother, United States, 1950 and 1967*

Age of mother	Total			White			Nonwhite		
	1950[a]	1967	Difference	1950	1967	Difference	1950	1967	Difference
Total	7.4	8.2	+0.8	7.0	7.1	+0.1	9.7	13.6	+3.9
Under 15 . . .	15.1	17.2	+2.1	15.9	12.5	−3.4	14.7	19.5	+4.8
15 to 19	9.0	10.5	+1.5	8.0	8.5	+0.5	12.0	15.7	+3.7
20 to 24	7.3	7.7	+0.4	6.9	6.7	−0.2	9.6	13.2	+3.6
25 to 29	6.7	7.2	+0.5	6.5	6.5	—[b]	8.4	11.8	+3.4
30 to 34	7.2	7.9	+0.7	7.0	7.0	—	8.8	12.6	+3.8
35 to 39	7.7	9.1	+1.4	7.5	8.3	+0.8	9.0	13.3	+4.3
40 to 44	7.7	9.6	+1.9	7.5	9.1	+1.6	8.9	12.2	+3.3
45 and over . .	6.1	8.6	+2.5	5.7	8.1	+2.4	7.4	10.8	+3.4

[a] Excludes all live births recorded in Massachusetts.
[b] Quantity zero.

Source: Reference 51.

1970 and 1972 in New York (9.3), California (9.3), and Washington (8.6)—States that had liberalized their abortion laws—and the rest of the United States (6.9).

Socioeconomic Factors

Prematurity may be strongly associated with factors like income and medical care. The National Natality Survey in 1963[56] found that the relationship between the percentage of infants weighing less than 2,500 g and maternal age was similar to that shown in table 7-16. When women are classified according to family income, however, their age had little effect on the percentages with premature infants (table 7-17). Approximately 47 percent of the mothers under age 20 had family incomes of less than $3,000 per annum, and another 33 percent fell in the next lowest category.

In the first four birth orders, the percent of mothers who received medical care early in pregnancy (by the end of the first trimester) was at least 40 percent higher for women aged 20 to 24 than for women aged 15 to 19 (table 7–18). Only approximately a third of the girls under age 15 and about half those aged 15 to 19 received prenatal care early in their first or second pregnancy.

In a study of infants in Baltimore between 1961 and 1965, birth weight was found to be related more, within each racial group, to the trimester of pregnancy in which prenatal care began than to age, parity, or socioeconomic status per se.[57] This finding supports the evidence of tables 7–17 and 7–18, since the timing of prenatal care was highly correlated wih socioeconomic status in the Baltimore study. The group under greatest risk of low birth weight was that of the unmarried black girl who had received no medical care, was under 15 years of age, was giving birth to her

Table 7-17.—*Percent of infants weighing 2,500 g or less at birth, by mother's age and family income, legitimate live births, United States, 1963*

Age of mother	Percent of infants, weighing 2,500 g or less				Percent of mothers by family income	
	Under $3000	$3000 to $4999	$5000 to $6999	$7000 or more	Under $3000	$3000 to $4999
Less than 20	10.9	6.9	4.9	4.1	47.2	33.3
20 to 24	10.6	7.8	6.5	5.5	22.8	31.5
25 to 29	11.1	7.6	3.8	4.1	13.6	25.4
30 to 34	11.4	6.7	6.4	4.4	13.9	21.1
35 and older	6.1	11.4	8.3	10.2	18.2	17.9

Source: Reference 56.

Table 7-18.—*Percent of mothers receiving medical care by the end of the first trimester of pregnancy, by age and parity, United States, 1975*

Age of mother	Parity[a]						
	1	2	3	4	5	6+	Total
All ages	72.3	76.5	72.6	66.7	61.1	50.6	72.4
Less than 15. . .	31.1	28.8	30.8	b—	—	—	30.9
15 to 19	54.9	48.6	40.3	37.5	26.5	53.2	53.3
20 to 24	78.9	73.1	60.6	49.1	42.3	37.6	73.4
25 to 29	87.3	85.4	77.7	66.8	56.1	45.7	81.3
30 to 34	85.2	86.2	81.8	75.1	67.1	52.1	78.9
35 to 39	79.5	81.8	78.5	73.6	68.0	53.0	70.3
40 to 44	72.4	74.5	72.0	69.2	65.7	50.1	61.0
45 to 49	60.2	58.7	53.2	54.3	51.4	46.0	49.5

[a] Total of 42 reporting States and the District of Columbia.
[b] Not applicable.

Source: Reference 19.

first child, and was in the study's lowest socioeconomic category. Just under 30 percent of the infants born to mothers in this group are estimated to weigh less than 2,500 g.

The dependence of the outcome of pregnancy on social factors was examined indirectly in another study of a very selected population. According to data on subscribers to the Health Insurance Plan of New York, fetal mortality was shown to be lowest for mothers under age 20 and to increase with each successive age group.[58] The average educational attainment and income are higher in this group than in the total population of New York. This age distribution within the group of women under age 20 is not given, but it is thought that fewer of them are very young teenagers than in the less selected populations from which previous data have come. Almost all received prenatal care early in pregnancy. The results of this study support the contention of investigators involved in the British Perinatal Survey, who stated that, "From the point of view of reproductive efficiency a woman is probably at her prime at about 18–20 years of age, just after she has attained full physical maturity."[45] In fact, analytical studies of their survey material showed, "that after allowance had been made for their relatively adverse parity and social class distribution the mortality in the under-20 age group was lower than at any other age period."[45] The previously discussed social and economic factors do, nonetheless, exist and appear to be strongly related to outcome of the pregnancy.

Other Problems of the Infants of Teenage Mothers

Increased mortality risks are not the only danger to infants of low birth weight. Prematurity is associated with the development of a host of seriously handicapping conditions. Lilienfeld and Pasamanick[59] carried out a series of landmark studies in Baltimore. One investigation located the birth certificates of epileptics who were born between 1935 and 1952 and who were followed in three hospital clinics. A control group was selected by searching the birth certificate records for the next infant born in the same place who matched the epileptic in race and maternal age. The proportion of infants weighing less than 2,500 g at birth was calculated. If prematurity and epilepsy were not associated, the proportion of epileptics and controls with birth weights under 2,500 g should have been the same. In fact, for whites, 12.9 percent of the epileptics and only 3.8 percent of the controls were premature, a highly significant result. The difference for nonwhites (15.3 percent of the epileptics against 12.3 percent of the controls were premature) is not as great, although it is in the same direction.

With similar methodology, links were established between prematurity and cerebral palsy and mental retardation.[60,61] Other investigators have followed groups of infants over a period of years and administered intelligence, motor development, and psychological tests. In all cases, scores improved as birth weight increased. In some cases, in comparisons of the smallest infants with infants who weighed 2,000 to 2,500 g at birth, differences of 6 to 10 points in mean IQ were detected.[62–66] Risks of deafness and blindness also are higher for the premature infant.[67,68] Thus, infants of young mothers may, by virtue of their high risks of prematurity, be unusually subject to severe neurological and sensory handicaps.

Maternal age alone also has been suggested as a determinant of the intelligence of the child. The evidence is, to some extent, conflicting. Pasamanick and Lilienfeld[69] found that the risk of mental retardation was high for mothers under age 20. In a Baltimore study by Lobl, Wilder, and Mellits,[70] IQ increased with age even when low birth weight infants were excluded from the study. Illsley[71] found that IQ increased with maternal age and the pattern of variation was similar to that of perinatal mortality, a finding indicating that environmental causes were at work. Record, McKeown, and Edwards[72] studied the verbal reasoning scores on standard examinations taken by 11-year-old British students who were born between 1950 and 1954. In examining the scores of these children according to the mothers' parity (0, 1, and 2), they found as much as 10 points difference between the scores of children born to mothers under age 20 and those of children whose mothers bore them at age 35 or more. The scores, however, at each age, decreased with the mother's parity. Investigating further, they found that there was only a slight difference between the scores of successive siblings within a family (i.e., first born against second in the same family, second against third, etc.). They concluded that the difference in intelligence is a result of the differences among families rather than within a family, as the mother's age increases.

The relationship of intelligence to maternal age may result from a direct relationship between a tendency to have children at a specified age and the intelligence of the offspring. They also believe that variation of the scores, in accordance with birth weight, may be due to familial differences in the risk of prematurity rather than birth weight per se. Their evidence on this point is less convincing because the lowest birth weight category was over 2,000 g.

Newcombe and Tavendale[73] linked increased risk of congenital defects to the two high-risk groups of mothers identified thus far: mothers under age 20 and over 35 years of age. Their data were extracted from the British Columbia Register of handicapped children and adults for 1953 to 1958 and from birth and death certificates for the Province. They found heightened risks of intracranial or spinal injury and of postnatal asphyxia and atelectasis for infants of young mothers irrespective of parity, and they found an increased risk of clubfoot for first births. They also noted an increased risk of epilepsy for the first two babies of mothers under 20 years of age.

Whether because of biological or environmental factors that affect the infant directly or indirectly through prematurity, the infant born to a teenage mother compared with an infant of a slightly older mother has a much higher risk of suffering severe handicaps that will certainly influence the child's life.

Maternal Mortality

Maternal mortality rates have undergone radical and rapid declines over the last 30 years. Between 1939 and 1941,[38] the rate was 364 per 100,000 live births; in 1973[74] it was 20. For whites, the rate dropped from 311 to 11; and for nonwhites, from 737 to 35. Although a large and rapid decline has occurred, nonwhite maternal mortality still is more than three times that of whites. For 1973, the rates were lowest for women under age 30 but they increased rather sharply thereafter. Racial differences in mortality increase steadily with maternal age. Mortality among whites is lowest (6.5 per 100,000 births) for mothers under age 20, but for nonwhites the rate for women aged 20–24 (18.2) is lower than that of younger women (26.7). For women under 20 years, the racial difference in maternal mortality is, to a large extent, a result of the differences in the death rates from toxemia, excluding abortion (9.1 for nonwhites against 2.6 for whites); abortion (3.2 against 0.2); and ectopic pregnancy (1.6 against 0.2). The rates for toxemia and for abortion with sepsis are approximately 50 percent higher for teenagers than for women aged 20 to 24 in each racial group.

Complications of Pregnancy

The complications of pregnancy most frequently reported for young mothers are toxemia, prolonged labor, and iron-deficiency anemia. Poor diets, late or inadequate prenatal care, and emotional and physical immaturity may well be contributing factors. Biological immaturity appears to be a problem for some while the mother is still growing.[36,75] Nevertheless, today's voluminous literature on the pregnant teenager overwhelmingly points toward social rather than medical problems as the primary concern.

This rather uniformly negative review ends with a single favorable relationship involving teenage pregnancies. A cooperative study carried out in the United States, Greece, Wales, Yugoslavia, Brazil, Taiwan, and Japan estimated ". . . that women having their first child when aged under 18 years have only about one-third the breast cancer risk of those whose first birth is delayed until the age of 35 years or more."[76] The relative risks of breast cancer according to age at first birth, taking the risk for women who never have a birth as 100, were estimated as less than age 20, 48; 20 to 24, 59; 25 to 29, 76; 30 to 34, 91; and greater than 35, 119. A steady increase in the chance of having breast cancer as age at first birth increases is thus indicated.

After a Teenage Pregnancy

Mothers who deliver babies out of wedlock represent a large segment of teenage mothers. Cutright[77] estimated that, in 1966, 64 percent of white infants and 6.4 percent of nonwhite infants born out of wedlock were adopted. He also speculated that few, probably less than 10 percent, were legitimized, in the sense of living with the mother and her husband, by later marriage. Zelnik and Kantner[25] found that only 18 percent of the 39 white illegitimate infants in their study, and 2 percent of the 221 blacks, were adopted, confirming speculation that many young girls are now keeping their infants. In their 1971 study, 41 percent of the 39 whites and 11 percent of the 221 blacks whose first births were illegitimate were married by the time they were surveyed at ages 15 to 19. Therefore, a much higher proportion of their infants may have been legitimized by later marriage.

The outlook for the premaritally pregnant is not particularly auspicious. They represent a rather large proportion of teenage brides. Estimates vary from at least 25 percent of the brides under age 20 to over 50 percent of the 15- to 17-year-old brides.[25,47,48,77] A long-term study of a sample of white couples who had a first, second, or fourth baby in Detroit in 1961 has described subsequent economic, social, and demographic variation among the families.[78] The premaritally pregnant, who comprised approximately a fifth of the sample, were found in 1961 and still in 1965 to be economically disadvantaged in terms of occupation, income, and assets, when compared with other couples. This situation was not accounted for by shorter marital duration, younger age at marriage, or the status of the couple's parental families.[79,80] In addition, the marital dissolution rate was higher for the premaritally pregnant (9.4 percent) than for other couples in the study (3.3 percent).

Other studies, too, have shown that the overall divorce rates for teenage marriages are very high.[81] Furthermore, women who marry or have a first child very early in life tend to add children rapidly. For example, a 1965 study of childspacing compares cumulative births, by successive intervals since first marriage for women aged under 22 and for those who married between 1960 and 1964. The average number of children 4 years after marriage was 1.51 for the younger women as compared with 1.24 for women

who were at least age 22 at marriage.[48] Similar findings come
from the 1960 Census for narrower categories of marital age (for
example, 14 to 17, 18 to 19, and 20 to 21).[47] In each case, fertility
at a given marital duration declined as age at marriage increased.
The differences usually were greater for whites than nonwhites.
Farley,[82] in his study of the fertility of black women aged 15 to 44
in 1960, estimated, "For each year marriage was delayed, fertility
was reduced by about one-eighth of a child." More recently, a
followup study of two groups of young black mothers compared
the fertility of those who bore a first child at age 15 or younger
with the fertility of those whose first birth took place at ages 20
to 24. The groups were matched for race and socioeconomic
background. The main difference was that 24 percent of the
teenagers went on to have at least three more children within the
7 years of followup, compared with 7 percent of those aged 20 to
24.[83]

The only study that examined the fertility experience of
teenagers, irrespective of marital status, was conducted several
years ago by Keeve and his coworkers in a Middle Atlantic
metropolitan county in 1969.[84] All birth certificates of infants born
to mothers aged 12 to 19 between January 1, 1958, and December
31, 1967, were scrutinized. Records of successive births to the same
mother were located, and cohort fertility tables according to age at
first birth were constructed. Actual parity is underestimated
because a study of this type could not search for the records of
later births to girls who either married, left the area, or delivered
elsewhere. The data suggest, however, that these girls are well on
their way to having large and closely spaced families.

Health Programs for Pregnant Adolescents

A number of special programs have been developed to reduce
the medical, educational, and social problems of pregnant
teenagers, especially those of school age, in the belief that the
outcome of their pregnancies can be altered favorably. Stress is
placed on early and adequate prenatal care, directed toward
reducing prematurity and infant mortality. Many health workers
suspect, although adequate studies have not been conducted, that
the combination of poor teenage diet, low income, and teenage
caloric needs may lead to more premature infants. Several
programs, although small scale, have succeeded in reducing
prematurity and infant mortality rates in their very young
clients.[75,85-87] They have found, however, only very limited success
or disappointing failure in preventing subsequent unplanned
pregnancies, even when family planning methods have been
introduced in ways intended to be sensitive to the feelings and
needs of teenagers.[88,89]

Although a program geared to the needs of the very young mother may have helped prevent obstetrical problems in one delivery, it may not affect conditions during a subsequent pregnancy. In New Haven, over 100 school-age mothers participated in a special program tailored to their needs. The health of the infants born while their mothers were enrolled in the program was compared with that of subsequent babies born within 5 years. According to Jekel et al.,[90] "Two factors were apparent. The study population delivered less healthy babies in subsequent deliveries than in initial ones despite the fact that the mothers were older. Second, prematurity was the most important immediate cause of perinatal death." Only 1.1 percent of index infants, compared with 8.8 percent of those born subsequently, died in the perinatal period. Therefore, the program was unable to alter the pattern observed earlier of infant mortality increasing with parity of the young mothers.

An interesting finding was that the girls sought less prenatal care for later pregnancies. "Perhaps the young mothers felt guilty about returning for care since the program personnel had expected that they would be successful contraceptors. . . . it was apparent that some of the girls felt keenly the expectation of the clinicians who gave them the contraception, because more than one stated at interviews 1 to 2 years later that they would not feel right about going back to the Young Mothers Clinic with another baby."[90]

Prevention of Adolescent Childbearing

Prevention of teenage childbearing is a difficult problem. Little research on contraceptive methods specifically for teenagers or for nulliparous women appears in the literature with the exception of studies of the intrauterine device (IUD). Although earlier reports suggested that the IUD was contraindicated for nulliparae, the insertion of smaller devices has somewhat alleviated problems with this method.[a] No recommendations have been made, at this writing, specifically for women under age 20, either for or against any contraceptive method.

Abortion is an alternative to childbearing and is widely used, as decribed earlier. For all ages, the short-term complications of abortion vary with the trimester of pregnancy when the abortion is performed and with the procedure used. The Joint Program for the Study of Abortion collected data on almost 73,000 abortions performed in the United States between July 1, 1970, and June 30, 1971.[91] Complication rates were calculated separately for patients with first-trimester abortions and those with later abortions. In

---

[a]Personal communication, Mary Grace Kovar.

this study, the youngest women had the highest proportions of abortions at week 13 of gestation or later. For girls 14 or less, 15 to 17, and 18 to 19, these proportions were 0.43, 0.38, and 0.27, respectively; in no age group of women over age 20 did more than 23 percent of the abortions occur after the first trimester. The complication rate in first-trimester abortions had a slight tendency to decline with age from its high of approximately 7 percent among women under age 20. The complication rate in later abortions rose with age from 22 percent in the youngest group to just over 25 percent in women age 25 and over. The overall complication rate from suction abortions was 5 percent. Because so many of the teenage abortions in this study occurred relatively late in pregnancy, it may be inferred that if the trend toward earlier abortion holds for teenagers as well as for all women, a decline in the overall age-specific short-term complication rate will have taken place.

The long-term complications of a particular abortion are difficult to study, and a number of recent investigations have produced conflicting results. Reports by Trussell[92] and the National Academy of Sciences[55] described a number of studies of the relationship between induced abortion and subsequent premature births, spontaneous abortions, ectopic pregnancies, infertility, and stillbirths.[93-96] Many of the samples are quite biased or small. Information requested retrospectively can create a problem, because it is the women with reproductive difficulties that may tend to report unusual events, such as an induced abortion more frequently. A World Health Organization group is at present undertaking studies in at least seven European countries to obtain a better delineation of abortion complications.[a]

The committee charged with preparing the report mentioned earlier for the National Academy of Sciences was also concerned that abortion might have been chosen as a substitute for contraception. The committee found, however, that insufficient data are available to reach any conclusion on the issue.[55] It did suggest that a "certain proportion of teenage women are introduced to contraception through the instruction and devices provided them at the time of their abortion [which] . . . serves as the primary entry into the system of fertility regulation, an entry otherwise denied them by relatively inaccessible or unavailable services."[58]

RECOMMENDATIONS

Infants of young mothers, especially very young mothers, are subject to higher risks of prematurity, mortality, and serious physical and intellectual impairment than children of older mothers. Research on the consequences and prevention of adolescent pregnancy is appropriate in a number of directions—some of which might include experimental action programs such as:

1. Separation of the effects of age from socioeconomic determinants.
2. Inquiry into the long-term medical effects not only on the infants born to adolescent mothers but also the infants' parents.
3. Research on methods and consequences of preventing early unanticipated childbearing.
4. Continued work on preventing young mothers, fathers, and their infants from experiencing the known possible consequences of early childbearing.
5. Identifying the social or economic determinants of pregnancy outcome in order to locate women of all ages at risk of experiencing reproductive problems associated with their status in an attempt to prevent these problems.

Separation of Age and Socioeconomic Factors

In many cases, except for very young mothers, no choice can yet be made between the two plausible explanations of the poor health observed in young mothers and their infants discussed in this report: maternal age itself or the socioeconomic forces that draw women who are more likely to experience problems into the early childbearing group. Obviously, when socially determined causes are primary, simply postponing childbearing to supposedly more favorable ages will not alter the outcomes of pregnancy. Other changes in living conditions might be necessary and should influence the policy and planning of health services for them.

Collecting and tabulating standard vital statistics of reproduction by single year of age for teenagers would be an obvious improvement in the currently available statistics. Recent volumes on *Natality*[4,5,7,9–20] have reported illegitimacy ratios by single year ages 15 to 19, and this practice should be extended to other data as well.

Additional socioeconomic questions might be included in the National Natality Survey and its coverage extended to include illegitimate births. The results could then be analyzed by age, race, education, and other measures of socioeconomic status.

Long-Term Medical Effects

Data may exist or could be collected to examine the health of the mother and child at various periods after the birth. Several mechanisms for gathering data could, with minor modifications or additions, provide relevant information:

1. The Health Interview Survey, which is conducted yearly, might add two questions: First, for the women, "What was your age at the birth of your first child (or, possibly, your first pregnancy) and the number of children you have given birth to before age 17 and age 20?" Then, for every respondent, "What was the age of your mother at the time of your birth?"

2. A question presently used in the Health Interview Survey, could be added to the National Family Growth Survey for the woman and each of her living children: "Compared to other people your age, would you say your health is excellent, good, fair, or poor?" The Health Interview Survey has found differential responses to this question by race, income, and other expected variables.[b]

If the prospective long-term cerebral palsy study conducted by the National Institute of Neurological Diseases and Stroke recorded maternal age at the child's birth, these extensive records might yield clues about the extent and importance of long-term effects. If questions regarding maternal age and socioeconomic status (currently and at the birth of the child) were asked or could be included in a followup, analysis of the responses might shed light not only on possible long-term effects but on the age-socioeconomic puzzle as well.

Prevention of Early Childbearing

The necessity for new ways of providing teenagers with adequate understanding of reproduction and with the means of controlling their fertility is obvious.

A radical approach would be to concentrate on teaching human (rather than vegetable or frog) biology starting in primary school. Many of the problems of adolescent health and childbearing described earlier reflect ignorance of normal body functioning.

In the medical sphere, it is essential to develop new methods of contraception and abortion, to consider the effects of various methods, and to plan their delivery in systems appealing to teenagers.

Preventing the Effects of Adolescent Childbearing

Finally, although many are disheartened by the paltry success of programs for the prevention of the deleterious sequelae of teenage childbearing, society cannot afford to ignore infants born with the unfavorable propsects known to affect the infants of adoles-

---

[b]Personal communication, C. Tietze.

cents. I have no new suggestions to offer, but I believe that continuing work on this approach is essential.

REFERENCES

1. Menken, J. "Teenage Childbearing: Its Medical Aspects and Implications for the United States Population." In C.F. Westoff and R. Parke, Jr., Eds., Commission on Population Growth and the American Future. *Research Reports* 1:351–357, 1972.
2. National Center for Health Statistics. *Vital Statistics of the United States, 1961,* Vol. 1, *Natality.* Washington: U.S. Government Printing Office, 1963.
3. National Center for Health Statistics. *Vital Statistics of the United States, 1968,* Vol. 1, *Natality.* Washington: U.S. Government Printing Office, 1970.
4. National Center for Health Statistics. "Summary Report: Final Natality Statistics, 1973." *Monthly Vital Statistics Report,* Vol. 23. No. 11, Supplement, Jan. 30, 1975.
5. National Center for Health Statistics. "Advance Report: Final Natality Statistics, 1975." *Monthly Vital Statistics Report,* Vol. 25, No. 10, Supplement, Dec. 30, 1976.
6. National Center for Health Statistics. Unpublished vital statistics data.
7. National Center for Health Statistics. "Summary Report: Final Natality Statistics, 1971." *Monthly Vital Statistics Report,* Vol. 23, No. 3, Suppl. 3, June 7, 1974.
8. Whelpton, P. K. and Campbell, A. A. *Vital Statistics: Special Reports.* No. 51, Part 1. National Center for Health Statistics, Washington: U.S. Government Printing Office, 1960.
9. National Center for Health Statistics. *Vital Statistics of the United States, 1964,* Vol. 1, *Natality.* Washington: U.S. Government Printing Office, 1966.
10. National Center for Health Statistics. *Vital Statistics of the United States, 1965,* Vol. 1, *Natality.* Washington: U.S. Government Printing Office, 1967.
11. National Center for Health Statistics. *Vital Statistics of the United States, 1966,* Vol. 1, *Natality.* Washington: U.S. Government Printing Office 1968.
12. National Center for Health Statistics. *Vital Statistics of the United States, 1967,* Vol. 1., *Natality.* Washington: U.S. Government Printing Office, 1969.
13. National Center for Health Statistics. *Vital Statistics of the United States, 1969,* Vol. 1, *Natality.* Washington: U.S. Government Printing Office, 1974.
14. National Center for Health Statistics. *Vital Statistics of the United States, 1970,* Vol. 1, *Natality.* Washington: U.S. Government Printing Office, 1975.

15. National Center for Health Statistics. *Vital Statistics of the United States, 1971,* Vol. 1, *Natality.* Washington: U.S. Government Printing Office, 1975.
16. National Center for Health Statistics. *Vital Statistics of the United States, 1972,* Vol. 1, *Natality.* Washington: U.S. Government Printing Office, 1976.
17. National Center for Health Statistics. *Vital Statistics of the United States, 1973,* Vol. 1, *Natality.* Washington: U. S. Government Printing Office, 1977.
18. National Center for Health Statistics. *Vital Statistics of the United States, 1974,* Vol. 1, *Natality* (in preparation).
19. National Center for Health Statistics. *Vital Statistics of the United States, 1975,* Vol. 1, *Natality* (in preparation).
20. National Center for Health Statistics. Summary Report: Final Natality Statistics, 1972. *Monthly Vital Statistics Report* Vol. 23, No. 8, Supplement, Oct. 31, 1974.
21. U.S. Bureau of the Census. *U.S. Census of Population: 1970. Subject Reports. Marital Status.* Final Report. PC(2)–4C. Washington: U.S. Government Printing Office, 1972.
22. Sklar, J. and Berkov, B. "The American Birth Rate." *Science* 189:693–700, 1975.
23. National Center for Health Statistics. Unpublished data.
24. Kovar, M.G. "Interval from First Marriage to First Birth." Paper presented at the Annual Meeting of the Population Association of America, 1970.
25. Pratt, W. "A Study of Marriages Involving Premarital Pregnancies." Ph.D. thesis. University of Michigan, 1965.
26. Zelnik, M. and Kantner, J. "The Resolution of Teenage First Pregnancies." *Fam. Plann. Perspect.* 6(2):74–80, 1974.
27. Center for Disease Control. *Abortion Surveillance Annual Summary, 1975.* Atlanta: Center for Disease Control, 1977.
28. Pakter, J., O'Hare, D., and Nelson, F. "Teenage Pregnancies in New York City: Impact of Legalized Abortions." Paper presented at the Annual Meeting of the American Public Health Association, 1974.
29. Pakter, J. and Nelson, F. "Factors in the Unprecedented Decline in Infant Mortality in New York City." *Bull. N.Y. Acad. Med.* 2nd series, July-Aug. 1974.
30. Sklar, J. and Berkov, B. "Teenage Family Formation in Postwar America." *Fam. Plann. Perspect.* 6(2):80–90, 1973.
31. Sklar, J. and Berkov, B. "Abortion, Illegitimacy, and the American Birth Rate." *Science.* 185:909–915, 1974.
32. Teele, J. and Schmidt, W. "Illegitimacy and Race: National and Local Trends." *Milbank Mem. Fund Q.* 48:127–145, 1970.
33. Siegel, E. and Morris, N. "The Epidemiology of Human Reproductive Casualties, with Emphasis on the Rate of Nutrition." *In Maternal Nutrition and the Course of Pregnancy.* pp. 5–40.

Committee on Maternal Nutrition, Food and Nutrition Board, National Resource Council. Washington: National Academy of Sciences, 1970.

34. Nortman, D. "Parental Age as a Factor in Pregnancy Outcome and Child Development." *Rep. Popul. Fam. Plann.* No. 16, 1974.

35. National Academy of Sciences Working Group Report. "Relation of Nutrition to Pregnancy in Adolescence." *In Maternal Nutrition and the Course of Pregnancy.* pp. 163–187. Committee on Maternal Nutrition, Food and Nutrition Board, National Resource Council. Washington: National Academy of Sciences, 1970.

36. Heady, J. A., Daley, C., and Morris, J. N. "Social and Biological Factors in Infant Mortality. II. Variations of Mortality with Mother's Age and Parity." *Lancet.* 1:395–397, 1955.

37. Chase, H. "Infant Mortality and Weight at Birth: 1960 United States Birth Cohort." *Am. J. Public Health.* 59:1618–1628, 1969.

38. Shapiro, S., Schlesinger, E., and Nesbitt, R. *Infant, Perinatal, Maternal and Childhood Mortality in the United States.* Cambridge: Harvard University Press, 1968.

39. National Center for Health Statistics. "Infant Mortality Rates by Legitimacy Status: United States, 1964–66." *Monthly Vital Statistics Report.* Vol. 20, No. 5, Supplement, August 11, 1971.

40. Heady, J. A. and Morris, J. N. "Social and Biological Factors in Infant Mortality. Variation of Mortality with Mother's Age and Parity." *J. Obstet. Gynaecol. Br. Commonw.* 66:577–591, 1959.

41. Morrison, S. L., Heady, A., and Morris, J. N. "Social and Biological Factors in Infant Mortality. VIII, Mortality in the Postneonatal Period." *Arch. Dis. Child.* 34:101–113, 1959.

42. Donnelly, J. F., Abernathy, J.R., Creadnick, R. N., Flowers, C. E., Greenburg, B. G., and Wells, H. B. "Fetal, Perinatal, and Environmental Factors Associated With Perinatal Mortality in Mothers under 20 Years of Age." *Am. J. Obstet. Gynecol.* 80:663–671, 1960.

43. MacMahon, B., Kovar, M. G., and Feldman, J. *Infant Mortality Rates: Socioeconomic Factors.* National Center for Health Statistics, Vital and Health Statistics Series 22, No. 14. Washington: U.S. Government Printing Office, 1972.

44. Chase, H. *The Relationship of Certain Biologic and Socioeconomic Factors to Fetal, Infant and Early Childhood Mortality. II. Father's Occupation, Infant's Birth Weight and Mother's Age.* (Mimeo.) Albany, N. Y.: Department of Health, 1962.

45. Baird, Sir A. and Thompson, A. M. "General Factors Underlying Perinatal Mortality Rates." In N. Butler and E. Alberman, Eds., *Perinatal Problems.* p. 27. Edinburgh and London: E. and S. Livingstone, Ltd., 1969.

46. Vavra, H. M. and Querec, L. *Age of Mother, Total Birth Order and Other Variables, 1960 Live-Birth Cohort.* National Center for Health Statistics, Vital and Health Statistics Series 20, No. 14. Washington: U. S. Government Printing Office, 1973.

47. U.S. Bureau of the Census. *U.S. Census of Population: 1960. Subject Reports. Childspacing.* Final Report. PC(2)–3B. Washington: U.S. Government Printing Office, 1968.

48. U.S. Bureau of the Census. *Current Population Reports. Marriage, Fertility, and Childspacing, June 1965.* Series P–20, No. 186. Washington: U.S. Government Printing Office, 1969.

49. Bumpass, L. "Age at Marriage as a Variable in Socioeconomic Differentials in Fertility." *Demography* 6:45–54, 1969.

50. Wray, J. "Population Pressure on Families, Family Size, and Childspacing." *In Rapid Population Growth.* pp. 403–461. Prepared by a Study Committee of the Office of the Foreign Secretary, National Academy of Sciences, with the support of the Agency for International Development. Baltimore and London: The Johns Hopkins Press (published for the National Academy of Sciences), 1971.

51. Chase, H. "Trends in prematurity: United States, 1950–1967." *Am. J. Public Health.* 60:1967–1983, 1970.

52. Loeb, J. *Weight at Birth and Survival of the Newborn, by Age of Mother and Total Birth Order, United States, Early 1950.* National Center for Health Statistics, Vital and Health Statistics Series 21, No. 5. Washington: U.S. Government Printing Office, 1965.

53. Chase, H. *International Comparison of Perinatal and Infant Mortality: The United States and Six West European Countries.* National Center for Health Statistics, Vital and Health Statistics Series 3, No. 6. Washington: U.S. Government Printing Office, 1967.

54. Armstrong, R. J. *A Study of Infant Mortality from Linked Records by Birth Weight, Period of Gestation, and Other Variables.* National Center for Health Statistics, Vital and Health Statistics Series 20, No. 12. Washington: U.S. Government Printing Office, 1972.

55. National Academy of Sciences. *Legalized Abortion and the Public Health.* Report of a study by a committee of the Institute of Medicine. IOM Publication 75–02. Washington, 1975.

56. Kovar, M. G. *Variables in Birth Weight, Legitimate Live Births, United States, 1963.* National Center for Health Statistics, Vital and Health Statistics Series 22, No. 8. Washington: U.S. Government Printing Office, 1968.

57. Wiener, G. and Milton, T. "Demographic Correlates of Low Birth Weight." *Am. J. Epidemiol.* 91:260–272, 1970.

58. Shapiro, S. and Abramowicz, M. "Pregnancy Outcome Correlates Identified Through Medical Record Based Information." *Am. J. Public Health.* 59:1629- 1650, 1969.
59. Lilienfeld, A. and Pasamanick, B. "Association of Maternal and Fetal Factors with the Development of Epilepsy. I. Abnormalities in the Prenatal and Paranatal Periods." *J. Am. Med. Assoc.* 155:719–724, 1954.
60. Lilienfeld, A., and Parkhurst, E. "A Study of the Association of Factors of Pregnancy and Parturition with the Development of Cerebral Palsy: Preliminary Report." *Am. J. Hyg.* 53:262–282, 1951.
61. Pasamanick, B. and Lilienfeld, A. "Association of Maternal and Fetal Factors with the Development of Mental Deficiency. I. Abnormalities in the Prenatal and Paranatal Periods." *J. Am. Med. Assoc.* 159:155–160, 1955.
62. Wiener, G. "The Relationship of Birth Weight and Length of Gestation to Intellectual Development at Ages 8 and 10 Years." *J. Pediatr.* 76:694–699, 1970.
63. Eaves, L. C. Nuttoll, J. C., Klonoff, H., and Dunn, H. G. "Developmental and Psychological Test Scores in Children of Low Birth Weight." *Pediatrics.* 45:9–20, 1970.
64. Drillien, C. M. "School Disposal and Performance for Children of Different Birth Weight Born 1953–1960." *Arch. Dis. Child.* 44:562–570, 1969.
65. Wiener, G., Rider, R., Oppel, W., Fischer, L., and Harper, P. "Correlates of Low Birth Weight: Psychological Status at Six to Seven Years of Age." *Pediatrics.* 35:434–444, 1965.
66. Clifford, S. H. "High Risk Pregnancy. 1. Prevention of Prematurity: The *sine qua non* for Reduction of Mental Retardation and Other Neurological Disorders." *N. Engl. J. Med.* 271:243–249, 1964.
67. Vernon, McC. "Prematurity and Deafness: The Magnitude and Nature of the Problem among Deaf Children." *Except. Child.* 33:289–298, 1967.
68. Goldberg, J. D., Goldstein, H., Quade, D., and Ragot, E. "Association of Perinatal Factors with Blindness in Children." *Public Health Rep.* 82:519–531, 1967.
69. Pasamanick, B. and Lilienfeld, A. "The Association of Maternal and Fetal Factors with the Development of Mental Deficiency. II. Relationship to Maternal Age, Birth Order, Previous Reproductive Loss and Degree of Deficiency." *Am. J. Ment. Defic.* 60:557–574, 1956.
70. Lobl, M., Wilder, A., and Mellets, E. D. "Maternal Age and Intellectual Functioning of Offspring." *Johns Hopkins Med. J.* 128:347–363, 1971.
71. Illsley, R. "The Sociological Study of Reproduction and Its Outcome." In S. A. Richardson and A. F. Guttmacher, Eds., *Child-*

bearing: Its Social and Psychological Factors. Baltimore: Williams and Wilkins, 1967.

72. Record, R. G., McKeown, T., and Edwards, J. H. "The Relation of Measured Intelligence to Birth Weight and Duration of Gestation." *Am. Hum. Genet.* 33:71–79, 1969b.
73. Newcombe, H. B. and Tavendale. O. G. "Maternal Age and Birth Order Correlations." *Mutat. Res.* I:446–467, 1964.
74. National Center for Health Statistics. *Vital Statistics of the United States, 1973,* Vol. 2., *Mortality,* Part A. Washington: U.S. Government Printing Office, 1977.
75. Stine, O. and Kelley, E. "Evaluation of a School for Young Mothers: The Frequency of Prematurity among Infants Born to Mothers under 17 Years of Age, According to the Mother's Attendance of a Special School During Pregnancy." *Pediatrics.* 46:581–587, 1970.
76. MacMahon, B., Cale, P., Lin, T. N., Lowe, C. R., Minna, A. P., Raonihar, B., Salker, E. J., Valooras, V. G., and Yuasa, S. "Age at First Birth and Breast Cancer Risk." *Bull. WHO.* 43:209–221, 1970.
77. Cutright, P. and Galle, O. *Illegitimacy: Measurement and Analysis.* (Mimeo.). Nashville: Vanderbilt University (Department of Sociology), 1966.
78. Freedman, R. and Coombs, L. "Childspacing and Family Economic Position." *Am. Sociol. Rev.* 31:631–649, 1966.
79. Coombs, L., Freedman, R., Friedman, J., and Pratt, W. "Premarital Pregnancy and Status before and after Marriage." *Am. J. Sociol.* 75:800–820, 1979.
80. Coombs, L. and Freedman, R. "Premarital Pregnancy, Childspacing, and Later Economic Achievement." *Popul. Stud. (London)* 24:389–412, 1970.
81. Coombs, L. and Zumeta, Z. "Correlates of Marital Dissolution in a Prospective Fertility Study: A Research Rate." *Social Probl.* 18:92–102, 1970.
82. Farley, R. "Fertility among Urban Blacks." *Milbank Mem. Fund Q.* 48:183–206, 1970.
83. Ting, R. Y. and Wang, M. H. "The Black Pregnant Teenager: What Becomes of Her and Her Offspring." *Fam. Plann. Dig.* 2(2):15, 1973.
84. Keeve, J. P. Schlesinger, E., Wight, B., and Adams, R. "Fertility Experience of Juvenile Girls: A Community-Wide Ten-Year Study." *Am. J. Public Health.* 59:2185–2198, 1969.
85. Sarrel, P. and Klerman, L. "The Young Unwed Mother." *Am. J. Obstet. Gynecol.* 105:575–578, 1969.
86. Dickens, H., Mudd, E., Garcia, R., Tomar, K., and Wright, D. "One Hundred Pregnant Adolescents, Treatment Approaches in a University Hospital." *Am. J. Public Health.* 63:794–800, 1973.

87. Jekel, J. F., Currie, J. B., Klerman, L. V., McCarthy, C. P. N., Sarrel, P. M., and Greensbert, R. A. "An Analysis of Statistical Methods for Comparing Obstetric Outcomes." *Am. J. Obstet. Gynecol.* 112:9–19, 1972.
88. Furstenberg, F. F., Masnick, G. S., and Ricketts, S. "How Can Family Planning Programs Delay Teenage Pregnancies?" *Fam. Plann. Perspect.* 4:54–60, 1972.
89. Graves, W. and Bradshaw, B. "Early Reconceptions and Contraceptive Use among Black Teenage Girls after an Illegitimate Birth." *Am. J. Public Health.* 65:738–740, 1975.
90. Jekel, J., Harrison, J., Bancroft, D. R. E., Tyler, N., and Klerman, L. "A Comparison of the Health of Index and Subsequent Babies Born to School-Age Mothers." *Am. J. Public Health.* 65:370–374, 1975.
91. Tietze, C. and Lewit, S. "A National Medical Experience: The Joint Program for the Study of Abortion (JPSA)." *In* H. J. Osofsky and J. D. Osofsky, Eds., *The Abortion Experience.* pp. 1–28. Hagerstown: Harper and Row, 1973.
92. Trussell, T. J. "Third Thoughts on Abortion." *Br. J. Hosp. Med.* May:601–604, 1973.
93. Hungary Central Statistical Office. Perinatalis Halalozas, 1972.
94. Pantelakis, S., Papadimitriou, G. C., and Doxiadis, S. A. "Influence of Induced and Spontaneous Abortions on the Outcome of Subsequent Pregnancies." *Am. J. Obstet. Gynecol.* 116:799–805, 1973.
95. Robb, L. H. and Aoyama, H. "Induced Abortion and Its Sequelae: Prematurity and Spontaneous Abortion." *Am. J. Obstet. Gynecol.* 120:868–874, 1974.
96. Hogue, C. J. "Prematurity Subsequent to Induced Abortion in Kospje, Yugoslavia: An Historical Perspective Study." Ph.D. thesis. University of North Carolina, 1973.

DISCUSSION

The following people were the major participants in the discussion: F. Jaffe, J. Trussell, P. Piotrow, R. Lincoln, S. Gustavus, J. Forbush, R. Faden, J. Kantner, A. Rosewater, J. McKigney, and A. Rossi.

The chief topics of discussion were the physical effects of early childbearing, the possible effects of oral contraceptives and abortion on fertility, some special socioeconomic problems of early adolescent childbearing, trends in adoptive placements, suggestions for research, and needs for reforms in population and sex education.

It was proposed that when the mother has not finished her physical growth, both the mother and child face definite childbearing risks. On the average, most girls have completed their growth by age 15. Some discussants pointed out that it was unlikely that a girl would become pregnant before the end of the physical growth spurt because this spurt is usually completed by the time she has reached menarche. After reaching menarche, she is unlikely to be fecund for a period of time. Full reproductive capacity appears to be related to the accumulation of a certain amount (22 percent) of body fat. This accumulation following menarche is strongly affected by the girl's nutritional level. Improvements in nutrition have lowered the age of puberty and have shortened the period between reaching menarche and reaching full reproductive potential. It would be more appropriate to think of the girl's gynecological age, rather than her chronological age, because of different levels of physical development among girls. Although most girls would have completed their growth spurt by the time they become pregnant, some pregnancy risks to the girl of marginal nutritional status could occur.

A question was raised as to what the physical risks of early childbearing actually are. Aside from possible nutritional risks, the major sources of difficulty would be uteroplacental (such as blood supply to the uterus, size of uterus, and ability to function normally). Apparently, no evidence exists that women under age 20 have more problems along these lines than women over that age.

It is almost impossible to untangle the specific physical effects of early pregnancy from the lifestyle and socioeconomic background characteristics of young pregnant girls. The kinds of young adolescents who become pregnant are apt to come from poverty backgrounds and to seek medical care late in their pregnancies. Early, optimal medical care for the girls might offset observed higher rates of maternal and child risk.

Some participants believed that nutritional supplements during pregnancy would have highly positive effects, but others thought that there is no firm evidence for this belief. The effects of nutritional supplements have not been definitively proved for expectant mothers of any age, although an extensive experimental study directed to this question is now under way.

The consensus was that, physically speaking, age 18 or 19 appeared to be the optimal age for the first pregnancy.

A question was raised concerning the possible effects of oral contraceptives on the young woman's later fertility. One speaker said that, theoretically, in a female with hypothalmic pituitary dysfunction, the use of oral contraceptives may produce a tendency toward subsequent infertility through suppressing the functioning of the hypothalmus and the pituitary gland. Fears that the estrogen content of the orals might accelerate growth seem to be unfounded.

The possible effects of abortion on fertility are not known at present. Currently, a large European research project is investigating this issue.

It was pointed out that concern about the possible effects of oral contraceptives on later fertility may be excessive. In 1976, Luker reported that physicians sometimes express this concern to young women, prompting them to abandon the pill and yet not substitute another form of contraceptive.

Childbearing by youngsters under the age of 18 creates a number of other problems for them, apart from the possible physical consequences already discussed. The problems often prompt a premature school departure and can place a girl in a vulnerable position since she lacks the legal status accorded to older people. Employment is difficult to find. Society tends to regard sexually active young women under the age of 18 as deviant. At a recent meeting of the National Alliance Concerned with School Age Parents, members of the youth panel pointed out their needs for help in obtaining housing, independent legal status, access to services (including contraceptive and abortion services), credit, jobs, and income.

Questions were raised as to whether young adolescents had reached the stage of psychological development at which they could understand the need for adequate prenatal and postnatal care and whether they would be able to provide adequate care for their children.

A lengthy discussion was held on the data available regarding the proportion of adolescents who place their children for adoption. No adequate information is available on adoptions, partly because there are so many informal and black market adoptive placements. A number of estimates, however, can be made. Increasing numbers of teenagers (including very young ones) seem to be keeping their babies, and it is more and more difficult for adoptive parents to find a child to adopt.

It is impossible to determine how many babies who are placed for adoption were illegitimate at birth because their official birth records are often changed. Thus, the effects on this group of infants of early, out-of-marriage births cannot be assessed.

Available data have shown for many years that white girls are more apt to place their babies for adoption than black girls. One reason is that the extended black family is more willing to accept and care for an illegitimate child of one of its members. Many black people also distrust formal adoption agencies, which are largely staffed by white, middle-class professionals.

The U.S. Bureau of Census does not gather specific information on the alternative custodial arrangements of the children if they are not living with either parent. Understandably, this topic is rather delicate.

Program research is needed to evaluate the effects of various intervention strategies, such as sex education, differing models of contraception and abortion services, and special programs for teen-age parents.

A particular opportunity exists at this time to evaluate the differential effects of service availability, in respect to abortions. The services are differentially available to adolescents in many communities at low, medium, and high levels of service availability.

Data on illegitimacy, by specific ages, will be increasingly available from the National Center for Health Statistics (NCHS). The topic has been so controversial in the past that it was difficult for NCHS to handle it.

More studies are needed concerning the effects of family planning services as an intervention strategy, primarily for prevention, namely, preventing the first pregnancy. All too often studies are carried out with girls who are already pregnant, because the already pregnant population is easier to reach for research. Although it is helpful to study never-pregnant girls known to family planning clinics, it is even more important to study those who do not apply for these services. This population is extremely difficult for researchers to reach.

Followup studies concerning the effects of programs are needed. For example, a recent New York City study by Christopher Tietze shows that following the liberal abortion law in New York, the birth rate declined for all age groups. The pregnancy rate also declined, but not so much for teenagers as for others. The decline in pregnancies probably was a result of increased use of contraceptives following an abortion: abortion services had been providing assistance with contraceptives after the abortion.

There are 623 special programs for school-age parents in the United States. It was originally hoped that these programs would bring about improved maternal and child health and would reduce further childbearing. An evaluation of a New Haven project by Dr. Jekel and Dr. Klerman, however, revealed that these goals were not reached for the most part. Many of the girls had a subsequent second pregnancy in a short period of time and did not return to the special medical services for prenatal or obstetrical care. Rates of infant mortality were high for the group. The young mothers, when asked, said they were embarrassed by their second pregnancies and failed to return for service because they did not want to disappoint the staff by their subsequent pregnancies. A later followup study showed that a large proportion of these girls had sought sterilization. A smaller proportion of the control group did the same.

The persons in charge of the special programs are eager for help in evaluating their programs, especially if adding an evaluation component will aid them in restoring the Federal funding they once had. It was pointed out that these and other programs should include a cost/benefit analysis component.

Some thought that the lifetime economic consequences of early childbearing were so costly that the prevention of even a few pregnancies would produce a favorable cost/benefit ratio for family planning services to teenagers.

Long-range followup research for the programs was recommended. Shortage of funds, among other factors, has put a 6-months' limit on followup of most of the school-age parent programs. For example, there is a dearth of information about how school-age parents finance themselves. Dr. Furstenberg has conducted one of the few longitudinal studies on the subject (see Ch. 11). Data are also available from Dr. Presser, who did a 1-year followup (see Ch. 10).

Better long-range followup studies on the effects of abortion are needed. All too often these studies consist of followup interviews while the young woman is still in the recovery room.

It was suggested that research be undertaken to study the effects of social organizations on adolescents. What are the attitudes and policies, for instance, of schools, religious organizations, and family planning programs toward sexually active adolescents? Dr. Ann Rosewater of the Children's Defense Fund said that the Fund has such a study in progress. Interviews with school administrators and teachers revealed that most school personnel do not want pregnant girls or young mothers in their programs. They fear parental objections if such girls are present in the schools. It was agreed that no social institution, including the family, really wants to deal with adolescent sexuality. More information about parent attitudes and behavior is needed.

More knowledge also is needed about what is being taught in the schools with respect to population and sex education. Dr. Forbush said she has recently undertaken a study of this topic with a select sample of teachers who have had special training in population education.

It was suggested that the effects of adolescent childbearing on the IQ of the children be studied. A proposal was made that it might be a good idea to undertake a retrospective study with older parents to obtain data on the ages at which they had children and to obtain their perceptions of the effects of childbearing at different ages. Such a study might provide information about the consequences over a long period of time and would also avoid the problem of using adolescents as research subjects. Changes in society and its norms, however, present a problem for these kinds of studies. The effects of adolescent childbearing and of childbearing outside of marriage today might be quite different than they were 10 or more years ago.

More information could be gained about the effects of maternal age at the birth of children by adding a few pertinent questions to the National Health Survey.

More should be known about the incidence of morbidity among children, as it relates to the age of the mother at the birth of a child. Too exclusive an emphasis seems to have been placed on infant mortality rates and low birth weights.

More research attention is needed in respect to males. Very little is known about their attitudes, knowledge, and behavior or the effects of them on such factors as contraceptive use, abortion, or early fatherhood. It was agreed that these questions are important but that male subjects are very hard to reach.

Extensive discussion ensued about the need for population and sex education in the schools and elsewhere. It was pointed out that what is being taught and the effects of what is being taught on attitudes and behavior are unknown. A participant commented that when she had shown films to groups about the possible adverse effects of adolescent teenage pregnancy, many persons reacted negatively, saying that they thought such films were merely propaganda.

Another participant said that education on population and sex was needed at home and at school and that these subjects should be treated naturally as they arise. Some thought that the usual sex education does not deal with the truly important topics, such as where contraceptive and abortion services can be obtained. There was general agreement that most teenagers understand neither the reproductive risks associated with coitus nor the concept of ovulation, including the times in the menstrual cycle when the risk of pregnancy is greatest.

It was suggested that sex education might be dealt with outside of the schools because so many schools are unwilling or unable to handle the topic. Others thought such an elaborate undertaking would be too expensive. The effectiveness of sex education had been questioned as a result of the few studies done on the subject, and more research is needed in this area.

Chapter 8

The Psychological Consequences of Adolescent Pregnancy and Abortion

E. James Lieberman

George Washington University

Adolescence may be defined as the developmental period between puberty, a biological transition, and adulthood, which is marked by social criteria of age, marital, and occupational status. The World Health Organization Expert Committee on Health Problems of Adolescence[1] accepted the age range of 10 to 20 within its purview. The term "youth" or "young people" has been used to describe the age group 20 to 24. It is reasonable to define the 5-year cohorts as follows: 10 to 14, early adolescence (pubescence); 15 to 19, adolescence (mid to late); and 20 to 24, youth or young adulthood.

A set of biopsychosocial factors accounts for contemporary prolongation of adolescence, with puberty coming somewhat earlier, and socialization to adulthood taking considerably longer than in the past. The study of adolescence has appropriately increased in recent years to the extent that some people say the whole phenomenon is a modern invention. While adolescence is not to be stereotyped (even as a period of storm and stress, since evidence varies on this point), neither is it merely an artifact of contemporary history or scholarship.

Every society has the collective task, as each family has the individual responsibility, to bring children to adulthood in a manner that equips them to function well in their sex roles, work, parenthood, leisure, and health maintenance. Adolescence, a period of transition in so many respects, is one which has prominently associated with it the risk of pregnancy and its sequelae, including abortion. The major psychological issues and psychiatric problems of adolescents are often related to sexuality, pregnancy, and abortion. Although the future of any given individual could never be predicted with certainty, in times past the patterns of society dictated a regularity of succession from generation to generation (barring external catastrophe). Today, even that regularity is upset by rapid social change. The adolescent bears a special burden of stress. The rules and roles that guided his or her grandparents, parents, and even older siblings are altered in the face of urbanization, mass communication, threat of nuclear catastrophe, overpopulation, and women's liberation.

The GAP Report *Normal Adolescence*,[2] an important contemporary statement, states: "Sexual potential is biologically given, but status must be socially achieved and accorded. . . . Socioeconomic responsibility for children, rather than sexual reproduction per se, would seem perhaps the ultimate criterion of adult status in most of the world. . . . Many 14-year-old girls are capable of bearing children and thus of functioning sexually as adults, yet there are no status categories to make this meaningful. Indeed, this functional capacity carries only potential penalty." An important distinction is to be made between adult status (as conferred by age, rites of passage, and parenthood) and adult function, that is, the taking of responsibility "for self, mate, offspring, and society in that order."

Previously, Erikson[3] had formulated the universal tasks of adolescence in similar terms: identity, intimacy, generativity, and integrity. In his epigenetic theory, each stage builds upon the previous one, and the failure of earlier stage mastery will be reflected to some extent in later development. Thus, adolescents and adults will not function optimally if the childhood tasks of basic trust, autonomy, initiative, and industry are left unfinished or flawed. Problems arise when too much or too little is demanded of the developing individual; when needed physical or emotional nurturance is lacking; or when familial, communal, or cultural upheaval alters or destroys the comprehensibility of the environment.

Problems also arise when, instead of fostering continuity of development, experience teaches the child only to be a good child and not how to be a good youth or adult. Related to this problem of discontinuity—exemplified by exaggerated adult reactions to puberty and adolescent sexuality—is the problem of rewards and penalties for "acceptable" social behavior in adolescence. Being "acceptable" in meeting society's criteria for certain roles does not always prove to be adaptive in the long run. Being "bad" or deviant, however, may sometimes be quite adaptive. If young people, in their quest for identity, see that adult models do not practice what they preach, their idealism and basic trust will change to cynicism and mistrust. They may become ill, delinquent, rebellious, withdrawn, or promiscuous. These reactions may be psychological coping maneuvers or "quitting" signs in response to stress that makes normal coping impossible.

PREMATURE PARENTHOOD

Although childbearing is an essential, honored, and protected function of every society, it can happen too soon in the life cycle, or too often, or under the wrong circumstances. Because motherhood has been regarded as virtually sacred, its abuse may be considered a sacrilege. Nonetheless, the attainment of motherhood has occurred until now primarily by accident rather than by design, and today the role does little to sanctify its occupant in such cases.

"Motherhood is often defined as the most sacred of women's roles; but, ironically, it is the social role women are most likely to adopt unintentionally."[4] This lack of intentionality has been dealt with, or accepted, throughout history and across diverse cultural systems with a variety of customs, rituals, and rationalizations. Individual informed consent for parenthood is still a radical proposal even in the United States, where self-determination and control of one's future have long been accepted in principle.[5] The desperate wish of many women to postpone or avoid motherhood created a hazardous but thriving illegal abortion business that only in this decade has faced competition from legal and safe abortion services. Primiparous single young women have been the major consumers of the services, expressing thereby the diagnosis of "premature pregnancy."

From the mental health standpoint, the most important pregnancy to plan is the first. The transition to parenthood is a critical phase of youth, a biopsychosocial commitment for years to come, one which completely changes the future of the pregnant woman— less so than that of her partner in fertility. Her education, economic status, health, and marital adjustment are all at stake. Yet she rarely has chosen motherhood deliberately when it happened, or had the knowledge or means to delay it, except by sexual abstinence.

In the United States in 1977, 11,455 girls under age 15 gave birth (about 2 births per thousand girls 12–14 years old). Although a few of the pregnancies were wanted, at least ostensibly, most were not. Objective observers would state that the pregnancies were premature and that they created an undesirable and severe stress on the girls. Among girls that young, about as many had abortions as gave birth. These girls and their families represent a major risk group in child mental health, but most have relatively little benefit of mental health care.

Most of these premature pregnancies are, of course, out-of-wedlock. Encompassing all school-age girls, over 225,000 births occur each year in the United States, most of which are premarital conceptions or out-of-wedlock births. These girls are not well motivated to seek good prenatal care—in many cases they are expelled

from school—married or not. Those who look forward to motherhood as emancipation from dependency in an unhappy home, or as
proof of womanhood, often find that the cost is too great to bear.
Teen marriages have a high rate of failure—about one out of two
end in divorce, and those couples who remain married are not
necessarily contented.

In her survey of first births in New York City,[4] Presser
found one-third were to adolescents aged 15 to 19; of those, 75
percent were out-of-wedlock conceptions, and 60 percent were illegitimate births; 81 percent were unplanned pregnancies (compared
with 56 percent in the 20 to 23 age group and 30 percent for
those aged 24 to 29). Fully half of the teen mothers wished they
could have postponed the first pregnancy.

Some people, even some with psychological expertise, maintain
that a woman does not become pregnant unless she wants to—this
desire can be an unconscious wish. No evidence supports this theory, which has, nevertheless, a substantial impact as a denigrating
label. The chance of impregnation with an unprotected act of sexual intercourse is about 4 percent. Thus, for 100 couples, it would
take 12 exposures before half of the women are pregnant. This
means that for every woman who is pregnant, a substantial number of others are engaging in the same degree of risk behavior
and are temporarily escaping impregnation. This statistical-biologi-
cal phenomenon is not well understood by young people. Many
young people not only have little understanding of the menstrual
cycle, but also have astonishing misconceptions about physiology, as
evidenced by, "Unless you are married you can't have a baby."
This belief is unwittingly fostered by well-meaning adults. Adolescents become pregnant through impulse, ignorance, desire, or some
combination.

ABORTION

Abortion, a controversial procedure that is widely used and
widely denounced, plays a significant role in the physical, psychological, social, and economic status of adolescents. Where it is illegal, abortion is a dangerous, costly, and in most cases, a humiliat-
ing procedure. Where abortion is legal, as in Japan and some other
countries, it can become a major, even dominant, form of birth
control. Although it is relatively easy and safe, legalized abortion
carries a risk that could be avoided with a contraception program.
In the United States, abortion is newly available as a secondary
prevention approach, or a backup method, in family planning.
(Women in privileged sectors of society have long been able to
obtain safe abortions even when it was illegal.)

Abortion's impact on the mental health of the patient may
either be a positive one (where abortion is legal, safe, and consid-

ered moral) or a negative one (where abortion is illegal, unsafe, and deemed immoral). The chief users of newly legalized abortion service in the United States have been first-time pregnant, young, unmarried women. Young women are declaring their independence from compulsory parenthood and compulsory marriage that, in the past, were so often precipitated by an unintended pregnancy. Over 90 percent of the young abortion clients adopted a good contraception method for the future, in contrast to the approximate one-third that had not practiced good contraception prior to the first pregnancy. Thus, the abortion service becomes a channel of contraceptive education and practice.[7]

Consideration of the risk of abortion must take into account the alternatives: carrying to term and keeping the child (with or without marriage), or placing the child in foster care or for adoption. Better ways are needed to measure the consequences of these alternatives. Over the past few years, research and clinical practice indicates that abortion is generally harmless psychologically. However, highly ambivalent patients are at greater risk.

Abortion ratios vary according to State or region. Thus, some useful research could be done until such time as health services and attitudes with respect to birth control for minors are equalized. In a remarkable study by Fingerer,[8] the most pathological scores on psychological tests were recorded by the following persons, in descending order: psychoanalysts simulating a postabortion patient; students role-playing a patient; the person accompanying the patient; the patient herself, preabortion; and least of all, the patient postabortion! In New York City, in 1973, there were 4.6 abortions for every live birth in the age group under 15. In five States, the ratio was greater than 2:1, but in others it was less than 1:2. For the age group 15 to 19, the overall ratio was 539 abortions per 1,000 live births.[4] It should be possible to compare sites with similar health care patterns, except for abortion.

PARENTHOOD

The psychological consequences of parenthood at any age are at the same time obvious and obscure. Having children is only now becoming something less than proof of normality in our society—a society that has usually penalized premature parenthood rather heavily. Young people evidently have more trouble with the tasks of parenthood, although social class factors confound the issue (for example, college-bound women are less likely to have children). Young parents are likely to be economically disadvantaged, ambivalent about child care, less skilled, and under the stress of no marriage or a new marriage with an even chance of being divorced within 5 years. Mothers under 18 compare less favorably with their elders on nurturing behavior and child development outcomes from birth to age 10.[9] The timing of births to young mothers, at least, is usually unwanted.

Recent research on life-stress events is highly relevant. Coddington[10] defines psychological trauma as, "Those events that require a readjustment on the part of the individual," and uses Life-change units (LCU's) to quantify it (but without a positive or negative evaluation). Rankings were made by 243 teachers, pediatricians, and mental health workers, with remarkable agreement. For junior high school age, unwed pregnant girls had the highest LCU's of 40 events; fathering a pregnancy out-of-wedlock ranked 7th, and pregnancy in an unwed teenage sister was 16th. For the senior high group, getting married and pregnancy out-of-wedlock were 1 and 2, ahead of death of a parent; fathering a pregnancy out-of-wedlock was 6th, and pregnancy in an unwed teenage sister was 12th. The incidence of these events was counted in 1971 in a normal Ohio sample. (The results are shown in table 8–1.) Both the weight and incidence of a sister's pregnancy and fathering a pregnancy are notable. The last item is for comparison: less weight but the most commonly reported event in the past year.

Today, adoption, in a period of a shortage of available babies, offers a viable alternative to young parenthood. A recent study reports on the adjustment period following out-of-wedlock births in Minnesota and the decision to raise or place a child. Dating patterns, marriage decisions, and sexual behavior varied with age and the adoption decision.[12] Too little attention has been given to the teenage father, or the unwed parent dyad: "It is as though a

Table 8-1.—*Incidence, ranking, and percent of life-stress events*

Event	Junior high[a]			Senior high[b]		
	LCU[c]	Incidence	Percent	LCU	Incidence	Percent
Pregnancy	95	7	0.7	92	17	1.9
Marriage	[d]—	—	—	101	10	1.1
Pregnant sister	60	61	6.0	64	36	3.9
Fathering a pregnancy	76	14	1.4	77	23	2.5
Breakup with boyfriend or girlfriend	47	362	35.7	53	411	45.0

[a] Number of students, 1,014.
[b] Number of students, 913.
[c] Life-change unit.
[d] Not applicable.

Source: Adapted from reference 11.

detached quality exists in the relationship, with the love of one for the other meeting personal rather than interpersonal needs."[13] Polsby[14] views premarital pregnancy and young parenthood, if the adolescent is properly supported by family and professionals, as opportunities for growth. A distant, hard-to-measure, but not surprising, consequence of early marriage and parenthood is "lost adolescence." The syndrome consists of failure to form strong identity (constriction of choices), lack of independence (space between child and parent roles), and lack of social experimentation with attendant regret in later years.[15]

THE RANGE OF CONSEQUENCES

Only as a convenience for discussion purposes can psychological consequences be separated from biological or social consequences. A perfect example of the need for comprehensive analysis is that of the ubiquitous incest taboo. Cohen,[16] an anthropologist, argues that the taboo has its source in the biological need for control of excess external stimuli, a need for privacy. Implications of this theory are relevant, including the idea that heterosexual shyness occurs, "in order to maintain the insularity and separateness that children need in the face of incipient and confusing sexuality."[16] He finds very early marriage quite atypical worldwide: "Most societies require that their members defer marriage until they are sufficiently mature emotionally to cope with the intense stimulation that is an integral part of sexuality within an institutionalized context. A society might permit premarital sexual intercourse rather freely to its adolescents, but the premarital relationship, unlike marriage, does not constitute a boundary-maintaining system."[16]

Adolescent pregnancy is a threat to privacy in more than one sense. It makes public what is intensely personal: a woman's participation in sexual intercourse. Depending on the circumstances, her feelings will vary from affirmation and celebration to shame and despair. And a mixture of conflicting feelings (i.e. ambivalence) is not unusual. In terms of identity formation, forced marriage is institutionalized intimacy for which neither partner is sufficiently prepared. Finally, the new child itself is a bundle of needs and stimuli that overwhelm the immature parent.

The most dramatic psychiatric outcomes are suicidal behaviors and postpartum psychosis. The former correlate with adolescent pregnancy in a study of 105 matched cases.[17] Paffenbarger[18] found no difference between 126 postpartum psychosis patients and controls on average age at marriage, illegitimacy, or parity. The afflicted group, with a mean age of 27.6, was older by 1-1/2 years than the controls.

Patterson[19] found fewer symptoms during pregnancy among young women who said they had planned the pregnancy than among those who said it was unplanned. In another study, unmarried pregnant women had more doubt, uncertainty, loneliness, and helplessness, according to Rorschach responses than a comparison group of married women with the same IQ. The differences were apparently the consequences rather than the causes of pregnancy out-of-wedlock.[20]

Recent literature[21] reports that pregnant adolescents cannot be stereotyped. One article shatters certain myths in finding a psychological profile of single pregnant women shared with accident-prone drivers, a profile defined in part as imaginative, assertive, intelligent, and enthusiastic.[22] Early pregnancy may be a psychosocially selective accident that penalizes many admirable human qualities. Those young people who are either more inhibited or calculating, for example, high on Machiavellianism,[23] escape the trap relatively often, increasing their proportion of academic and socioeconomic success and reinforcing societal norms favoring their own psychological profiles.

Jessner[24] cites research indicating that the motivation for pregnancy is more important in couples' handling (of pregnancy) thereof than whether the pregnancy was planned or not. The separation of "wantedness" factors is needed in sophisticated research on psychological outcomes. Vincent[25] presents counseling problems of males and females who are unwed parents. Their situation, he states, combines a tacitly reinforced cause, coition, with a negatively sanctioned result, illegitimacy. "Although many such fathers are quick to assert either that they had no feelings of guilt and responsibility, or that they quickly resolved such feelings, they just as quickly supply explanations which suggest the contrary."

Pregnancy is not only a cause of life stress but is also likely to be preceded by high life-change scores.[26] In the same symposium, Gersten et al.[27] point out that "locus of control or responsibility for the events" is important, as is their desirability, and also feelings about events which might have occurred but did not. Adolescent pregnancy is a prime focus for enlargement of this research approach. Coping and competence, inner versus outer locus of control, moral reasoning,[28] and attitude toward life are psychological dimensions that must be affected by adolescent pregnancy, desired or undesired, and its avoidance.

It is well known that adolescent pregnancy is the major cause of girls' leaving school. This is a psychosocioeconomic consequence of import not only for the dropout but also for the next generation. Mayeske found that the quality of parent-child interaction had more to do with school achievement and attitude toward life than did family structure and stability. Reading to a child at the preschool stage and discussing schoolwork later on were found to be especially important. Aborting a girl's education because she is pregnant not only scars her mind but visits a scourge on the generations that follow.

The psychological dilemma of the helping professions and the policymakers must be considered. Ways must be found to help adolescents be better parents without encouraging them to become parents. And ways must be found to protect young people against unplanned parenthood without penalizing those who slip past the protections and without punishing their children.

REFERENCES

1. World Health Organization. May, A. R., Kahn, J. H., and Cronholm, B. *Mental Health of Adolescents and Young Persons. Public Health Papers No. 41.* Geneva: WHO, 1971.
2. Group for the Advancement of Psychiatry. *Normal Adolescence.* New York: GAP, 1968.
3. Erikson, E. *Childhood and Society* (2nd Ed.). New York: Norton, 1963.
4. Presser, H. B. "Early Motherhood: Ignorance or Bliss?" *Fam. Plann. Perspec.* 6:8–14, 1974.
5. Lieberman, E. J. "Informed Consent for Parenthood." In C. Reiterman, Ed., *Abortion and the Unwanted Child.* pp. 77–85. New York: Springer, 1971.
6. Center for Disease Control. *Abortion Surveillance Report 1976.* U. S. DHEW Publ. No. CDC 78–8276, August 1978.
7. Osofsky, H. and Osofsky, J. *The Abortion Experience.* New York: Harper, 1973.
8. Fingerer, M. "Psychological Sequelae of Abortion: Anxiety and Depression." *J. Comm. Psychol.* 1:221–225, 1973.
9. Dickens, H. O. "Teen-Age Pregnancy and Abortion." In D. W. Abse, E. M. Nash, and L. M. R. Louden. *Marital and Sexual Counseling in Medical Practice* (2nd Ed.). pp. 341–347. Hagerstown: Harper & Row, 1974.
10. Coddington, R. D. "The Significance of Life Events as Etiologic Factors in the Diseases of Children. I—A Survey of Professional Workers." *J. Psychosom. Res.* 16:7–18, 1972.
11. Coddington, R. D. "The Significance of Life Events as Etiologic Factors in the Diseases of Children. II—A Study of a Normal Population." Ibid. 16:205–213, 1972.
12. Nettleton, C. and Cline, D. W. "Dating Patterns, Sexual Relations, and Use of Contraception of 700 Unmarried Mothers During a Two Year Period Following Delivery." *Adolescence:* X:45–57, 1975.
13. Juhasz, A. M. "The Unmarried Adolescent Parent." *Adolescence* IX:263–272, 1974.

14. Polsby, G. M. "Unmarried Parenthood: Potential for Growth." *Adolescence.* IX:273–284, 1974.
15. Jurich, A. P. and Jurich, J. A. "The Lost Adolescence Syndrome." *Fam. Coord.* 24:357–361, 1975.
16. Cohen, Y. A. *The Transition from Childhood to Adolescence.* Chicago: Aldine, 1964.
17. Gabrielson, I. W. et al. "Suicide Attempts in a Population Pregnant as Teen-agers." *Am. J. Public Health.* 60:2289–2301, 1970.
18. Paffenbarger, R. "The Picture Puzzle of the Postpartum Psychoses." *J. Chron. Dis.* 13:161–173, 1961.
19. Patterson, et al. 1960, cited but not referenced in Baizerman, op. cit.
20. Wagner, E. E. and Slembowski, J. "Psychological Reaction of Pregnant Unwed Women." *J. Clin. Psychol.* 24:267–269, 1968.
21. Baizerman, M. et al. *Pregnant Adolescents: A Review of Literature with Abstracts 1960–70. Sharing* supplement, Dec. 1971.
22. Olley, P. C. "Age, Marriage, Personality and Distress." *In* R. B. Sloane, Ed., *Abortion.* pp. 131–141. New York: Grune & Stratton, 1971.
23. Christie, R. and Geis, F. *Studies in Machiavellianism.* New York: Academic Press, 1970.
24. Jessner, L. "Pregnancy as a Stress in Marriage." *In Marital and Sexual Counseling in Medical Practice* (2nd Ed.). pp. 292–304. Hagerstown: Harper & Row, 1974.
25. Vincent, C. E. "Counseling Cases Involving Premarital and Extramarital Pregnancies." *In* B. N. Ard and C. C. Ard, Eds., *Handbook of Marriage Counseling,* pp. 279–288. Palo Alto: Science & Behavior Books, 1969.
26. Holmes, T. H. and Masuda, M. "Life Change and Illness Susceptibility." Ibid. pp. 45–72.
27. Gersten, J. et al. "Child Behavior and Life Events." In B. S. Dohrenwend and B. P. Dohrenwend, Eds., *Stressful Life Events.* pp. 159–170. New York: Wiley, 1974.
28. Kohlberg, L. and Gilligan, C. "The Adolescent as Philosopher." *In* J. Kagan and R. Coles, Eds., *Twelve to Sixteen: Early Adolescence.* pp. 144–179. New York: Norton, 1972.
29. Mayeske, G. W. et al. *A Study of the Attitude Toward Life of Our Nation's Students.* U. S. DHEW Publ. No. OE 73–01700. Washington: U. S. Government Printing Office, 1973.

DISCUSSION

The following people were the major participants in the discussion: J. Trussell, R. Faden, F. Furstenberg, A. Rossi, C. Westoff, R. Hill, H. Presser, K. Terhune, J. Kantner, H. David, and E. Moore.

The chief topics of discussion were the possible psychological consequences of adolescent childbearing for mothers, fathers, children, and grandparents, the possible psychological barriers within the adolescent that inhibit the use of contraceptives and abortion, and the contribution of social science research to judicial decisions.

Some participants thought that young adolescents need a good deal of personal privacy. An intimate relationship, such as marriage, is too difficult for many of them to handle.

Actually, very little is known about the psychological consequences on young women of early childbearing. It is assumed that the consequences are adverse. Grave problems such as suicide, psychopathology, and psychosis, may be possible consequences of adolescent childbearing, but other, more subtle, consequences should also be studied. However, to discriminate between antecedent psychological characteristics and those characteristics that might be said to be a consequence of having a child may be difficult.

It was suggested that the consequences of having a child might be viewed by older educated women who have launched a career as an interruption of their life plans.

Dr. Furstenberg said that the young mothers in his study did not feel a greater sense of incompetency, when dealing with parenting, than older mothers. Other studies have shown that many teenage mothers appear to gain psychological strength from their responsibilities and adapt well to their changed life circumstances. Some largely anthropological studies performed with low-income black adolescents reveal that they feel motherhood gives them a more adult status in their communities and a greater sense of personal maturity.

Perhaps, some adolescents would do better to have their children early, grow through this experience, and return to their education and employment later.

Very little is known about the possible psychological effects on children of early childbearing. In addition to checking for such problems as neurological defects, investigators need to study more subtle measures in the behavioral and self-security realm.

There was considerable discussion about the effects of "wantedness" on a child. It was agreed that this is a very difficult category to measure. It is common to find that an originally unwanted pregnancy becomes accepted in time, and that the previously unwanted child becomes one that is very much loved.

Dr. David described a Czechoslovakian study of 200 children whose mothers were twice denied abortions. These children are now 9 years old and appear not to be different, on the average, from a control group of wanted children. A host of factors clearly affect developmental outcomes for children.

Considerable speculation about the psychological characteristics of young women who fail to use contraceptives or resolve early pregnancies through abortion was noted. Some people seem to be more comfortable in accepting what occurs and making the best adjustment possible to a life situation. They get recognition for their ability to endure. Some are disturbed about using modern technologies and find it stressful to make planned decisions about the management of their own lives. Others actively use the opportunities at hand to help achieve the goals they have for themselves.

A number of suggestions were made for research. Many child-development studies have been carried out in the past. It should be possible to reanalyze the data with the age of the mother at the child's birth being the dependent variable. In such studies, however, it would be necessary to consider a large number of variables that may affect developmental outcomes of children, including the socioeconomic status of their parents.

A large study of life satisfactions has just been completed by the Institute of Survey Research at the University of Michigan. More studies are planned for the future. It should be possible to assess life satisfactions in terms of age at first and later births with the necessary control for confounding variables, such as race, socioeconomic status, marital status, and completed family size.

More studies are needed concerning the psychological differences between adolescent contraceptive users and nonusers and between those who resolve pregnancies through abortions and those who do not. Studies also are needed concerning what psychological differences, if any, characterize adolescents who become pregnant and those who do not. Pregnancy, to a considerable extent, may come about largely as a matter of luck.

There is a need for better long-term measurement methods to assess parent attitudes and behaviors as well as developmental outcomes for children.

When the child is between age 8 months and 18 months, a number of child psychologists find that parent-child interactions are crucial to his/her cognitive development. It should be possible to follow children for the first 4 years of life and assess levels of cognitive development. Results could be analyzed in terms of maternal age at the birth of these children. However, it would be necessary to control for other variables that might affect cognitive development. These variables include the composition of the family in which the child is living. For example, a few recent studies suggest that children achieve higher levels of cognitive development if they are living with two adults rather than one, although the two-adult household need not necessarily be composed of the child's mother and father. The second adult may be a grandparent, another relative, or a friend.

Although a few inadequate investigations show that the psychological reactions to abortion are more negative following a second trimester abortion, more systematic research fails to support these results. It is important in such studies to control for age, race, and socioeconomic status of the patients. A recent study at Johns Hopkins University showed that, when these variables are controlled, psychological reactions to second trimester abortions are not more negative than to those performed in the first trimester.

Studies of attitudes toward abortion, the adverse consequences of illegal abortions, and the general lack of negative effects when abortions are legalized have been used in testimony in court cases considering the legalization of abortion. The presentation of these findings have had a marked and favorable impact on judicial decisions. Education of the voters relative to abortion can be extremely useful in attempts to affect legislation.

Continuing efforts are needed apart from obtaining favorable court decisions and needed legislation. Decisions and laws should be implemented through the establishment of programs. The availability of services and a supporting social climate are probably more important in promoting the use of contraceptives and needed abortions than are the psychological traits of individuals.

Chapter 9

Economic Consequences of Teenage Childbearing

T. James Trussell
Princeton University

Economists since the time of Malthus have attempted to unravel the interrelationship between fertility and various economic variables, primarily income. These analyses have concentrated mainly on two aspects of the economic determinants and consequences of fertility decisions. Starting with Malthus, economists have studied the macroeconomic impact of fertility on development and growth.[1-8] More recently, the economic determinants of fertility have been analyzed through the new home economics approach that employs microeconomic models, in part, to analyze fertility decisions.[9-16]

Unfortunately, neither the findings nor the approach of previous analyses of the economics of fertility is particularly helpful in determining the economic effects of teenage childbearing. Moreover, the consequences of teenage childbearing, per se, except perhaps for the medical consequences, have been neglected by disciplines other than economics. We can, however, sift through studies that concentrate on variables other than age of childbearing, such as age at first marriage or premarital pregnancy, to predict the magnitude and direction of the effect of very young childbearing on various economic variables. Our focus can be enlarged to include the consequences of teenage pregnancy that ends in abortion.

Ideally, it would be helpful to the individual woman (and to society) to find the economic difference of becoming pregnant while a teenager versus not becoming pregnant. We may call the microeconomic consequences the economic differential between two average women, who are identical, except that one had become pregnant in her teens. The impact of many such pregnancies produces a macroeconomic effect. It does not follow that eliminating 10,000 teenage pregnancies would have 10,000 times the individual effect.

This point is not very profound; in fact it is quite obvious, but the literature on the impact of birth prevention on economic development has often failed to make clear the distinction between micro and macro effects.[17-19] For instance, in his seminal article published in 1966, Enke[17] estimated that the value of each birth prevented in India would be $263. Compared with the cost of preventing a birth, he concluded that, in raising income per capita, the net effect of birth prevention has an effect 100 times greater than policies to accelerate economic growth. Simon[18] rightly replied that the benefit of a prevented birth depends upon the number of other prevented births. Only in a macro model can the effect of change in the age structure, the capital—labor ratio, and savings propensity be assessed. Virtually all the studies mentioned hereafter are micro studies in the sense used above. Analysis of the macro impact of teenage childbearing, though much more difficult, of course, is also needed.

One caveat is in order here. If teenage fertility is planned, and if teenagers can correctly assess the costs of becoming pregnant and bearing children early, then there are no real economic net private costs of early childbearing. If the private benefit did not outweigh the private cost, then the girl—or the couple—would not have a child. An individual (couple), however, would not include in their cost/benefit calculus either the costs or benefits that are external and accrue to society at large. To the extent, then, that all costs or benefits are not internalized, there will be net social costs that do need to be assessed.

The new household economics, with Becker as mentor, does postulate such economic models of individual fertility decisions and other decisions of consequence—marriage[20,21] and suicide[22]. The new home economics, however, would not claim that all children are wanted, nor that all individuals can, without error, calculate costs, many of which would be in the future. It seems unlikely that the bulk of teenage fertility is planned[23] or that teenagers can calculate costs very well. Nevertheless, the following discussion of the costs of teenage childbearing must be matched against the benefits, if any. Such benefits might include the satisfaction of being a mother and mothering, the comfort of conforming to some social norm, and the pleasure of (pro)creating.

DIRECT EFFECTS ON FUTURE
EARNINGS OF WOMEN

A woman's earnings can be viewed as a product of the wage rate available to her if she works and the extent of her labor force participation. (Strictly, the employment rate, and not the labor force participation rate, is the relevant variable. A woman can be in the labor force and also be unemployed.) In this section, the effects of teenage childbearing on both variables will be considered. Though there have been many studies of women's labor force participation and their wage rates, none have been concerned with the impact of the timing of the first child per se. In many studies, the data imposed this limitation; in a few others, relatively simple modifications could be employed to test whether teenage childbearing has any measurable effect.

Wage Rate

Recent studies of the determinants of wage rates are based upon models of human capital formation.[24,25] To the extent that the wage rate commanded in the labor market is a function of the human capital stock accumulated by the individual, a sequence of positive net investment gives rise to growing earning power over the life cycle. When market skills are eroded by depreciation, net disinvestment occurs. Two distinct sources of human capital accumulation—formal schooling and learning by doing (formal or informal on-the-job training)—have long been recognized, and measures of schooling and length of work experience are usually included in wage equations. Most such equations are empirically estimated by regression techniques.

Variables other than schooling and work experience, such as marital status, health, geographic region, and mobility, often have been found to have explanatory power. The primary impact of teenage childbearing on wages is likely to operate through the two sources of human capital formation, though perhaps in opposite ways. Education is likely to to be curtailed by pregnancy, especially if it occurs in high school. On the other hand, the woman may enter the labor market earlier and thus acquire more labor market experience. Another possible effect, particularly for husbands, is that those who have children early may also have to take jobs that offer less on-the-job training; that is, they take jobs that have higher wage rates in the present, relative to deferred higher wages in the future. Moreover, their opportunity to search for higher paying jobs may be curtailed.

One representative study by Oaxaca,[26] in which women's wage equations were estimated, can be used to sort out the relative effects. Oaxaca used data from the 1967 Survey of Economic Opportunity (SEO, described in the appendix). As these data unfortunately do not include the length of work experience, he used potential work experience (current age minus number of years of education minus 6 preschool years) as a proxy. Such a proxy overstates women's work experience and therefore biases the estimated experience coefficient downward. Equating potential and actual work experience is not the only source of error; further error arises from the assumption that all individuals start school at the same age and advance one grade with each passing year. Since only 68.0 percent, 63.4 percent, 52.4 percent, and 46.5 percent of white females, white males, black females and black males, respectively, aged 16, are in the modal grade for their age group, substantial error is introduced even into the measure of potential work experience.[27] As a rough attempt to handle the problem of lost experience, Oaxaca controlled for the number of children born to the female.

A further potential source of bias is that the wage equation is based only upon the experience and characteristics of women who have earnings (specifically, in the week preceding the survey). From Oaxaca's wage equations based on personal characteristics, it is possible to derive the wages women would receive at age 30 if they left school after completing different grades but are otherwise alike at that age. Table 9–1 shows such calculations assuming that grade 12 is completed at age 18. Clearly a year of education is more important than a year of work experience. Moreover, the trade-off between work and experience is more pronounced for urban blacks than for urban whites.

What if education is held constant? Does teenage childbearing affect the accumulation of earning power beyond the effect on work experience? Though the question cannot be answered for teenagers, Mincer and Polachek[28] found that the number of chil-

Table 9-1.—*Index of comparative wage earnings based on a ratio comparing earnings at age 30 to various assumed ages of leaving school*

School grade	Age	Urban black women	Urban white women
9	15	0.90	0.92
10	[a]16	1.00	1.00
11	17	1.07	1.04
12	[b]18	1.17	1.09
13	19	1.29	1.15
14	20	1.44	1.22
15	21	1.63	1.32
16	22	1.69	1.43

[a] Index: age 16 = 1.
[b] Assuming that age 18 represents high school completed.

Source: Calculated according to Oaxaca's[26] personal characteristics wage regressions for urban females, assuming: same number of children at age 30, same proportion part-time, same proportion in each marital status, same proportion with health problems, same degree of mobility, and same distribution by size of urban area.

dren affected the wage rate only by reducing work experience. Inclusion of a children variable did not add significantly to the explanatory power of the regression. This finding is important, since the authors used the National Longitudinal Survey of Work Experience (NLS, described in the appendix) that contains detailed work histories of a large sample of women aged 35 to 44. With this data file available, no need to use a less precise proxy for work experience exists.

In both these studies of female wage equations, a dummy variable could be added to test directly for an effect of early first childbearing on wages; this dummy should be assigned different values for various subdivisions of ages from, say, 14 through 22 and be set equal to zero otherwise. Similar tests could be run for children other than the first.

Labor Force Participation Rates

No study of female labor force participation rates (LFPR) has included the age of first childbearing as a dependent variable. Much, however, is known about the general effect of children on the labor force participation of women. In their monumental study of the economics of labor force participation, Bowen and Finegan[29] found that LFPR of women are highly dependent upon the presence and ages of children in the household. As a rule, the younger the age of children, the lower the proportion of women in the labor force; this inverse relationship is especially pronounced for children under the age of 6. Moreover, it is well known, that even if marriage cohort and the time of last birth are controlled, LFPR vary inversely with the total number of children.

Data from the childspacing volume of the 1960 census, shown in table 9–2, illustrate this relationship. These data indicate that if age at first marriage and number of children are held constant, then the earlier the first child is born, the greater the labor force participation rate is of women in 1960. Of women with two children, married between 1945 and 1949 and whose first child was born after 1950, 36.4 percent were working in 1960; similar results hold for women with three or more children. Hence, there is some indication that earlier childbearing, ceteris paribus, leads to higher rates of labor force participation.

Such a conclusion is admittedly very weak, since the data may simply be measuring the babysitter effect noted by Bowen and Finegan.[29] Although the youngest children of the two groups of women were the same age, the oldest child of the women who had their first child at a younger age would be older and could function as a babysitter, thereby freeing the mother for work. If a control for the ages of all children were established by comparing the cohort of 1950–1954 with the cohort of 1945–1949 in the bot-

Table 9-2.—*Labor force participation rate (LFPR) in 1960 for women whose most recent birth occurred between 1950 and 1954*

First child born	Number of children	LFPR for marriage cohort	
		1950 to 1954	1945 to 1949
Before 1950	4 or more	[a]—	0.324
	3	—	0.335
	2	—	0.364
1950 to 1954 . . .	3 or more	0.300	0.283
	2	0.336	0.302
	1	0.457	0.417

[a]Not applicable.

Source: Reference 29.

tom panel of table 9–2, it could be seen that the women who married between 1950 and 1954 and had their first child and subsequent children at a younger age also had higher LFPR. These rates, however, are only marginally higher, and comparison of two different marriage cohorts captures women at different points in their life cycle.

On the other hand, an extensive economic analysis by Ross,[30] using the NLS data of the timing of births and women's LFPR, found that the age of first childbearing was positively related to the rate of labor force participation if wife's and husband's education, income, number of children, and age were held constant. (In these regressions, age at first birth was the dependent variable; for our purposes, it would appear more appropriately as an independent variable. Still, the sign of the partial correlation between any two variables, with all others held constant, is invariant with choice of the independent variable in regression analysis.) Because in another regression, Ross found the age of first childbearing and wife's education to be strongly positively correlated, omission of this control from table 9–2 might explain the contradictory results. Both of Ross's findings are gratifyingly consistent with human capital theory.

Two caveats are, however, in order. First, there are compelling reasons to believe that the relationship between LFPR, education, and age at first childbearing could only be captured by estimation of a simultaneous equation system; there is no justification for using ordinary least squares. Second, and more important, Ross completed her research before an error was discovered in the coding of the work histories of mature women who were not working at the time of the interview in 1966. The error resulted in the omission of the record of their most recent work experience, and its effect on Ross's findings is unknown. In newer files of the NLS data, the mistake has been corrected. It can only be concluded that the effect of early childbearing on women's LFPR is not fully understood; additional analysis of either the NLS or SEO data could yield more information about the relationship.

Human capital theory predicts a strong positive association between years of school completed and LFPR. Primarily, higher schooling increases a woman's expected market wage and encourages her to substitute time in the labor market for time she might otherwise have spent in the home. Moreover, additional education gives opportunities for more stimulating work, and the psychic income derived from work is undoubtedly an important component of real income. Such expectations are supported by empirical tests.

The study by Bowen and Finegan[29] has shown that for various age and sex groups in the U.S. population, a strong positive relationship between LFPR's and educational attainment exists. Hence, we see that education is positively related not only to wage rates but also to LFPR's. It is important, therefore, to determine whether teenage pregnancy curtails the number of years of education completed by the female.

Education

As Bacon[31] has stated, it is often very difficult to distinguish variables that are clearly antecedent from those that are clearly consequent in order to establish unambiguously the causal connection and temporal sequence of events. Hence, it is difficult to determine ex post whether early pregnancy curtailed a woman's formal educational experience or whether her education had been terminated prior to childbearing. Undoubtedly, for many women, especially those with 8 or fewer years of education, the negative relationship between age of first childbearing and years of education is merely associative, and early pregnancy cannot be interpreted as causing low educational achievement. Nevertheless, an analysis[31] of the 1967 SEO data has shown that age of first childbearing and educational attainment *are* clearly associated; Bacon's findings[31] are shown in table 9-3. Furthermore, since pregnancy and motherhood have been the primary reasons for dropping out of school, it would appear that the figures in table 9-3 display more than simple association. Among those women with very low educational attainment, only the very young childbearers are distinct: 15 percent of those who became mothers at 13 to 15 years had less than 4 years of schooling. Yet only 6 percent of those who became mothers at any other age had less than 4 years of schooling. The proportion of women who went on to college increased monotoni-

Table 9-3.—*Educational attainment by age women become mothers, by race, 1957, United States*

Age women became mothers	Years of schooling completed					Total	
	0 to 4	5 to 8	9 to 11	12	13 and more	Thousands	Percent
All races							
13 to 15	14.5	43.3	30.0	10.6	1.6	1,325	100.0
16 to 17	6.2	33.5	40.5	17.5	2.2	4,680	100.0
18 to 19	4.5	24.5	26.2	38.7	6.1	9,023	100.0
20 to 21	4.6	21.0	18.6	41.5	14.2	9,230	100.0
22 and older	4.2	18.8	14.5	38.4	24.1	21,014	100.0
All ages	4.8	22.6	20.8	36.1	15.6	45,272	100.0
White							
13 to 15	13.3	47.1	28.5	9.3	1.7	807	100.0
16 to 17	5.4	33.3	41.6	17.8	1.9	3,760	100.0
18 to 19	3.5	24.6	25.7	40.1	6.0	8,063	100.0
20 to 21	3.8	20.7	18.6	42.6	14.3	8,473	100.0
22 and older	3.7	18.5	14.3	39.3	24.3	19,782	100.0
All ages	4.0	22.1	20.2	37.6	16.1	40,885	100.0
Black							
13 to 15	16.9	37.1	32.0	12.9	1.2	510	100.0
16 to 17	9.2	33.7	36.9	17.3	3.0	881	100.0
18 to 19	11.4	23.9	31.2	26.9	6.8	897	100.0
20 to 21	13.0	25.9	19.2	29.7	12.4	684	100.0
22 and older	11.4	25.8	18.3	23.0	21.4	1,012	100.0
All ages	11.9	28.6	27.2	22.5	9.9	3,984	100.0

Source: Reference 31.

cally from 2 percent at the earliest ages of childbearing to 24 percent of those who became mothers at 22 years of age or later. Similarly, the proportion of women who completed high school rose with increased age at motherhood. Among those who bear children below age 18, very little differential between whites and blacks is shown; only 20 percent of this group ever complete high school. For ages at first childbearing above 18, whites are more sensitive to age at first birth than blacks. The sample included only ever married mothers, so that (young) mothers who had not married by the time of the survey are excluded. As our interest is in all young mothers and not just those who are married or later marry, this omission is unfortunate.

It is also unfortunate that reliance must be placed on information gathered indirectly through surveys that are not primarily concerned with educational attainment to determine whether pregnancy curtails education. Inasmuch as in many school districts in the past, pregnancy, motherhood, and marriage were all causes for revocation of the right to attend public schools, a more straightforward approach would be to survey school districts directly.

One such study[32] of the 153 school districts in the continental United States with populations of 100,000 or more found that statistics concerning teenage pregnancy and marriage, even in large school districts, were inadequate. Only 127 of 153 superintendents replied. Of those who did reply, only 58 to 71 percent, depending on the question, could specify their 1940 policies and statistics. Only 27 had made a study of any aspect of the problem that culminated in a written report. A related question showed that only 12 percent of the districts had made studies or gathered statistics concerning the incidence of teenage pregnancy in various socioeconomic and cultural groups. Nevertheless, the study found that a definite shift had taken place in the major cities since 1940 to accommodate a higher percentage of youths who were married, were mothers, or were pregnant. Ordinarily, if such students were permitted in school at all, they were allowed to attend regular classes; but there was also a tendency to assign them to adult evening school.

Another study,[33] which surveyed by questionnaire the administrators of various agencies in the 150 cities in the United States with a population of 100,000 or more, found that the officials of almost half the cities were unable to provide information on the population of teenage mothers and the number of live births to women under 20 years of age. Officials in one-fourth of the cities could supply only partial information. In addition to discovering a paucity of vital and program statistics, the authors found a narrow scope and limited extent of community efforts to address the needs of pregnant teenagers.

Forced exclusion from public schools of teenagers who are mothers or who are married or pregnant is now illegal. Moreover, these students cannot be excluded from regular classes except at their own request. The rules and regulations of Title IX of the Educational Amendments of 1972, effective July 12, 1975, prohibit schools who receive Federal funding from excluding any student from any aspect of its educational program on the basis of "pregnancy, childbirth, false pregnancy, termination of pregnancy or recovery therefrom," unless the student requests voluntarily to participate in a separate portion of the program.[34]

Therefore, one obstacle to educational achievement has been eliminated. It is still not known, however, what proportion of such women would continue school if they are allowed to participate. Several small studies are less than sanguine. One such study[35] in Philadelphia followed 100 girls in their first pregnancies at ages 17 or younger from September 1967 to September 1970. During pregnancy, 61 dropped out of school. Of the 61, however, 24 continued school in one of the special programs begun by the Philadelphia School Board in early 1968, before girls were permitted to stay in regular school beyond the sixth month of pregnancy. Only 33 percent are known to have returned to school after delivery, though the percentage is higher (56 percent) for those attending a special teenage obstetrical clinic. Another study[36] of 180 girls under age 19 residing in New Haven who registered for prenatal care at the Yale-New Haven Hospital from 1967 to 1969 found that at the time of registration, 83 percent were still in school. Moreover, 77 percent had either graduated or were enrolled in school 2 months post partum.

Morbidity and Mortality

Maternal mortality rates have shown a rapid decline in the past 35 years. Rates for nonwhites are still very much higher than those for whites, and this difference increases with age.[37] Moreover, young women, in general, have higher rates of pregnancy complications resulting from toxemia, prolonged labor, and iron-deficiency anemia.[38] Incidence of breast cancer in young mothers, however, appears to be lower.[39] Since both wage rates[27] and LFPR's[40] are negatively affected by poor health, a higher incidence of maternal morbidity among young women, if it persists into later life, would constitute a definite social and private welfare loss. The effect could be quantified in a straightforward manner.

Direct Effect on the Child and Husband/Father

Nearly every study of infant, fetal, neonatal, or postneonatal mortality and prematurity has found marked differences by age of mother, even when parity is controlled. Both Menken[38] and Nortman[41] have written excellent reviews of the findings. Almost without exception, most studies have found that infants of young mothers are subject to relatively high risks, a result, probably, of the relatively low birth weight of such infants. The monetary costs of increased early mortality risks could be quantified in terms of the medical expenses incurred by the mother and child and the mother's lost work experience. All costs in excess of the costs at later ages constitute a net social welfare loss in that the pregnancy/childbirth that ends in death of the fetus or child at an early age has little or no benefit. Furthermore, infants of low birth weight are subject to increased risks of morbidity; prematurity has been associated with higher incidence of epilepsy,[42] cerebral palsy,[43] mental retardation,[44] deafness,[45] and blindness.[46] Motor development and scores on various psychological and IQ tests also increase with birth weight.[47-49] Unfortunately, the authors of many of the studies

of maternal age and mortality or prematurity do not control for
standard of living of the mother. Menken[38] has demonstrated that
when income is controlled, maternal age has little effect on prematurity. Whether other risks operate through socioeconomic status is
not known.

The effect of early childbearing on the husband-father has
not been analyzed, but the studies by Freedman and Coombs[50,51]
are very suggestive. The data for their analyses were derived from
interviews with 1,113 married women in the Detroit area in 1962
who had a first, second, or fourth birth in July 1961. These women
were reinterviewed in 1962, 1963, and 1966 (see appendix for a
description).

The authors investigated the effect of premarital pregnancy
and the length of the childspacing interval on later economic
achievement. They divided the sample of wives according to whether the first birth had resulted from a premarital pregnancy (PMP),
had occurred within 1 year of marriage (short spacers), or had
occurred more than a year after marriage (long spacers). In 1961
and 1966, long spacers had both higher family income and greater
family assets than short spacers; and the short spacers, in turn,
were substantially richer and earned more than the couples who
were premaritally pregnant. These results held for an analysis of
husband's income alone, indicating that the wife's income or work
experience was not the important determinant of the differential
across groups. If marriage duration or age at first birth or current
age was held constant, differences between short and long spacers
disappeared. The premaritally pregnant, however, suffered a substantial disadvantage. Their income differential disappeared only if
education and marriage duration were controlled; moreover, with
such controls, their unfavorable asset position was merely reduced.
Hence, the husband's education is particularly important in cases of
premarital pregnancy. The information in table 9–4 shows that
long and short spacers differed very little in years of schooling
completed by the husband, but among couples with a premarital
pregnancy, the husbands had markedly fewer years of schooling.
The PMP couples were much more likely to be married at an
early age; they were on the average 1.7 years younger at marriage
than the others, and many were so young that marriage may have
interrupted their education. Thirty-seven percent of the husbands
whose wives were pregnant before marriage, but only 18 percent
of other husbands, started but did not complete high school. Husbands of PMP wives were only one-third as likely as other husbands to have finished college.

Interruption of education by early marriage does not, however, entirely explain the lower educational achievement of the
premaritally pregnant. In only a quarter of the cases were the
husbands under age 20 at marriage. As with mothers, the link

Table 9-4.—*Number of years of school completed by husband, by first birth interval, and husband's age at marriage (percent distribution)*

Length of first birth interval	Years of school completed by husband						
	Less than 9	9 to 11	12	13 to 15	16 or more	Total	Couples (N)[a]
All couples							
PMP[b] couples	8	37	34	14	7	100	208
Non-PMP couples							
Less than 1 year	6	13	41	20	20	100	342
1 year or more	7	21	34	18	20	100	503
Total	7	22	36	17	18	100	1,053
Husband 16 to 19 years old at marriage							
PMP couples	4	50	39	5	2	100	56
Non-PMP couples							
Less than 1 year	22	24	40	14	0	100	37
1 year or more	8	45	29	18	0	100	57
Total	10	41	36	12	1	100	144
Husband 20 to 22 years old at marriage							
PMP couples	3	34	37	20	6	100	90
Non-PMP couples							
Less than 1 year	2	17	50	20	11	100	117
1 year or more	6	22	40	19	13	100	187
Total	4	23	42	20	11	100	394
Husband over 22 years old at marriage							
PMP couples	19	31	24	13	13	100	62
Non-PMP couples							
Less than 1 year	5	9	35	20	30	100	188
1 year or more	7	16	30	17	30	100	265
Total	8	15	31	18	28	100	515

[a] Number.
[b] Premaritally pregnant.

Source: Reference 50.

between educational achievement and early childbearing and marriage seems to run in opposite ways for different segments of the sample. Among one group, pregnancy leads to dropping out of school, perhaps because of the necessity for marrying young. Among the other group, factors predisposing to little education or resulting from it are also conducive to premarital pregnancy.

Although the structure of the Freedman and Coombs analyses and the limitations of their data preclude direct assessment of the effect of early childbearing on later economic achievement, early childbearing does appear to have a negative impact on income and assets, though it is not clear whether this effect operates only by reducing educational attainment. Reanalysis of their data, using age of first childbearing as the control variable, could determine this effect, at least, for married couples.

SOCIAL WELFARE COSTS:[a]
EXCESS SOCIAL COSTS OF
EARLY PREGNANCY OVER LATER PREGNANCY

Medical Costs

Some excess costs of early childbearing resulting from increased prematurity were discussed earlier. In addition to the costs of caring for infants and children who suffer lasting disabilities as a result of prematurity, the special care required for low-weight infants at the time of birth also constitutes a social cost. Furthermore, increased complication rates during pregnancy for young mothers impose higher measurable, but as yet unquantified, medical costs. Finally, it has been found that pregnant teenagers generally do not enroll in ordinary prenatal clinics. In order to attract these women, special programs must be devised. These programs have been found to decrease risks of prematurity and mortality, but the cost is substantial. The cost in excess of ordinary prenatal care is a definite social cost.

There appears to be no greater risk if a pregnancy is terminated at an early rather than at a later age. Tietze and Lewit[52] found that the complication rate fell slightly with increased age for women who terminated a pregnancy at less than 12 weeks gestation but rose slightly with age for those who terminated later. In light of the fact that young women terminate pregnancies later in pregnancy than older women do, and that the complication rate rises with length of gestation, there is some excess cost associated with termination of pregnancies in young women.

Public Aid

Bacon[31] found that the incidence of poverty rose substantially as the age at which women became mothers fell. These results, shown in table 9–5, hold for both whites and blacks. A very real possibility exists, however, that the causation runs the other way. Perhaps the poor are more likely to become pregnant when young,

---

[a] To the economist, welfare costs are not expenditures for public assistance; they are costs to society at large resulting from inefficient allocation of resources.

Table 9-5.—*Incidence of poverty by age women become mothers, by race, 1967, United States*

Age women become mothers	Total	Poverty	Percent in poverty
All races			
13 to 15	1,325	410	30.9
16 to 17	4,680	1,084	23.2
18 to 19	9,023	1,430	15.8
20 to 21	9,230	1,327	14.4
22 and over	21,014	2,216	10.5
All ages	45,272	6,467	14.3
White			
13 to 15	807	160	19.8
16 to 17	3,760	733	19.5
18 to 19	8,063	1,087	13.5
20 to 21	8,473	1,065	12.6
22 and over	19,782	1,884	9.5
All ages	40,885	4,929	12.1
Black			
13 to 15	510	246	48.2
16 to 17	881	342	38.8
18 to 19	897	327	36.5
20 to 21	684	251	36.7
22 and over	1,012	295	29.2
All ages	3,984	1,461	36.7

Source: Reference 31.

thereby curtailing their education and perpetuating a cycle of poverty. Cutright[53] estimates that 60 percent of white and 80 percent of nonwhite illegitimate children born between 1964 and 1966 were delivered to women below the near-poverty line. Berkov[54] reports that, in 1967, medical expenses were paid from public funds for 52 percent of white illegitimate but only 10 percent of white legitimate births. The corresponding figures for blacks are 76 percent and 40 percent, respectively. Neither of the studies controls for age at birth; but the bulk of illegitimate births (53 percent in 1973) occurs to young women below the age of 20.[55] Although neither of these findings is conclusive, both lend support to a hypothesis that poverty leads to early childbearing. It would appear, moreover, that illegitimacy imposes an extra cost upon the public.

Income and Early Pregnancy

Kantner and Zelnik[56] found that at every age from 15 to 19, unmarried girls from poor families were more likely to have had intercourse than unmarried girls from nonpoor families and that the poor knew less about the risks of pregnancy than the nonpoor. They also reported[57] that the poor were less likely to use contraception, though among those who did, the black poor were more likely than the black nonpoor to use effective methods. Hence, it appears likely that poor teenagers would become pregnant more often than nonpoor teenagers, though Kantner and Zelnik had not tested this hypothesis.

On the other hand, Coombs et al.,[51] found that among their sample, the social background of the family of origin of the couples whose first child was premaritally conceived did not account for their disadvantaged position after marriage and that those couples were not drawn from lower status groups. This finding most likely is a result of their sample—poor women are less likely to marry if they become pregnant and unmarried women are not included in the sample. In summary, a definitive test for the possible simultaneity of income and early pregnancy has not yet been formulated.

Unwanted Children

Excess costs of unwanted children over those of wanted children, have, however, been demonstrated. Forssman and Thuwe,[58] in a longitudinal study of 120 Swedish children born after applications by the mothers for therapeutic abortion were refused, found markedly higher social pathology among those children than among a control group. Laing[59] has estimated the excess public expenditure from supplementary benefits, child care and sickness benefits, and temporary accommodations in Britain to be substantial for the illegitimate and average unwanted child. Although equivalent studies for an American population have not been conducted, it would appear that children of teenage mothers, to the extent that they are disproportionately unwanted, would constitute a heavy social cost. Presser[23] found that the percentage of planned first births rose steadily from 19 to 44 to 70 in age groups 15 to 19, 20 to 23, and 24 to 29, respectively. Although unplanned births are certainly not necessarily unwanted, the findings are suggestive that children of young mothers may be disproportionately unwanted.

It may prove difficult to find an operational definition of an unwanted birth for young women that is as neat and precise as the one for married women developed in the Indianapolis survey[60] and refined in the National Fertility Surveys.[61,62] Births to the latter groups of women were judged to be unwanted if they constituted excess fertility. By this definition, few young women could have unwanted births. Nevertheless, births to young women could very well be unwanted in the literal sense of the word, and the motivation underlying the concepts of preventing or delaying pregnancy will undoubtedly prove to be as powerful a predictor for young women as it has for older women.

Illegitimacy

Are there any excess costs attributable to a birth solely because it is illegitimate? Previously cited statistics[54] indicate that the expenses for illegitimate childbirth are more likely to be paid from the public coffers than those of legitimate childbirth. Clearly, however, these costs, though real to the taxpayer, are not, properly, social costs as the economist would measure them. Unless illegitimate births cost more in terms of real resources, regardless of their source of financing, they would create no excess social costs. It is not known if bearing a child out-of-wedlock affects subsequent educational attainment and economic achievement. The excess social costs of an illegitimate child compared with a legitimate one have not been quantified either. Nevertheless, because illegitimate births comprise a large proportion of births to teenagers (35 percent in 1973), the question should be addressed.[55]

INDIRECT EFFECT OF EARLY CHILDBEARING ON SUBSEQUENT CHILDBEARING

It has been clearly established[63,64] that the earlier the age of first marriage, the greater is cumulated fertility. Examination of the *Children Ever Born* volume[65] of the 1970 census indicates that the differential is quite large. The same result almost certainly holds for age at first birth, though the census does not tabulate cumulated fertility by duration since first birth in this manner. Preliminary data from the 1973 National Survey of Family Growth[65] shown in table 9-6 reveal the strong inverse association of completed fertility and age of first birth; unfortunately, there is no life-cycle control such as current age, duration since first birth, or marriage cohort.

Several small studies have found that the incidence of repeat pregnancy among teenage mothers is quite high. Currie et al.[67] estimated that between 29 percent (of mothers in a special program) and 53 percent (of mothers in a control group) became pregnant again within 2 years. Dickens et al.[35] report that 20 percent of women in their study became pregnant a second time at an average of 14.5 months after the first birth; 2 years later, over 40 percent were found to have become pregnant again. If early childbearing causes higher completed fertility, and if higher fertility imposes heavier social costs, then this indirect effect should be included in an accounting of costs. Early childbearing may, however, simply reflect higher fecundability (or inept contraceptive practice). Higher fecundability, which cannot be directly

Table 9-6.—*Number of children ever born, additional births expected, and total births expected per 1,000 mothers under 45 years old, 1972 and 1973, United States*

Sociodemographic characteristics	Number of mothers (thousands)	Percent of mothers	Children ever born	Additional births expected	Total births expected
	National Natality Survey, 1972				
All mothers	2,818	100.0	2,245	788	3,033
Age at first birth					
Under 18 years . . .	293	10.4	2,633	760	3,393
18 to 19 years	542	19.2	2,346	780	3,126
20 to 21 years	600	21.3	2,284	822	3,106
22 to 24 years	721	25.6	2,026	878	2,904
25 to 29 years	522	18.5	2,112	742	2,854
30 or more years . .	139	4.9	2,498	439	2,937
	National Survey of Family Growth, 1973				
All mothers	21,201	100.0	2,682	339	3,022
Age at first birth					
Under 18 years . . .	[a]—	12.6	3,439	327	3,766
18 to 19 years	—	24.1	2,896	328	3,224
20 to 21 years	—	23.6	2,728	322	3,050
22 to 24 years	—	23.4	2,443	344	2,787
25 to 29 years	—	13.6	2,100	394	2,494
30 or more years . .	—	2.7	1,756	388	2,144

[a]Not applicable.

Source: Reference 62.

measured, may cause the observed association between early and greater childbearing.

Several researchers have estimated the private cost of an additional child.[68-71] Presumably, however, the private costs are exceeded by private benefits if the child is wanted, or the couple would decide not to have the child. If rational decision-making models of fertility are correct, these studies have little relevance here. Leasure[72] has estimated the cost to the North Carolina taxpayer of rearing a child from birth to entry into the labor force. He included costs of education, aid to dependent children, prenatal and delivery care, and institutional care. These costs are, however, not net of the discounted taxes the individual may be expected to pay back once he enters the labor force; and, furthermore, not all these costs are social costs. In conclusion, very little is known about the link between early childbearing and total fertility and even less is known about the excess social costs imposed by greater fertility.

SUMMARY AND RECOMMENDATIONS

Although little is known with certainty about the economic effects of teenage pregnancy and childbearing, minor refinements of existing methodology could yield useful results without enormous cost or effort. Data from both the SEO and NLS have yet to be mined fully. The SEO data have the twin advantages of being surprisingly clean and containing rather complete fertility histories, but they have the disadvantage of becoming increasingly dated; data from the NLS are much less clean and contain paltry fertility information. The NLS data are, however, nearly current; the NLS cohort of women aged 14 to 24 in 1967 provides an ongoing opportunity to analyze childbearing and labor market decisions as they occur. Several answers could be provided by analyzing these data, specifically:

1. The effect of early childbearing on wage rates. Addition of dummy variables to the regressions run by Oaxaca[26] and Mincer and Polachek[28] would allow an easy test.
2. The effect of early childbearing on LFPR. Methodology like that of Bowen's and Finegan's[29] employing dummy variables similar to those used for age of children seems appropriate. Hill's[40] framework, although used for men only, could also be adapted.
3. The effect of early pregnancy on the probability of dropping out of high school. Although the reason for dropping out of school was asked of everyone leaving school in the NLS survey of young men and women, their answers have never been analyzed. Pregnancy was an acceptable response, but it is not clear whether such responses would be biased. Further, the youngest women, who were 14 years of age in 1967, are now too old to be still in high school. Hence, the effect of the recent change in the guidelines of the Office of Education could not be assessed. In view of the impact of a high school education on wages, LFPR, and economic opportunity in general, the collection and analysis of data on high school dropouts should be given high priority.
4. The effect of early pregnancy and childbearing on later economic position. The same type of exhaustive analysis of Freedman and Coombs,[50,51] using age of first childbearing as a control variable, is needed. Their data would allow analysis only of ever-married women, but such an analysis would be relatively simple.

Other answers will be harder to find. Determining whether a differential between illegitimacy and legitimacy exists requires data on mothers and families of illegitimate children that are not yet available. Quantification of the excess medical costs of teenage childbearing must await specification of the increased risks of childbearing resulting from age alone. Finally, assessment of the macroeconomic impact of teenage fertility would necessitate the construction of a more elaborate demographic-economic model than is currently available. Only with such a macro model, however, can the really interesting problems be analyzed.

APPENDIX

Description of Data Sets

National Longitudinal Survey

The National Longitudinal Survey (NLS) is a longitudinal study of the labor market experience of four groups in the U.S. population: men 45 to 59 years of age, women 30 to 44 years of age, and young men and women 12 to 24 years of age. For convenience, these groups have been labeled men, women, boys and girls, respectively. Women were interviewed in 1967, 1969, 1971, and 1972; a brief questionnaire was mailed to them in 1968. Girls were interviewed annually from 1968 through 1973. Each cohort was represented by a national probability sample of approximately 5,000 individuals. The shrinkage of the samples has been very small; 88 percent of women and 86 percent of girls, respectively, were interviewed in the last scheduled survey. It has been decided that the surveys will be continued for 5 more years by means of a short telephone interview. There are to be 2 biennial surveys of this type for each cohort; and, if this experience is favorable, a final face-to-face interview is scheduled for the end of the second 5 years of the program.

The data collected on labor market experience and human capital formation are quite extensive. Information on the current school enrollment status of girls has been collected at every survey. Thus, movement in and out of the formal educational system can be discerned. There also is an index of high school quality; high school curriculum, field of specialization in college, and amount of scholarship aid in college illustrate the kinds of information collected.

The fertility history of older women is inadequate. The month and year of entry of the first child into the family are included on the tapes, but it cannot be positively determined if the child is her own. Similarly, the number of children ever born is not asked specifically; it can only be estimated indirectly by the use of answers from several questions. The year of birth of the first child was not asked of girls. Moreover, their fertility history is not adequate.

Further information is available in the *NLS Handbook,* which may be obtained free of charge from the Center for Human Resource Research at Ohio State University.

Survey of Economic Opportunity

The Survey of Economic Opportunity (SEO) was conducted by the U.S. Bureau of the Census at the request of the Office of Economic Opportunity. In 1966, 30,000 households (18,000 white and 12,000 drawn from areas with a high concentration of nonwhites) were surveyed; in 1967, the people living in the locations chosen in 1966 (not necessarily the same families) were reinterviewed.

Questions about labor force experience and participation, income, wages, and health were asked. The fertility history is quite complete; dates of birth of first, second, next to last, and last child were asked of ever-married women or women with their own children in the household; moreover, the number of children ever born is available for such women.

More information is available from the SEO clearinghouse at the University of Wisconsin. The *SEO Newsletter* contains an index to all known research using the SEO data.

Detroit Family Growth Study

The Coombs et al.[50] analyses are based on interviews with 1,113 women in the Detroit metropolitan area in 1962, selected to constitute a probability sample of all married white women in the area who had a first, second, or fourth birth in July 1961. This panel was reinterviewed three times, mainly by telephone, in the fall months of 1962, 1963, and 1965. Those pregnant at the final interview were later reinterviewed so that all birth data are based on completed pregnancies. Eighty-five percent of women eligible for the original sample were interviewed all 4 times. The data contain extensive information on pregnancy histories, family size expectations, and a wide range of social and economic variables.

ACKNOWLEDGMENTS

I should like to thank Rachel Thurston for her invaluable help in locating and interpreting the mass of data used in preparing this paper. Bryan Boulier, Ansley Coale, Jane Menken, Norman Ryder, and Charles Westoff provided thoughtful criticisms and comments. I should also like to express my appreciation for the editorial help given by Winifred Proctor.

REFERENCES

1. Hansen, Alvin. "Economic Progress and Declining Population Growth." *Am. Econ. Rev.* 29(1):1–15, 1939.
2. Leibenstein, H. *Economic Backwardness and Economic Growth.* London: Chapman and Hall, 1957.
3. Coale, A. J. and Hoover, E. *Population Growth and Economic Development in Low Income Countries.* Princeton: Princeton University Press, 1958.
4. Hagen, E. "Population and Economic Growth." *Am. Econ. Rev.* 49(3):310–327, 1959.
5. Enke, S. *Economics in Development.* Englewood Cliffs: Prentice Hall, 1963.
6. Enke, S. "Birth Control for Economic Development." *Science.* 164(3881):798–801, 1969.
7. Enke, S. "Economics of Preventing Births." *Popul. Stud. (London).* 24(3):455–456, 1970.
8. Enke, S. and Zind, R. G. "Effects of Fewer Births on Average Income." *J. Biosocial Sci.* 1(1):41–56, 1969.
9. Becker, G. "An Economic Analysis of Fertility." *In Demographic and Economic Change in Developed Countries.* Princeton: Princeton University Press, 1960.
10. Blake, J. "Are Babies Consumer Durables." *Popul. Stud. (London).* (22)(1):5–25, 1968.
11. Simon, J. "The Effect of Income on Fertility." *Popul. Stud. (London).* 23(3):327–341, 1969.
12. Mueller, E. "Economic Motives for Family Limitation." *Popul. Stud. (London).* 26(3):383–403, 1972.
13. Becker, G. S. and Lewis, H. G. "On the Interaction between the Quantity and Quality of Children." *J. Polit. Econ.* 81(2):S279–S288, 1973.
14. Cain, G. and Weininger, A. "Economic Determinants of Fertility: Results from Cross-Sectional Aggregate Data." *Demography.* 10(2):205–224, 1973.
15. Schultz, T. P. "A Preliminary Survey of Economic Analysis of Fertility." *Am. Econ. Rev.* 63(2):71–78, 1973.
16. Leibenstein, H. "An Interpretation of the Economic Theory of Fertility: Promising Path or Blind Alley." *J. Econ. Lit.* 12(2):457–479, 1974.
17. Enke, S. "The Economic Aspects of Slowing Population Growth." *Econ. J.* 76(301):44–56, 1966.
18. Simon, J. "The Value of Avoided Births to Underdeveloped Countries." *Popul. Stud. (London).* 23(1):61–68, 1969.
19. Leibenstein, H. "Pitfalls in Benefit/Cost Analysis of Birth Prevention." *Popul. Stud. (London).* 23(2):161–170, 1969.
20. Becker, G. "A Theory of Marriage: Part I." *J. Polit. Econ.* 81(4):813–846, 1973.

21. Becker, G. "A Theory of Marriage: Part II." *J. Polit. Econ.* 82(2):S11–S26. 1974.
22. Hamermesh, D. and Soss, N. "An Economic Theory of Suicide." *J. Polit. Econ.* 82(7):83–98, 1974.
23. Presser, H. B. "Early Motherhood: Ignorance or Bliss." *Fam. Plann. Perspec.* 6(1):8–14, 1974.
24. Johnson, T. "Returns from Investment in Human Capital." *Am. Econ. Rev.* 60(4):546–560, 1970.
25. Mincer, J. "The Distribution of Labor Incomes: A Survey with Special Reference to the Human Capital Approach." *J. Econ. Lit.* 8(1):1–26, 1970.
26. Oaxaca, R. "Male-Female Wage Differentials in Urban Labor Markets." *Internat. Econ. Rev.* 14(3):693–709, 1973.
27. U.S. Bureau of the Census. *U.S. Census of Population, 1970. Special Reports: Years of Schooling.* PC(2)–5A. Washington: U.S. Government Printing Office, 1973.
28. Mincer, J. and Polachek, S. "Family Investments in Human Capital: Earnings of Women." *J. Polit. Econ.* 82(2):S76–S108, 1974.
29. Bowen, W. and Finegan, T. A. *The Economics of Labor Force Participation.* Princeton: Princeton University Press, 1969.
30. Ross, S. G. "The Timing and Spacing of Births and Women's Labor Force Participation: An Economic Analysis." National Bureau of Economic Research Working Paper No. 30, 1974.
31. Bacon, L. A. "Early Motherhood, Accelerated Role Transition and Social Pathology." *Social Forces.* 52(3):333–341, 1974.
32. Atkyns, G. C. "Trends in the Retention of Married and Pregnant Students in American Public Schools." *Sociol. Educ.* 41(1):57–65, 1968.
33. Wallace. H. M. et al. "A Study of Services and Needs of Teenage Pregnant Girls in the Large Cities of the United States." *Am. J. Public Health.* 63,I(1):5–16, 1973.
34. *Federal Register.* June 4, 1975, p. 24142.
35. Dickens, H. O. "One Hundred Pregnant Adolescents, Treatment Approaches in a University Hospital." *Am. J. Public Health.* 63,II(9):794–800, 1973.
36. Foltz, A., Klerman, L., and Jekel, J. "Pregnancy and Special Education: Who Stays in School?" *Am. J. Public Health.* 62,II(12):1612–1619, 1972.
37. National Center for Health Statistics. *Vital Statistics of the United States, 1970.* Vol. II, *Mortality,* Part A, Tables 1–15, pp. 1–72. Washington: U.S. Government Printing Office, 1974.
38. Menken, J. A. "Teenage Childbearing: Its Medical Aspects and Implications for the United States Population." *Demographic and Social Aspects of Population Growth.* Washington: U.S. Government Printing Office, 1972.

39. MacMahon, B., Cole, P., Lin, T., Lowe, C., Mirra, A., Ravnihar, B., Salber, E., Valoaras, V., and Yuasa, S. "Age at First Birth and Breast Cancer Risk." *Bull. WHO* 43(2):209–221, 1970.

40. Hill, C. R. "Education, Health, and Family Size as Determinants of Labor Market Activity for the Poor and Nonpoor." *Demography.* 8(3):379–388, 1971.

41. Nortman, D. "Parental Age as a Factor in Pregnancy Outcome and Child Development." *Reports on Population/Family Planning.* August, 1974, pp. 1–5.

42. Lilienfeld, A. and Pasamanick, B. "Association of Maternal and Fetal Factors with the Development of Epilepsy." *J. Am. Med. Assn.* 155(8):719–724, 1954.

43. Lilienfeld, A. and Parkhurst, E. "A Study of the Association of Factors of Pregnancy and Parturition with the Development of Cerebral Palsy: Preliminary Report." *Am. J. Hyg.* 53(3):262–282, 1951.

44. Pasamanick, B. and Lilienfeld, A. "Association of Maternal and Fetal Factors with the Development of Mental Deficiency." *J. Am. Med. Assn.* 159(3):155–159, 1955.

45. Vernon, McC. "Prematurity and Deafness: The Magnitude and Nature of the Problem Among Deaf Children." *Except. Child.* 33:289–298, 1967.

46. Goldberg, I. D., Goldstein, H., Quade, D., and Rogot, E. "Association of Prenatal Factors with Blindness in Children." *Public Health Serv. Rep.* 82(6):519–532, 1967.

47. Wiener, G. "The Relationship of Birth Weight and Length of Gestation to Intellectual Development at Ages 8 to 10 Years." *J. Pediat.* 76:694–699, 1970.

48. Drillien, C. M. "School Disposal and Performance for Children of Different Birthweight Born 1953–1960." *Arch. Dis. of Child.* 44:562–570, 1969.

49. Wiener, G., Rider, R., Oppel, W., Fischer, L., and Harper, P. "Correlates of Low Birth Weight: Psychological Status at Six to Seven Years of Age." *Pediatrics.* 35:434–444, 1965.

50. Coombs, L. and Freedman, R. "Premarital Pregnancy, Childbearing and Later Economic Achievement." *Popul. Stud. (London).* 24:389–412, 1970.

51. Freedman, R. and Coombs, L. "Childspacing and Family Economic Position." *Am. Sociol. Rev.* 31:631–649, 1966.

52. Tietze, C. and Lewit, S. "A National Medical Experience: The Joint Program for the Study of Abortion." *In* H. Osofsky and J. Osofsky, Eds., *The Abortion Experience.* New York: Harper and Row, 1973.

53. Cutright, P. "Illegitimacy in the United States: 1920–1968." *Demographic and Social Aspects of Population Growth.* Washington: U.S. Government Printing Office, 1972.

54. Berkov, B. "Illegitimate Fertility in California's Population." Unpublished manuscript, University of California, Berkeley, 1971.

55. National Center for Health Statistics. "Summary Report: Final Natality Statistics, 1973." *Vital Statistics Reports*. January 30, 1975.

56. Kantner, J. and Zelnik, M. "Sexual Experience of Young Unmarried Women in the United States." *Fam. Plann. Perspec.* 4(4):9–18, 1972.

57. Kantner, J. and Zelnik, M. "Contraception and Pregnancy: Experience of Young Unmarried Women in the United States." *Fam. Plann. Perspec.* 5(1):21–35, 1973.

58. Forssman, H. and Thuwe, I. "One Hundred and Twenty Children Born After Application for Therapeutic Abortion Refused." *Acta Psychiatr. Scand.* 42(1):71–78, 1966.

59. Laing, W. A. *The Costs and Benefits of Family Planning*. London: Population and Economic Planning (PEP), February 1972.

60. Whelpton, P. K. and Kiser, C. V., Eds. *Social and Psychological Factors Affecting Fertility*. Vol. I, 1946. Vol. II, 1950. Vol. III, 1953. Vol. IV, 1954. Vol. V, 1958. New York: Milbrook Memorial Fund.

61. Ryder, N. B. and Westoff, C. F. *Reproduction in the United States, 1965*. Princeton: Princeton University Press, 1971.

62. Westoff, C. F. and Ryder, N. B. *The Contraceptive Revolution*. Princeton: Princeton University Press, 1977.

63. Bumpass, L. "Age at Marriage as a Variable in Socio-Economic Differentials in Fertility." *Demography*. 6(1):45–54, 1969.

64. Busfield, J. "Age at Marriage and Family Size: Social Causation and Social Selection Hypotheses." *J. Biosocial Sci.* 4(1):117–134, 1972.

65. U.S. Bureau of the Census. *U.S. Census of Population, 1970. Special Reports: Women by Number of Children Ever Born* PC(2)–3A. Washington: U.S. Government Printing Office, 1973.

66. Bonham, G. and Placek, P. "The Impact of Social and Demographic, Maternal Health and Infant Health Factors on Expected Family Size: Preliminary Findings from the 1973 National Survey of Family Growth and the 1972 National Natality Survey." Presented at the 1975 PAA meetings in Seattle, Washington, April 1975.

67. Currie, J. B., Jekel, J. F., and Klerman, L. V. "Subsequent Pregnancies Among Teenage Mothers Enrolled in a Special Program." *Am. J. Public Health*. 62,II(12):1606–1611, 1972.

68. Dublin, L. and Lotka, A. J. *The Money Value of a Man*. Rev. Ed. New York: Ronald Press, 1946.

69. Campbell, A. *Family Planning and the Reduction of Parity in the U.S.* Attachment to a Consultant Report to the DHEW on Family Planning and Population, September 1967.

70. Espenshade, T. "The Price of Children and Socio-Economic Theories of Fertility: A Survey of Alternative Methods for Estimating the Parental Cost of Raising Children." *Popul. Stud. (London).* 26(2):207–221, 1972.
71. Espenshade, T. *Estimating the Costs of Children and Some Results from Urban United States.* Berkeley: International Population and Urban Research Center, 1973.
72. Leasure, W. "Some Economic Benefits of Birth Prevention." *Milbank Mem. Fund Q.* XLV(4):417–426, 1967.

DISCUSSION

The following people were the major participants in the discussion: R. Hill, H. Presser, C. Chilman, S. Gustavus, J. Kantner, F. Furstenberg, F. Jaffe, and L. Coombs.

The chief topics of discussion were the possible economic consequences of adolescent childbearing for young parents and their children, effects upon the education of teenagers and their later education, and suggestions for research.

A question was raised about the assumption that early childbearing might have positive economic consequences because the mother could reenter the labor market while she was still young, leaving an older child to care for younger children. Some participants felt that this is not an optimal method of child care; such an arrangement might well have an adverse effect on the development of the children involved, thereby creating later adverse economic consequences for them.

A question also was raised about the presumption that early childbearing causes later poverty. Many adolescent parents come from poverty families. Thus, they start their earning careers with handicaps engendered by their derived low socioeconomic status and frequently adverse developmental experiences. These factors may be more central to their continuing unemployment than the fact of early childbearing.

Somewhat the same might be said for early school leaving. Adolescent girls drop out of school for many reasons besides pregnancy. Dr. Kantner found in his study that only one-third of the school dropouts had left because of pregnancy. It was remarked that studies of early school leaving show that dropping out of school is associated with educational problems going back to the early grades, such as an inability to read, poverty, racism, poor family relationships, low self-esteem, and alienated attitudes. Some of the same characteristics also seem to be associated with becoming an adolescent parent. Moreover, both Presser and Furstenberg found in their studies that many of the young mothers who dropped out of high school returned later, especially if they had high educational aspirations.

It was remarked that the mere fact of graduating from high school does not assure employment. Studies have shown that many other factors are involved, including the state of the economy. Being a high school graduate enhances, but does not assure, employment potential.

A question was raised as to whether studies indicated differences in consumer patterns between adolescent and older parents. It was suggested that if a mother has a child when she is very young, she may have neither the experience nor the resources to allocate money for such child care investments as medical and dental care or high quality education. Would she, perhaps, develop a lifestyle that would persist so that her children would have less invested in them over a period of years, thus depriving them of aids to their optimal development? In broad terms, are adolescent parents less effective consumers than older ones?

Dr. Hill said that his study of family consumer patterns showed that the younger generation (but not differentiated in terms of adolescents) showed more shrewdness and careful planning as consumers than the parent and grandparent generations. Of course, they were more active as consumers because of their stage in the life cycle. Several people pointed out that consumer patterns seemed to be determined more by income and life cycle stage than by age per se.

Some of the group members wondered whether macro studies could be done on the probable economic consequences of adolescent childbearing. This would be difficult. Many other factors affecting the economy would develop, if a large number of teenagers had children. These factors would include changes in the population structure and consumer expenditure patterns. Not enough data are available to make accurate predictions of the consequences of a major decline in adolescent births. Some participants thought that a simulation model might be devised, but others commented that the data are not available to put into such a model with any degree of confidence.

Mr. Jaffe said that predictions of the macroeconomic effects of preventing all births to mothers under age 18 would be very useful in impressing policymakers about the importance of preventing such births.

It was suggested that longitudinal studies might include questions regarding income resources and consumer patterns. Asked to discuss her experience with longitudinal research in the Detroit area studies, Ms. Coombs said that she has recently found that it is possible to locate people who were first interviewed almost 20 years ago. Followup studies had been previously carried out, every year, with a group of white married couples, some of whom had experienced a premarital pregnancy.[1] She and her associates have recently experimented with a 10-percent sample of that study population and have found that they can reach 90 percent of the group by telephone (sometimes by long-distance calls). Ms. Coombs suggested that it should be possible to do a longitudinal study with a sample in the early childbearing years, obtain retrospective data at that time, and follow the group over a period of years.

Dr. Kantner commented that followup studies may be less expensive than others, in which a new sample must be located. In his study of adolescent girls, it was necessary to contact over 80,000 homes to find the less than 5,000 respondents for his research project.

It also was suggested that studies of the economic consequences of adolescent childbearing consider the economic consequences for the parents of the adolescents involved.

Chapter 10

Social Consequences of Teenage Childbearing

Harriet B. Presser
University of Maryland

Teenage childbearing is widely regarded as a serious social problem in the United States, primarily because of its strong association with out-of-wedlock childbearing. Although only about a third of teenage mothers are unmarried at the time of birth,[1] it is this subpopulation that typically has been studied. The focus of such study is usually on the determinants of nonmarital fertility, such as attitudes toward sex, contraceptive knowledge and practice, family relationships, and various cultural factors.[2-5] Empirical studies on the consequences of out-of-wedlock childbearing, moreover, are generally limited to the problems of recidivism, dropping out of school, and welfare dependency.[6-12]

Underlying these studies is the assumption that some negative social consequences of early motherhood could be avoided if childbearing were postponed until at least age 20 and until the women were married. A priori, this seems to be true: The limited social and economic resources of teenagers seem to be a major handicap for childrearing. However, it is difficult to document this assertion. By limiting the samples to unmarried teenage mothers, investigators are unable to compare them to older mothers, married teenage mothers, or teenagers without children. One exception is the study by Furstenberg[13] on the social consequences of early childbearing, based on a clinic sample of mothers aged 15 to 17. From a comparison with female classmates 5 years later, the author concluded that there is "a sharp and regular pattern of differences in the marital, fertility, educational, and occupational careers of the

young mothers and the classmates." The latter were more successful in realizing their aspirations.[a]

According to other studies, pregnant teenagers who choose to
marry rather than undergo an abortion or have a child out of
wedlock may also experience negative social consequences. Premarital conceptions are associated with economic difficulty and shorter
birth intervals,[16,17] as well as with high rates of separation and
divorce.[18] Whether responding to a pregnancy by marrying young is
socially more advantageous than being an unmarried mother (or
father) has never been shown.

This study empirically examines some specific ways in which
early childbearing—and rearing—affects women's lives. It is based
on a sample of New York City women who recently became mothers. A comparison will be drawn between those who had their first
births in their teens with those in their twenties, focusing on
differences in aspirations and behavior with regard to motherhood,
marriage, education and employment. The birth of the first child is
viewed as a critical transition that may markedly alter a woman's
life. The basic hypothesis is as follows: The earlier the age at the
first birth, the more restrictive the effect of motherhood on nonmaternal roles. The analysis is limited to a few years after the
first birth, and thus to its important early effects. The data permit comparisons by age and hence an assessment of what is distinctive about teenage childbearing.

THE SAMPLE

The sample consists of 408 respondents randomly drawn from
the birth records of women residing in three New York City bor-
oughs (Brooklyn, the Bronx, and Queens) who had their first child
in July of 1970, 1971, or 1972. Only those women born on the
United States mainland were eligible; thus first-generation mi-
grants from Puerto Rico and elsewhere were excluded. Nonwhites
other than blacks were also excluded. Women who gave birth to
twins were omitted, as were those whose first child was not residing with them. About 90 percent of first births in New York City
are to women aged 15 to 29, and the sample was restricted to this
age range.

Of all New York City mothers meeting these criteria, 38 percent were black, and 30 percent were unmarried at the time of
their first birth. The population was stratified by mother's race,
marital status, and age at first birth, to assure a representative

---

[a]Furstenberg's study differs also in that fathers were interviewed. The men
were extremely difficult to locate, a fact which may explain why there are so few
studies on unmarried fathers (refs. 14 and 15). Without them, however, no analysis
of the determinants and consequences of early parenthood can be complete.

sample in this respect. Women were disproportionately drawn into the sample, however, by year of first birth to comprise about a quarter whose first birth was in July 1970, about a quarter in July 1971, and about a half in July 1972. (The major consideration here was the difficulty in finding those women whose addresses on the birth records were over 1 year old.) Women were interviewed during the period from January 15 to March 14, 1973. For about one-half of the sample, then, the first child was about 7 months old at the time the mother was interviewed; the remainder of the sample was divided equally between those whose first child was about age $1\frac{1}{2}$ and those whose first child was about age $2\frac{1}{2}$ at the time of the interview.

Personal interviews were conducted by the staff of the National Opinion Research Center (NORC). Of the 709 cases originally compiled, 541 were located and eligible, and, of those, 75 percent (408) were interviewed. For a breakdown of those not interviewed and an evaluation of the reliability of the data, see Presser.[19] There appears to be little selective bias among those initially interviewed (determined by an analysis of birth record data) or among those reinterviewed (determined by an analysis of the first interview).

Of the women who participated in the first interview, 88 percent (358) were reinterviewed by NORC approximately 1 year later (February 1974), regardless of whether they were still residing in New York City. Most reinterviews were by telephone (85 percent), although some were conducted in person when a respondent could not be reached by telephone.

TEENAGE CHILDBEARING AND WOMEN'S ROLES

By the time they became mothers, the majority of women in the sample (72 percent) were married, most (72 percent) had graduated from high school, and most (74 percent) had worked, part or full time, at least 6 months. But the percentages vary considerably by the mother's age at first birth (table 10-1). The younger the woman, the less likely she was to be included in these majorities. Thus, of teenage mothers,[b] only 39 percent were married, 33 percent had graduated from high school, and 39 percent had worked—facts suggesting that a first birth at a relatively young age restricts these role attainments. This suggestion, however, assumes that few or none of these teenagers chose early motherhood as an alternative to other roles, and that they would otherwise have

---

[b]"Teenage mothers" is used throughout this paper to refer to women who had their first births at ages 15 to 19; some were no longer teenagers at the time of the survey.

Table 10-1.—*Percent of New York City mothers who by the time of their first birth graduated from high school, worked, and were married*

Status of mother	Age at first birth			
	15 to 19	20 to 23	24 to 29	Total
Percent who were married at time of first birth	39	84	92	72
Percent who graduated high school before first birth	33	87	94	72
Percent who worked before first birth[a]	39	84	98	74
Total number of cases	129	154	125	408

[a]Only jobs of at least 6 months' duration are included.

been more likely to marry and to obtain more education and more work experience. It assumes also that younger mothers will not eventually catch up with older mothers.

These assumptions can be tested by considering whether the aspirations of women prior to their first birth differed by their age and whether the timing of motherhood differentially altered these aspirations. To do this testing with the data available, it is necessary to rely largely on retrospective reporting. With regard to the mother role, it is possible to examine the association between the age at first birth and reported family-size desires just before becoming pregnant. Regarding marriage, school, and work, it is possible to make an assessment on the basis of the reported role aspirations before motherhood.

The Onset of Motherhood

Asked whether, just before they became pregnant with their first child, the respondents had any idea of the total number of children they wanted, almost all (92 percent) said they did, and there was almost no variation by the age at first birth. As shown in table 10–2, 38 percent wanted two children, and 24 percent

Table 10-2.—*Percent distribution of New York City mothers by family size desires before becoming pregnant with her first child, according to age at first birth*

Age at first birth	Family size desires (percent)						Total	Number of cases	Mean[a]	
	0 to 1	2	3	4	5 or more	No idea			Number of children desired	Number of cases
15 to 19 ...	10	38	20	12	12	8	100	129	2.9	118
20 to 23 ...	8	34	25	8	7	8	100	154	2.9	142
24 to 29 ...	5	43	26	15	5	6	100	125	2.7	117
Total	8	38	24	15	8	7	100	408	2.8	377

[a]$\chi^2 = 10.48; P > 0.05$: excludes women who had no idea.

wanted three children, again with little difference by the age at first birth.[c] Presumably, teenage mothers did not start their families early because they wanted larger families.

Supporting this view is the fact that only 20 percent of the teenage mothers planned the birth of their first child,[d] as contrasted with 44 percent of mothers aged 20 to 23, and 70 percent of those aged 24 to 29 ($P<0.05$). Of *all* first births, most were unplanned—56 percent. Although respondents with unplanned births were not choosing to become mothers at that time, none of them decided to abort the pregnancy (a legal option for three-fourths of the women—those who had their first birth in 1971 or 1972), or put the child up for adoption. Once pregnant, they accepted motherhood instead of these alternatives.

[c]Family size desires at age 16, retrospectively reported, are also not related to age at first birth. Moreover, the older the mother at the time of the first birth, the more likely she was to have most wanted at age 16 to be a housewife or mother rather than to have a specific occupation (ref. 20).

[d]Respondents were asked whether contraception was consistently practiced during the month the woman became pregnant with her first child, and if not, the reason(s). A card listing several possibilities included a category in which additional reasons could be volunteered. First births were classified as planned by women who said that at least one reason they did not use contraception was that they were trying to have a baby. All other first births were classified as unplanned. For the distribution of other reasons stated for not using contraception, see reference 19.

Marriage

As noted earlier, most of the teenage mothers were unmarried (see table 10–1). For an unmarried woman who becomes pregnant, does not want an abortion, and prefers to keep the child, it is not altogether clear that she would benefit by marrying the child's father. Almost all the unmarried mothers wanted eventually to marry, but over half said that when they learned they were pregnant, they did not want to marry the child's father. "He was irresponsible," "a drug addict," "an alcoholic," and so forth. Among married women in the study, no relation between the age at first birth and self-ratings of marital happiness was found.

The study indicates that the unmarried fathers had less education than the married ones. Among those paired with teenage mothers, for instance, 51 percent of the unmarried fathers, but only 34 percent of the married, were not high school graduates. Although not statistically significant, this difference suggests that many unmarried mothers may not have derived much economic benefit from marriage with the child's father.

Many women unmarried when their first child was born will marry later, although not typically soon after motherhood begins. Only 16 percent of the mothers unmarried at the time of their first birth had married within the following 1½ years. The amount of face-to-face contact between the unmarried mothers and the fathers after the child's birth varied considerably. Among the 80 unmarried mothers asked on this point in the reinterview (excluding the seven cases in which the father had died), the distribution was as follows:

Amount of contact	Percent
At least once a week	29
1 to 3 times a month	22
Less than once a month	22
Never	27

For at least half of the cases, then, a consequence of unmarried motherhood apparently is the added social responsibilities of fatherhood. There was no difference in the amount of contact by the mother's age at her first birth.

Education

As noted earlier, women who had early first births were less likely to have graduated from high school: Only 33 percent of the teenage mothers had done so (see table 10–1). Whether pregnancy and subsequent childbearing were responsible for the low level of education is difficult to ascertain, but the study provides an opportunity for some analysis.

Of the mothers in the study, 13 percent were attending school at the time of the first interview—that is, when their first child was between 7 months and 2½ years old. The younger the mother, the more likely she was to be in school: 25 percent of the teenage mothers, 7 percent of those aged 20 to 23 at the first birth, and 6 percent of those aged 24 to 29 ($P < 0.05$). The contrast is striking, especially since many of the teenage mothers were unmarried and poor, but the data suggest that many more would have been in school had they postponed their first births.[e]

Those not currently attending school at the time of the first interview were asked the main reason they had dropped out. Of the teenage mothers, 36 percent said it was a result of their pregnancy. Among the teenage mothers not attending school, moreover, the younger their age at the first birth, the more likely they were to give this reason for leaving school. The percentages by age were as follows:

Age	Percent
15–16	74
17	38
18	28
19	19

Sixty of the teenage mothers not in school, or almost two-thirds, had not graduated from high school, and, of these, about half said the main reason for leaving school was their pregnancy.

Pregnancy may have restricted the education of many teenage mothers, but it may also be that many had low aspirations and would not have continued in school in any event. As declared

---

[e]The New York City Board of Education's policy to provide several options for pregnant teenagers in high school was spelled out in a statement to superintendents and secondary school principals, and was still in effect in the mid-1970's: "These girls should be permitted to remain in their regular school program as long as their physical and emotional condition permits. An individual decision is necessary to determine what is in the best interest of each student found to be pregnant. The girl's parents and physician should be consulted in developing the educational plan to fit her needs. If she is a short time away from completing the term's work or from graduation, and, if her physician advises that she may attend classes, she should be encouraged to continue at her home school. Should this consultation lead to the conclusion that continued attendance at the home school may be detrimental to her physical or mental well-being, she should be transferred to one of the special centers or other suitable arrangements should be made for continuing her education. As in other school matters, the final decision will rest upon the good judgment of the principal of the home school who will consider all the factors involved" (ref. 21).

retrospectively, what were the educational aspirations of the respondents prior to their first birth? Women not in school were asked whether, just before they had their first child, they had gone as far in school as they wanted. Almost three-fourths had wanted to go further, especially those who had not graduated from high school. In short, for many teenage mothers, regardless of whether or not they were high school graduates, pregnancy seemingly interfered with their educational plans.

The contrast is sharp between teenage and older mothers not in school. The percent who stated that prior to their first birth they had wanted to go further in school was 72 for those aged 15 to 19 at the first birth, 42 for those aged 20 to 23, and 43 for those aged 24 to 29 ($P < 0.05$). This finding does not necessarily mean, of course, that younger mothers wanted to achieve a higher level of education than older mothers: They had had substantially fewer years of schooling prior to motherhood. As can be seen in table 10–3, if the educational aspirations of those not currently attending school had been realized, the teenage mothers would still be less educated than the older ones. Having a child early certainly cannot explain all the variation in education. On the other hand, among those not in school who postponed motherhood until after their teens, educational aspiration differed little by whether they became mothers in their early or late twenties.

What happens to the educational aspirations of women after the birth of the first child? Those not enrolled at the time of the first interview were asked whether they planned to go back to school, and, if so, whether they planned to do so within the next few years. Over half of the respondents (52 percent) said they

Table 10-3.—*Percent distribution of New York City mothers not currently attending school, by level of educational aspirations just before first birth according to age at first birth*[a]

Age at first birth	Level of educational aspirations (percent)				
	12 grades[b]	13 to 15 grades	16 or more grades	Total percent	Number of cases
15 to 19	42	22	36	100	69
20 to 23	8	30	62	100	61
24 to 29	8	25	67	100	51
Total	21	25	54	100	181

[a] $\chi^2 = 30.64; P < 0.05$.
[b] Includes one case of less than 12 grades.

intended to return to school some time, and, of these, 81 percent were planning to go back within 5 years (42 percent of the total sample).

As can be seen in table 10-4, teenage mothers were more likely than older mothers to plan to return to school, especially if before their first birth they had wanted to go further: 73 percent of these teenage mothers planned to go back to school within 5 years. At all ages, educational aspirations before the first birth were positively related with current plans to return to school. However, of the substantial minority in each age group who before their first birth felt they had gone as far as they wanted, some planned after having the child to continue in school. The reverse also occurred: Some who had wanted more schooling changed their

Table 10-4.—*Percent distribution of New York City mothers not currently attending school by whether and when they plan to go back to school according to educational aspirations just before first birth and age at first birth*

Age at first birth and when plan to go back to school	Educational aspirations just before first birth		Total
	Went as far as wanted	Wanted to go further	
15 to 19[a]			
Go back within 5 years	39	78	67
Go back after 5 years	7	3	4
Never go back	54	19	29
Total percent	100	100	100
Number of cases	28	68	96
20 to 23[b]			
Go back within 5 years	29	55	40
Go back after 5 years	8	12	10
Never go back	63	33	50
Total percent	100	100	100
Number of cases	83	60	143
24 to 29[c]			
Go back within 5 years	28	56	40
Go back after 5 years	9	26	16
Never go back	63	18	44
Total percent	100	100	100
Number of cases	67	50	117

[a] $\chi^2 = 13.36; P < 0.05.$
[b] $\chi^2 = 12.26; P < 0.05.$
[c] $\chi^2 = 23.69; P < 0.05.$

plans after having a child. Although both responses were by a minority, they suggest that, for some women, becoming a mother altered their educational ambitions.

Employment[22]

Prior to their first birth, three-fourths of the respondents had worked outside the home for at least 6 months (see table 10–1). The older the woman, the more years she had had in which to work. Accordingly, of women who became mothers when they were 20 to 23, 84 percent had been in the labor force; of those aged 24 to 29, 98 percent; and, of those aged 15 to 19, only 39 percent. Of the women who had worked before their first birth, over three-fourths were employed during pregnancy: 72 percent of teenage mothers, 74 percent of those aged 20 to 23 at the first birth, and 84 percent of those aged 24 to 29. The differences are not statistically significant.

Shortly after the first births, teenage mothers were less likely to be working than older mothers. By age at the first birth, the percentages employed when the first child was 7 months old were as follows ($P<0.05$):

Age	Percent
15–19	10
20–23	13
24–29	22
Total	15

By the time the first child was 19 months old, the percentage distribution was as follows ($P<0.05$):

Age	Percent
15–19	13
20–23	23
24–29	32
Total	22

As mentioned earlier, many women were in school soon after their first birth, especially those in their teens. Does school attendance explain the lower employment rates of women with early first births? Among those not attending school at the time of the first interview, was there a difference in employment status by age at first birth?[f] Of this group, only 9 percent of those aged 15

---

[f]The ten women both attending school and employed at the time of the first interview were excluded from the analysis. Employment at the time of first inter-

to 19 at the first birth were employed, as compared to 16 percent of those aged 20 to 23 and 24 percent of those aged 24 to 29 ($P<0.05$). School attendance apparently does not explain the lower employment rates of women who had become mothers in their teens.

The lack of the work experience or occupational skills needed to obtain a reasonably remunerative job may be the explanation. Work experience before and after the first birth is often merely interrupted, and young mothers were least likely to have worked prior to motherhood. Of those with earlier work experience and not currently in school, the percent employed at the time of the first interview differed little by age at first birth: 17 percent of those aged 15 to 19 at the first birth, 16 percent of those aged 20 to 23, and 23 percent of those aged 24 to 29. Thus, for women with some work experience prior to motherhood, the age at first birth seemingly did not affect employment soon after. The postponement of motherhood apparently provides opportunities for a first job and also has consequences for subsequent employment. Regardless of age, women who become pregnant when they are employed have a special advantage in obtaining work later, since they often return to the same job. Other women may find young children a serious impediment to both seeking and obtaining a new job. Previously employed women may also be more highly motivated than other women to work soon after the birth of their first child, having experienced some of the advantages of paid employment.

Although less likely to be employed at the time of the first interview, teenage mothers were more likely to be planning to go to work soon. Among those not employed, 61 percent of teenage mothers intended to work within 1 year, in contrast to 24 percent of those aged 20 to 23 at the first birth, and 16 percent of those aged 24 to 29 (table 10–5).

How much do these aspirations predict behavior a year later? Plans at the time of the first interview can be compared with employment status at the time of the second interview (1 year later). Only 23 percent of those who planned to return to work within 1 year were in fact employed. The younger the woman at her first birth, the less likely she was to realize her intention: only 16 percent of those aged 15 to 19, 24 percent of those aged 20 to 23, and 54 percent of those aged 24 to 29 ($P<0.05$).

---

view is considered here rather than at a specific age of the child (as in the previous analysis of employment), since school enrollment relates to the time of the first interview.

Table 10-5.—*Percent distribution of New York City mothers not employed at time of first interview by when planning to go to work according to age at first birth*[a]

Age at first birth	When planning to work (percent)						
	Less than 1 year	1 to 2 years	3 to 5 years	5 years or more	Not at all	Total percent	Number of cases
15 to 19	61	18	10	8	3	100	115
20 to 23	24	20	11	32	13	100	128
24 to 29	16	9	16	41	18	100	95
Total	35	16	12	26	11	100	338

[a] $x^2 = 77.32; P < 0.05.$

Public Assistance

As we have seen, only a minority of the mothers were employed soon after their first birth. Teenage mothers, least likely to be working and most likely to be going to school, were also disproportionately without husbands to help support them or their children. How, then, did they make ends meet?

The data on public assistance are revealing. Asked whether any of their household income came from public assistance or welfare, including aid to dependent children, over a fourth of the sample said at least some was from this source. This reply undoubtedly overstates the proportion of women personally receiving public assistance, but not by much. Public assistance was more prevalent among younger mothers: 55 percent of the teenage mothers were in households receiving public assistance at the time of the first interview, in contrast to 17 percent of mothers aged 20 to 23, and 9 percent of mothers aged 24 to 29 ($P<0.05$). (For further discussion and an analysis of the relationship between public assistance and early family formation based on this sample of women, see Presser and Salsberg.[23])

Public assistance apparently enables many mothers to go to school. Not only were teenage mothers most likely to be enrolled and disproportionately receiving public assistance, but 75 percent of those in school were in households receiving public assistance. Looking at the relationship in the reverse direction, public assistance did not affect the proportion of either the total sample or teenage mothers specifically who were home full time: It was about two-thirds of either category. Recipients differed, however, between work and school: Among the remaining third, those receiving welfare were more likely to be in school, and nonrecipients were more likely to be at work (table 10–6).

Table 10-6.—*Percent distribution of New York City mothers by public assistance status at first interview according to activity last week, for total sample and for women aged 15 to 19 at time of first birth*

Activity last week	Public assistance status		Total
	Recipients	Nonrecipients	
Total sample[a]			
Employed[b]	8	23	19
In school	22	4	9
Home full time	69	73	72
Total	100	100	100
Number of cases	107	300	407
Aged 15 to 19 at first birth[c]			
Employed[d]	9	23	15
In school	26	10	19
Home full time	65	67	66
Total	100	100	100
Number of cases	70	58	128

[a] $\chi^2 = 40.98; P < 0.05.$
[b] Includes 10 women who were both employed and going to school.
[c] $\chi^2 = 8.10; P < 0.05.$
[d] Includes five women who were both employed and going to school.

Motherhood after the First Birth

For a period soon after their first births, most women were full-time homemakers supported by their husbands, families, or public assistance. Many, especially teenagers, had dropped out of school when they became pregnant, and many others had left the labor force or never had a chance to enter it. The educational aspirations of those not in school were well beyond realistic expectations once they were mothers. Almost all women planned to go (back) to work, and probably most will, although not as soon as they expect. How do such alterations in their day-to-day lives, the "reality shock" of motherhood, affect women's desired family size and subsequent fertility? Do these differ by age at first birth?

When the family-size desires of women just before they became pregnant with their first child (table 10–2) were compared with their desires at the time of the first interview, about one-fourth of the respondents indicated a change. Reportedly, 21 percent wanted fewer children, only 3 percent wanted more, 67 percent wanted the same number, and 9 percent had no specific idea at one or both times. There was, however, no strong relation between change in family-size desires during this period and age at the first birth, even when one controlled for the age of the first child.

With the reinterview it was possible to note changes in family-size desires 1 year later, without depending on retrospective data. Fewer than half of the women (48 percent) gave the same response at both interviews, and the shift was again toward smaller families. Of the reinterview sample, 29 percent wanted smaller families, but 17 percent wanted larger families. Although teenage mothers were most likely to change their family-size desires in either direction, differences by age at the first birth were not substantial.

Between pregnancy and the time of the second interview, however, the absolute number of children the respondents wanted declined markedly. Whereas just before pregnancy only 8 percent wanted fewer than two children (table 10-2), at the second interview 17 percent gave this preference (table 10-7). The two-child family, however, remained the most popular, especially among women who had had their first birth in their late twenties. Those who had become mothers in their teens were most likely to prefer either very small families (fewer than two children) or large families (four children or more). Shifts in the desired family size between pregnancy and the second interview seemingly differ by age at the first birth.

Turning now from attitudes to behavior, can any difference be discerned in subsequent fertility by age at first birth? This question can be examined with regard to the spacing of the second child. At the time of the second interview, the minimum interval since the first birth was 19 months, and 12 percent of the mothers had a second child during this interim. Teenage mothers did not

Table 10-7.—*Percent distribution of New York City mothers by family size desires at second interview according to age at first birth: Reinterview sample*

Age at first birth	Family size desires						Number of cases	Mean number of children desired[a]	Number of cases
	0 to 1	2	3	4 or more	No idea	Total percent			
15 to 19	24	36	17	17	6	100	111	2.2	104
20 to 23	17	47	26	6	4	100	132	2.2	128
24 to 29	9	60	19	9	3	100	115	2.3	112
Total	17	48	21	10	4	100	358	2.2	343

[a] $\chi^2 = 23.56$; $P < 0.05$. Excludes women who had no idea.

differ, however, from women aged 20 to 23: 14 percent of both had their second child within this interval, but only 7 percent of the women aged 24 to 29. These differences by age at the first birth are not statistically significant.

It is important to note that the study covered a relatively short span since the first birth. The long-term consequences of early motherhood on subsequent fertility may be substantial. Those who began childbearing as teenagers can be expected to have larger completed families than mothers who started later, not only because they will have had more reproductive time but because their role options over this span will be narrower. A third interview of the sample, conducted over 2 years after the second interview, can test these assertions.[g]

SUMMARY AND IMPLICATIONS

Although teenage mothers approached motherhood with family-size desires similar to those of women who were older at first birth, they were less likely to plan the timing of motherhood. Being young, they had less time than older mothers to find a suitable husband, to go to school, or to work before their first child was born. Almost all who were unmarried wanted to marry, although not necessarily the child's father. Many teenage mothers stated that before they became pregnant they had wanted to go further in school. With more child-free time, presumably some would have obtained more education prior to their first birth. It would also have given them a greater chance to work prior to motherhood, which seems to be an important determinant of subsequent employment. Unencumbered by a child, more unmarried women might have found a husband who could provide the kind of emotional and financial security they sought. To the extent that marriage, schooling, and employment are socially advantageous to women, and women themselves have such aspirations, the data indicate that teenage motherhood has negative social consequences.

The findings support the general view that childrearing responsibilities restrict the nonmaternal role activities of women. Many dropped out of school or out of the labor force when they became mothers; some never got the chance to work. Most became full-time homemakers. A few mothers were in school or working soon after their child was born, reflecting their strong motivation or great economic need. Teenage mothers were more likely to be

[g]This chapter was initially written in 1975, before the third series of interviews was conducted. This series was undertaken in 1976, and the results from this study are reported in Harriet B. Presser, *The Social and Demographic Consequences of Teenage Childbearing for Urban Women,* final report to NICHD (Contract NO1-HD-62836) published by the National Technical Information Service, 1980.

in school than older mothers, but less likely to be employed. They were also more likely to plan to return to school or work. However, their work plans were not good predictors of their subsequent behavior. Teenage mothers were less likely than women who became mothers in their twenties to have realized their work aspirations 1 year later.

Between pregnancy and the time of the second interview, the family-size desires of mothers changed considerably, more often downward than upward. At the time of the second interview, many teenage mothers wanted either no more than one child or four or more, while older mothers were more likely to prefer two and three children. The wider dispersion of family-size desires among teenage mothers suggests that their ability to cope with children, given their current lifestyle, may have varied more.

This chapter has focused on the relation between women's role aspirations and behavior over a limited time after their first birth. Further research is needed on the long-term consequences of teenage childbearing and rearing, comparing teenage mothers not only with older mothers but with teenagers who have not (yet) had children. If early parenthood is indeed socially disadvantageous for women (and perhaps also for men and children), then the problem could be alleviated by three policies: (1) increasing young people's motivation to postpone parenthood, as by increasing wages and job opportunities for women outside the home; (2) improving access to birth control knowledge and services for teenagers, as with innovative programs that deal also with sexuality; and (3) providing greater support to teenage parents, such as child care, so that they can more easily combine childrearing with school or work. These general strategies need further specification, of course, at the program level. Although there are problems of implementation associated with each, they need not be viewed as alternative strategies. But before their potential effectiveness can be assessed in reducing the negative social consequences of early parenthood, more information is needed about what these consequences are, and how serious they may be for the individual, the family, and society.

ACKNOWLEDGMENTS

This is a revision of a paper presented at the Conference on the Consequences of Adolescent Pregnancy and Childbearing, held in Bethesda, Maryland, October 29 and 30, 1975. The research upon which this paper is based was performed pursuant to Contract No. N01-HD-2-2038 with the National Institutes of Health, DHEW. The field work for the reinterview was funded by The Population Council. The author gratefully acknowledges the research assistance of Katherine Brown and Liliane Floge, and the computer programming assistance of Pi-Yu Ting.

REFERENCES

1. National Center for Health Statistics. *Vital Statistics of the United States, 1971.* Vol. I, *Natality.* Washington: U.S. Government Printing Office, 1975.
2. Vincent, C. E. *Unmarried Mothers.* New York: The Free Press, 1961.
3. Roberts, R. W., Ed. *The Unwed Mother.* New York: Harper and Row, 1966.
4. Furstenberg, F. F., Jr. "Birth Control among Pregnant Adolescents: The Process of Unplanned Parenthood." *Social Problems.* 19(2):192–203, 1971.
5. Rains, P. M. *Becoming an Unwed Mother.* Chicago: Aldine-Atherton, 1971.
6. Pakter, J., Rosner, H. J., Jacobziner, H., and Greenstein, F. "Out of Wedlock Births in New York City. I. Sociological Aspects." *Am. J. Public Health.* 51(5):683–696, 1961.
7. Stine, O. C., Rider, R. V., and Sweeney, E. "School Leaving Due to Pregnancy in an Urban Adolescent Population." *Am. J. Public Health.* 54(1):1–6, 1964.
8. Crumidy, P. M. and Jacobziner, H. "A Study of Unmarried Mothers Who Kept Their Babies." *Am. J. Public Health.* 56(8):1242–1251, 1966.
9. Sarrel, P. M. "The Young Unwed Primapara." *Am. J. Obstet. Gynecol.* 95(5):722–725, 1966.
10. Currie, J. B., Jekel, J. F., and Klerman, L. V. "Subsequent Pregnancies among Teenage Mothers Enrolled in a Special Program." *Am. J. Public Health.* 62(12):1606–1611, 1972.
11. Foltz, A., Klerman, L. V., and Jekel, J. F. "Pregnancy and Special Education: Who Stays in School?" *Am. J. Public Health.* 62(12):1612–1619, 1972.
12. Jekel, J. F., Klerman, L. V., and Bancroft, D. R. E. "Factors Assocated with Rapid Subsequent Pregnancies among School-age Mothers." *Am. J. Public Health.* 63(9):769–773, 1973.
13. Furstenberg, F. F., Jr. "Unplanned Parenthood: The Social Consequences of Teenage Childbearing." Final Report to Maternal and Child Health Service, 1975.
14. Vincent, C. E. "Unmarried Fathers and the Mores: 'Sexual exploiter' as an Ex Post Facto Label." *Am. Sociol. Rev.* 25:40–46, 1960.
15. Pannor, R., Massarik, F., and Evans, B. *The Unmarried Father.* New York: Springer, 1971.
16. Freedman, R. and Coombs, L. "Childspacing and Family Economic Position." *Am. Sociol. Rev.* 31(5):631–648, 1966.

17. Freedman, R. and Coombs, L. "Economic Considerations in Family Growth Decisions." *Popul. Stud. (London)* 20(2):197–222, 1966.
18. Monahan, T. P. "Premarital Pregnancy in the United States." *Eugen. Q.* 7(3):133–147, 1960.
19. Presser, H. B. "Early Motherhood: Ignorance or Bliss?" *Fam. Plann. Perspect.* 6(1):8–14, 1974.
20. Presser, H. B. Sex-Role Socialization for Motherhood. Paper presented at the Annual Meeting of the Population Association of America, New York, April 1974.
21. Board of Education of the City of New York. Special Circular No. 10 (1968–1969), 1968.
22. Presser, H. B. Female Employment and the First Birth. Paper presented at the Annual Meeting of the American Sociological Society, San Francisco, August 1975.
23. Presser, H. B. and Salsberg, L. "Public Assistance and Early Family Formation: Is There a Pronatalist Effect?" *Social Problems.* 23(2):226–241, 1975.

Chapter 11

The Social Consequences of Teenage Parenthood

Frank F. Furstenberg, Jr.
University of Pennsylvania

In recent years, there has been an upswing in social concern about early childbearing—that is, teenage parenthood has become less socially acceptable as it has become more publicly visible. Unfortunately, this surge of interest has not been matched by an expansion of information about the problem, or by the development of effective programs to help resolve it.

The widespread conviction that early childbearing precipitates a number of social and economic problems is founded, however, on surprisingly little evidence. Systematic research on the consequences of adolescent parenthood is virtually nonexistent. Nor is the narrow scope of existing studies on the consequences of adolescent parenthood their most serious shortcoming. The major defect is their failure to contrast the experiences of young mothers with those of their peers who avoid early parenthood. Moreover, most existing research on the careers of adolescent mothers has concentrated on the immediate postpartum experience, offering little or no information on the long-range impact of the pregnancy.

In this article, we describe some of the findings of a 6-year study of some 400 young adolescent mothers, their partners, progeny, and parents. We explore when, how, and why childbearing before the age of 18 jeopardizes the life prospects of the young mother and her child; and we compare the experiences of the young mothers to those of a peer group who managed to avoid premature parenthood.

THE BALTIMORE STUDY

Between 1966 and 1968, interviews were conducted with every adolescent under the age of 18 and never before pregnant who registered at the prenatal clinic of Baltimore's Sinai Hospital.[a] A total of 404 interviews were conducted. Interviews were also completed with 350 (87 percent) of the mothers of the pregnant teenagers.

Only two of the adolescent mothers indicated unwillingness to participate in the study. Our population consisted almost exclusively of women residing in low-income households. Since Sinai was easily accessible to the black community in northwest Baltimore and many blacks could not afford private medical care, the women in our study were predominantly black. However, the participants turned out not to be very different from the sample we might have expected had it been drawn from the entire population of pregnant adolescents who delivered a child in Baltimore during the period of the study.

The adolescent mothers were interviewed three times subsequently: 1 year after the child was born, again in 1970, and once again in 1972 when the child was about 5 years old.

Interviews were also attempted in 1970 with 301 of the former classmates of the adolescent mothers—women who had not become pregnant in early adolescence—in order to have a basis for assessing the impact of the very early pregnancy on the career of the young mother. We were able to contact more than 70 percent of the designated sample and to interview most of those whom we were able to locate. Only 7 percent of the classmates we located refused to participate in the study. The classmates were reinterviewed in 1972.

We also attempted to follow up all of the fathers who could be located. However, we managed to find only slightly more than half of the 260 men for whom we had some residential information. Interviews were completed for only 33 percent of the fathers,

---

[a]The study was originally conceived as a relatively short-term evaluation of the effectiveness of a special "comprehensive" program for pregnant teenagers as compared to the hospital's regular prenatal program. The pregnant teenagers were assigned on a random basis to either the special program or the regular clinic. Although there were some significant short-term differences in the two programs' effects on later fertility, the differences were largely attenuated after the first year, both because the special program was not geared to long-term assistance for the adolescent mothers and their children, and because the regular clinic program included many of the same services provided by the special program. Eventually, the study was broadened to become a 6-year longitudinal study of the consequences of adolescent parenthood. In this article, no distinction is made between the young mothers who attended the special and the regular prenatal clinics.

over half of whom were residing with the young mothers and their children when the interviews took place.

In addition, interviews were attempted with all the firstborn children of the adolescent mothers and with the classmates' children who were at least 42 months old in 1972. The attrition of the samples over the study period is summarized in table 11–1.

In the original sample of pregnant adolescents, only 13 percent were white. At the completion of the study, the sample was even more homogeneous: Only 9 percent of the women interviewed in the 5-year followup were white. The whites who remained in the sample, no doubt, were not representative of all white adolescent mothers or even of those who originally entered the prenatal clinics at Sinai.

Table 11–2 compares the family backgrounds of the young mothers and their former classmates. With the exception of the educational achievement of their parents, the two samples accorded rather well. Like the young mothers, the classmates came mostly from working- and lower-class homes. Before their first child was born, the young women who found their way into the study population could not have been easily differentiated from their peers who managed to avoid such an early pregnancy. Premarital pregnancies even during adolescence had occurred among many of the classmates as well. Nearly half (49 percent) of them acknowledged at Time 4 (six years after initiation of the study) one or more pregnancies before marriage; about half occurred during adolescence, and one in three happened before the classmates turned 18. Thus, comparisons between the classmates and young mothers probably slightly understate the impact of an early and unplanned pregnancy on the subsequent life course, because some of the classmates shared this experience with the young mothers. In the analysis that follows, we subdivide the classmates by their premarital pregnancy experience wherever this breakdown affects the reported findings.

BECOMING PREGNANT

Most theories about the etiology of out-of-wedlock pregnancy, while differing significantly in their particulars, rest on the assumption that the unwed mother becomes pregnant because she is motivated, consciously or unconsciously, to have a child outside of marriage.

An alternative, but equally plausible, assumption is that most women who become unwed mothers do not engage in sexual activity for the purpose of becoming pregnant, but rather are initially recruited into the ranks of unwed motherhood without possessing any advance commitment. The data collected from the adolescents

Table 11-1.—*Design of the Baltimore study, 1966 to 1972*

Interview schedule	Interview dates	Participants	Number of attempted interviews	Completed interviews[a]	
				Number	Percent
Time 1: during pregnancy	1966 to 1968	Adolescent mothers	404	404	100
		Grandmothers	379	350	92
Time 2: 1 year after delivery	1968 to 1970	Adolescent mothers	404	382	95
Time 3: 3 years after delivery	1970	Adolescent mothers	404	363	90
		Classmates	361	268	74
Time 4: 5 years after delivery[b]	1972	Adolescent mothers	404	331	82
		Children of adolescent mothers	331	306	92
		Classmates	307	221	82

[a] This category includes a small number of interviews that were excluded from the analysis because of a large amount of missing or falsified information.
[b] Interviews were also obtained with about one-third of the fathers at this time.

Table 11-2.—*Percent distribution*[a] *of adolescent mothers and classmates by selected characteristics, Baltimore, 1966 to 1972*

Characteristic	Adolescent mothers (N = 323)	Classmates (N = 221)
Age at Time 4[b]		
Less than 20	11	12
20	17	19
21	30	24
22	26	26
More than or equal to 23	15	19
Mean Age	21.2	21.1
Race at Time 4[b]		
Black	91	87
White	9	13
Living arrangements of unmarried adolescents at Time 1		
Lived with both parents	51	59
Lived with mother	38	32
Lived with father	3	2
Lived with neither parent	8	7
Education of mother when present in home at Time 1[c]		
High school graduate	22	45
Not high school graduate	78	55
Education of father when present in home at Time 1[c]		
High school graduate	17	41
Not high school graduate	83	59
Occupational status of parents		
One or both skilled	20	27
Mother working	60	66
Neither parent working	20	7
Welfare status during childhood[c]		
No	76	83
Yes	24	17
Marital status at Time 1[c]		
Single	81	98
Married	19	2

[a] Percent may not add up to 100 because of rounding.
[b] Five years after delivery.
[c] Information for adolescent parents was supplied at the first interview. The classmates reported the information at the second followup, 3 years after the adolescent mother's delivery.

in the Baltimore study afforded an opportunity to examine the process leading up to unplanned pregnancy.

All of the young mothers in our study had initiated sexual intercourse by their early or mid-teens. About half of their classmates were sexually active by age 16, and 77 percent were no longer virgins before they reached the age of 20. (The proportions sexually active in this predominantly black population were similar to those found among U.S. black teenagers of the same age by Kantner and Zelnik in the 1971 Johns Hopkins Study of Teenage Sexuality, Contraception and Pregnancy.[1]) It would appear, then, that in their sexual practices, the young mothers did not sharply diverge from their classmates or from the larger population of black adolescents.

Dating not only provided the adolescent with the opportunity, but often made it necessary for her to engage in sexual relations. Approximately one-fifth of the abstainers from sex compared to 6 percent of the nonvirgins did not date at all in early adolescence. Frequent dating over a long period of time is eventually accompanied by sexual intercourse, and few adolescents are able to remain sexually active for long before pregnancy occurs. We observed this pattern among the young mothers, who were unusually socially active at an early age. (At the time they conceived, nearly two-thirds of the adolescent mothers were going out at least several times a week.) Four out of five became pregnant within 2 years following the onset of intercourse, which typically occurred at age 15.[b] In addition to the likelihood that fecundity was low in this youthful population, a sporadic pattern of intercourse helped to reduce the probability of conception. Two-fifths of the young mothers indicated that they had had intercourse as frequently as once a week, and fewer than one-fifth had relations several times a week or more. These self-reports suggest an unsteady pattern of sexuality, and imply the lack of an advance commitment to becoming pregnant.[c]

Other studies have found that a majority of both adult and adolescent black women did not approve of premarital relations.[4-7] The data collected from our study were consistent with these findings. A substantial proportion of the pregnant adolescents and their parents disapproved of premarital sex. Nearly half of the

---

[b]This same pattern was evident among the classmates. They became sexually active several years later, but by age 20, half of those who had been sexually active in their teens had experienced a premarital pregnancy. Zelnik and Kantner reported almost identical figures. Nearly half of the black adolescents who had intercourse during their teens became pregnant before age 20. (See ref. 2.)

[c]The figures on sexual activity also correspond to the incidence reports collected by Zelnik and Kantner. The respondents in their sample had a very low frequency of sexual activity, too. (See ref. 3.)

mothers of the pregnant teenagers stated that they thought it was "very wrong" for a girl to have sexual relations before she married, and another quarter said they felt it was "somewhat wrong." The adolescents' views on premarital sex closely resembled those of their parents. Nearly half of the teenagers stated that it was very important for a woman to wait until marriage to have sex.

Undeniably, there was an obvious discrepancy between the words and the deeds of the respondents. Many of the parents and the youths were paying allegiance to a sexual code to which they were unable to adhere. This ambivalence made it especially difficult for these women to deal with the consequences of their sexual behavior.

Few of the adolescents in this population believed that they would or should marry before their early twenties. In the meantime, they were repeatedly provided with opportunities for sexual experience. While direct information on their boyfriends' views about premarital sex was not available, it is safe to assume that the men's views were considerably more permissive than those of the adolescent mothers. By age 14, two-thirds of the males were sexually active, and they reported more frequent and more varied sexual patterns than the females. It is not surprising, then, that when the pregnant teenagers were asked why a female begins to have sexual relations, the most common response was inability to successfully resist pressure from the male. It would be naive to believe the female is invariably the innocent and exploited victim of her boyfriend's dishonorable intentions. Nonetheless, under different circumstances, many women probably would wait at least until their late teens to begin having sexual relations. Only one-quarter of the adolescents thought that a female should have relations before age 18.

The young mothers invoked a number of justifications that permitted them to depart from their ideal norms. Seeing themselves as persuaded or coerced by their boyfriends was obviously one such rationalization. Another was the notion that "everyone else is doing it." (Indeed, this observation is nearly correct, and it is a testimony to the tenacity of ideal norms that they can survive at all in the face of widespread violation.) Another rationalization helped to offset the fear that negative consequences would result from sexual activity, namely, the belief, shared by most participants in our study, that they could avoid "getting caught." A number mentioned that they did not think it was possible to become pregnant "right away." Others thought that if they had sexual relations only "every once in a while," they would not become pregnant.[d] Finally, their behavior had a self-reinforcing quality.

[d]The study of Zelnik and Kantner documented in depressing detail the woefully inadequate knowledge of the reproductive process possessed by adolescents. In their

Because many were not yet fecund, as time went on they became increasingly convinced that they would not become pregnant. The longer they went without conceiving, the more likely they were to assume greater risks.

Fewer than one in four of the teenagers' mothers admitted that they had known that their daughters were having sexual relations prior to the pregnancy. As a check on whether the parents were misrecollecting their previous observations, those with other adolescent daughters residing in the home were asked if those children were sexually active. Only 16 percent of the parents suspected, or made a statement to the effect, that their nonpregnant teenage daughters were currently having sexual relations. Extrapolating from the figures provided by Kantner and Zelnik[8] on the incidence of sexual relations among teenagers, we found the mothers' estimates so low as to suggest that the parent has a certain stake in remaining misinformed. By so doing, she is able to preserve the fiction that her daughter is "staying out of trouble." This, in turn, releases her from the responsibility of having to take some action to prevent a pregnancy from occurring. Since most of the mothers did not know what measures to take even if they were aware of their child's sexual activity, they preferred to keep themselves uninformed.

So long as sexuality is safeguarded from public view, it poses little danger to either mother or daughter. Paradoxically, the techniques for concealment ultimately increase the risk of pregnancy. But it is important to recognize that from the point of view of the adolescent, using contraception may be extremely costly because it involves open acknowledgement of sexuality and thereby increases the threat of public exposure. Therefore, it was not surprising to find that prior to pregnancy, experience with birth control was quite limited.

BIRTH CONTROL KNOWLEDGE, EXPERIENCE

Most of the adolescents had some limited knowledge of birth control. Almost all were aware that drugs and devices to prevent conception existed; only 6 percent were unable to identify any method of birth control, and most were able to mention at least two or three techniques. This information, usually acquired from casual conversations with relatives and friends or through the mass media, was, however, extremely superficial. The young women

---

study, fewer than one-third of the respondents could correctly state the time of the month when the risk of pregnancy is greatest. It is a reasonable assumption that the young women in our sample would not have fared as well as the average adolescent in that national study. (See ref. 3.)

tended to be most aware of those forms of birth control to which they had least access and about which they had only limited practical knowledge. Over 80 percent mentioned the pill as a "method of keeping you from having babies," but only two women had ever used oral contraceptives. In both instances, the pills had been borrowed from their mothers.

Whatever practical knowledge and experience the adolescents had with birth control was confined largely to "getting the boy to use something." More than half of these respondents (37 percent of the total sample) had had some experience with condoms. As with the other methods, however, experience for the most part had been sporadic; only 15 percent of the women reported that condoms had been used more or less regularly when relations occurred. There are many reasons for such irregular use, but by far the most common (mentioned by 54 percent of the users) was that the boyfriend was either unprepared or unwilling most of the time.

PARENTAL HELP

The lower-class family is, if anything, even more puritanical and prudish about sexual matters than families with higher incomes.[9] Despite this, 59 percent of the mothers in our study had frequently attempted to talk to their daughters about sex, and 92 percent had had at least occasional discussions on the subject. It seems that most talks, however, involved the mother's admonishing her daughter not "to get mixed up with boys" or to do anything she would "be sorry for later."

Slightly more than 61 percent of the mothers and 45 percent of the daughters said that birth control had been explicitly discussed in the family. Quite clearly, however, most of the instruction was casual and oblique. Rarely were the adolescents told about effective contraceptive devices.

Even when the mothers did recognize the need for specific instruction, they could not offer much assistance. They were frequently poorly informed themselves, and at the time of the study in 1966, there was no place that a mother could send or take her teenage daughter for information. Thus, it is understandable that most mothers, if they provided instruction at all, were inclined to give only general advice and admonitions. Nevertheless, this limited instruction apparently had a definite impact. Fifty-two percent of the adolescents from families in which both the mother and daughter reported discussing birth control had had some experience with contraception, compared to 23 percent from families in which no guidance was given. Moreover, the young mothers' reports revealed that the specific content of the discussion had a decided effect on whether or not birth control was practiced. If the mother had counseled her daughter to use a specific method (typically, she urged her daughter to insist that the male use a condom), the adolescent was more likely to have had some birth control experience. However, when contraceptive instruction was extremely vague, its effect on the adolescent's behavior was hardly greater than that of no instruction.

Apparently, then, the family can and does play a part in transmitting expectations about birth control use. In addition to imparting specific information, parents may promote contraceptive use for quite another reason. In raising the issue of contraception, the mother reveals an explicit awareness that her daughter is or may be having sexual relations. The adolescent, in turn, is allowed to acknowledge her own sexuality and hence may regard sex less as a spontaneous and uncontrollable act and more as an activity subject to planning and regulation.

The nature of the teenage couple's relationship greatly influenced whether and how often birth control was used. The single most important factor was the extent of involvement between the adolescent and her sexual partner. Contraception was much more likely to be practiced by couples who had a stable romantic relationship. Indeed, of those women who were still "going with" the fathers of their unborn babies at the time of the initial interview, nearly twice as many had attempted contraception as those whose relationships had been broken off for one reason or another.

ATTITUDES TOWARD PREGNANCY

Only 9 percent of the sample said that they had deliberately failed to use contraception in order to get pregnant. It is perhaps not surprising, therefore, that pregnancies were greeted by most adolescents and their parents with astonishment. Three-quarters of the adults reported that they were "very surprised" to learn their daughters were pregnant. A large number of the adolescents related this same feeling of disbelief.

Usually a feeling of despair accompanied the initial reaction of astonishment. Only one adolescent in five indicated that she had been happy about becoming pregnant. And even these women qualified their responses by saying that they felt "kind of good" or "sort of happy" about getting pregnant. Another fifth of the sample reported mixed feelings about becoming pregnant or indicated that they had not been affected much one way or the other. Three-quarters of the expectant mothers said they wished they had not become pregnant, and three-fifths stated their first reactions in unambivalently negative terms. Half of them could not bring themselves to tell their parents of the pregnancy for several months. More often than not, the adolescents never actually told their parents; the mothers learned about it elsewhere or detected it on their own.

By the time of first interview, 70 percent of the teenage parents indicated that they were feeling less negative about the pregnancy than they had been initially. However, fewer than one-third described themselves as "very happy"—scarcely an indication that parenthood was preceded by a commitment. Virtually the only women in the sample who were unambivalently positive about impending parenthood were to be found among the 20 percent who had married by the time of the first interview. More than three times as many married as single women (51 percent versus 14 percent) classified their feelings as positive. It seems, then, that adolescents view pregnancy more favorably when it enhances, or at least does not diminish, their prospects for marriage. Yet even the married women retained many misgivings about becoming parents.

The classmate interviews conducted in 1970 provided some information on how unmarried, sexually active women in their late teens feel before conception about the possibility of having a child. In general, the sentiments of the sexually active classmates who had conceived corresponded to the retrospective reactions of the adolescent mothers at the initial interview. In each case, about two-thirds indicated that they had not wished to become pregnant.

Regardless of their feelings about becoming pregnant in the immediate future, few of the sexually active classmates at risk were using contraception on a regular basis. Although the interviews with the classmates were conducted in 1970, 3 years after the young mothers became pregnant, and the classmates accordingly were several years older than the young mothers had been at the time of the initial interviews, little had changed in the interim. Like the adolescent mothers, more than half (53 percent) of the classmates were leaving matters to chance; and many, no doubt, were soon to become premaritally pregnant. (By this time, more than two-thirds of the adolescent mothers were using contraception.)

GETTING MARRIED

Unwed motherhood is not the only possible consequence of premarital teenage pregnancy. Only one-third of premarital pregnancies to teenagers result in out-of-wedlock births; about half are terminated by induced or spontaneous abortion.[10-14]

Traditionally (although increasingly less so), marriage has been a popular solution to impending parenthood for the adolescent pregnant for the first time. We looked at the marriage patterns of the adolescent mothers who were interviewed at the 5-year follow-up interview in 1972. Only 3 percent had been married at the time of conception, but nearly 20 percent had wed by the time of their first visit to the prenatal clinic, and by delivery nearly one-quarter of the mothers were married (see figure 11–1). All but a few of these women had married the father of the child. By the 5-year followup, just 36 percent of the young mothers remained single.

Of those who married, more than one-third had done so by the time of delivery, three-fifths by the 1-year followup, and three-quarters within 2 years after delivery. These statistics underscore how significant the pregnancy was in determining the timing of matrimony, and strongly suggest that were it not for the birth, most of the marriages would not have taken place when they did.

The marriage patterns of the adolescent mothers and their classmates differed sharply. By age 18, only 21 percent of the classmates were married, as compared to 41 percent of the young mothers. The difference was sharper still for marriages that occurred among women not yet 18—30 percent versus 11 percent. Had the pregnancy not occurred, many fewer of the young mothers obviously would have married before the age of 18.

Premarital pregnancy was not a covert tactic used by the teenage mothers to bring about marriage. Most who married did so with obvious reluctance. Only one in three felt that the timing of her marriage corresponded with her wishes for the future. Fewer than one in three of those who were married by the 5-year followup had wed at the age they considered to be most desirable. At the 3-year followup, approximately two-thirds of those who were married claimed, in retrospect, that under normal circumstances they would have chosen to marry at a later age.

If most of the marriages that came about after conception were indeed forced, how can we explain the fact that some women succumbed to the pressure to marry while others resisted? The young mothers who had higher educational and career aims were more reluctant to jeopardize their plans by an early marriage. Indeed, only 10 percent of the most educationally ambitious students married before delivery, compared to 43 percent of the least ambitious, and a greater proportion were still single at the 5-year followup (47 percent versus 23 percent). Similarly, the women who married early were less able students, and by their own accounts did not perform well in the classroom. Two-fifths of the women who married before delivery characterized themselves as "poor" or "so-so" students. By comparison, only one-third of the young mothers who deferred marriage and one-quarter of those who never married described their academic abilities in such negative terms.

The marriage rate began to rise sharply as the young mothers reached their late teens. By this time, they had had a chance to complete their education and to gain some working experience. More important, the fathers were beginning to find steady employment, suggesting that the economic situation of the males was an important determinant in the decision to wed and in the timing of marriage.

Figure 11–1.—*Percent of adolescent mothers married**
by months from delivery, Baltimore, 1966-1972

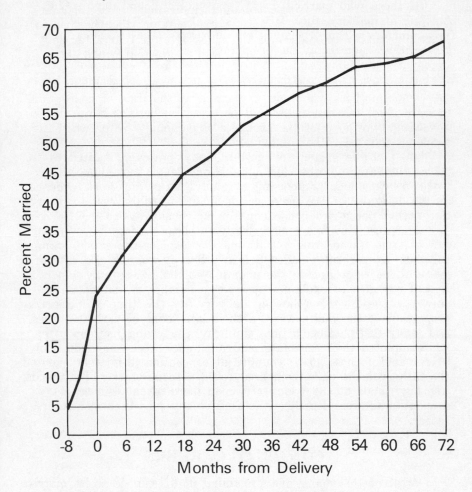

*Cumulative probability using life table procedure.

THE ECONOMICS OF MARRIAGE

Two-thirds of the single teenagers indicated during their pregnancy that there was at least a good chance that they would eventually marry the father of the child. Even a year after delivery, half of those women who were still single reaffirmed this intention.

These projected marriages took place among nearly half of the young mothers who were unmarried at the time of conception. Indeed, of all the marriages that occurred during the study period (involving two-thirds of the sample), 70 percent were between the teenager and the father of her child.

Most of the participants in our study, however, wanted to marry the father of the child only *if* and *when* they thought he would be capable of supporting a family. Although direct evidence on the attitudes of the male was lacking, his willingness to marry the mother perhaps depended on similar considerations.[15–18]

Marriage was much more likely to occur during the prenatal period if the father held a full-time job. Among the men working full-time, 34 percent married before delivery; whereas the rate of prenatal marriage among the unemployed males was only 4 percent. This helps to explain why a large number of marriages occurred in the 2 years following delivery. By this time, a higher proportion of the males were in their late teens or early twenties, and many had obtained a job; similarly, the young mothers often had completed their schooling, and a number were employed. Only 31 percent of those 15 or younger at conception ultimately married the father of the child, compared to 53 percent of the 17-year-olds. The boyfriends of the younger women more often were school dropouts and were less likely to find steady jobs than the other fathers.

CONJUGAL CAREERS

Most of the young mothers found it difficult to resist matrimony for very long. After a year or 2 of protracted courtship negotiations, many women simply decided that it was time to "give it a try." Although their chances for success were miniscule, it is not surprising that they were willing to assume the risks, given their problematic and often deteriorating economic situations.

Other studies have shown consistently that premarital pregnancy greatly increases the probability of eventual marital dissolution.[19–24] The mothers in this study proved no exception. Figure 11–2 shows the mortality of marriages entered into by the young mothers and their classmates. Among the former, marriages that took place during the study had less than an even chance of surviving beyond the first 4 years. About one-fifth of the marriages broke up within 1 year and nearly one-third were dissolved within 2 years. Three out of five of the marriages were destined to break up within 6 years.

By any standard, these rates are incredibly high. Carter and Glick[25] reported that in a population of white women married for at least 10 years by 1960, about 13 percent of the marriages had dissolved; the figure for nonwhites, 28 percent, was high, but still less than half that for teen mothers in our sample.

The rate of marital breakup among the classmates was only about half as great as the rate for the adolescent mothers during the first $3\frac{1}{2}$ years of marriage. After 2 years of marriage, the mothers had already experienced a higher proportion of marital dissolution (32 percent) than the classmates had after 4 years of marriage (30 percent). When the classmates who had married after conception were separated out, the differences were even more striking, as figure 11-2 shows. Among those who had not conceived premaritally, the probability of the marriage breaking up within the first 2 years was half that calculated for the adolescent mothers. Apparently, the mothers were especially disadvantaged in marriage because their pregnancies had occurred earlier in adolescence than those of the classmates, raising the possibility that marrying young in itself reduces conjugal stability.

RESOURCES AND MARITAL STABILITY

Almost all existing studies show that economic resources are strongly linked to marital stability. The willingness of black women to work at menial jobs that are poorly paid, dirty, and irregular creates a double problem in the family. The husband feels that his role as provider is being undercut; his wife, at the same time, is likely to resent his inability to support the family.

There is every reason to suspect that this situation was common within our sample. Most of the married men were young, inexperienced, and unskilled. More than one out of every four women explicitly attributed the failure of her marriage to her husband's inability to support his family. As a rough measure of their earning potential, we classified husbands as lower status if they had not completed high school and held an unskilled job. High school graduates and/or skilled workers were classified as higher status. This crude index turned out to be the single best predictor of marital stability. Among the lower status males, the probability of separation within two years of the wedding date was .45, while it was only .19 for the men classified as higher status.

This finding strongly suggests that the most important link in the chain between an unplanned pregnancy and later marital failure is the weak economic position of the male who fathers a child

Figure 11–2.—*Percent of adolescent mothers and classmates**
separated,+ by number of months from marriage date,
Baltimore, 1966-1972

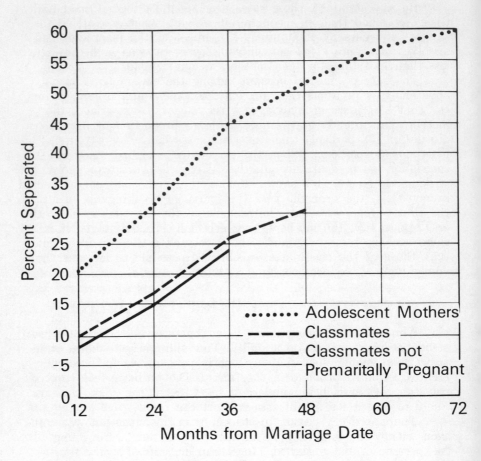

*Probability not reported when base <10.

†Cumulative probability using life table procedure.

out of wedlock or marries a single mother. Most of these men have a low earning potential before they ever wed. An ill-timed marriage may further limit their prospects for economic advancement by compelling them to terminate school and enter the labor force under less than favorable circumstances. Consequently, the fathers of unscheduled children are hard-pressed to find good jobs.

One way of putting this speculation to the test is to compare the economic status of the men who married the classmates with the spouses of the young mothers. There was a noticeable difference in status level between the two groups of men, especially after we separated out the couples who married following a premarital pregnancy. Half the husbands of the young mothers were in the higher socioeconomic category, as compared to three-fifths of the spouses of the premaritally pregnant classmates and 85 percent of the husbands of those classmates who married before becoming pregnant.

THE AFTERMATH OF MARITAL EXPERIENCE

Although our study spanned only 5 years in the lives of the young mothers, our data suggest that a substantial proportion of the separated women will be permanently disinclined to marry as a result of their first unsuccessful attempt. Only one-fifth of the women whose marriages were no longer intact at Time 4 were divorced, although over half had been separated for 2 or more years, providing ample time for a formal termination of the marriage. Most remained technically married even after 4 or more years of separation. The majority showed no inclination to divorce although they no longer considered their marriages to be binding.

The major reason for the low incidence of divorce among the sample, apparently, is that few of the young women had current plans to marry again. However, women like those in our study also face certain objective barriers to remarrying. Most of the adolescent mothers had at least two children by the time their marriages broke up, a situation which presents a formidable challenge to the earning power of potential mates. To add to her difficulties, the young mother usually has limited economic assets to contribute to a new marriage.

Ironically, most of the young mothers who managed to avoid single parenthood by marrying either before or shortly after delivery ended up as single parents several years later. And many of these women no doubt will never remarry. Therefore, it might be said that once an unplanned pregnancy occurs in adolescence, it hardly matters whether the young mother marries. In time, she may be almost as likely as the unwed mother to bear the major, if not the sole, responsibility for supporting her child.

FURTHER CHILDBEARING

Although some teenagers welcome a second child soon after the first, even when the initial pregnancy was unplanned, the second child more often represents a major setback to the future plans of the young mother, damaging especially her prospects of economic self-sufficiency. Existing evidence seems to support the prevailing belief that pregnancy in early adolescence signals the beginning of a rapid succession of unwanted births. Although estimates vary, depending on the experiences of the women following the first birth, most published studies show that at least one-half of teenage mothers experience a second pregnancy within 36 months of delivery.[26]

Explanations of why adolescent mothers often become pregnant again shortly after the birth of the first child have been based largely on speculation. Not surprisingly, the commentaries are reminiscent of the disputes over the etiology of unplanned parenthood. One school of writers argues that the high parity of teenage parents is consonant with their cultural aspirations and life-styles. They become pregnant again primarily because they want additional children.[27] Sharply diverging from this position are the researchers who contend that childbearing patterns reflect not parental aspirations but the availability of resources for controlling unwanted pregnancies. These authors assert that more family planning services would sharply reduce repeat pregnancies.[28]

FAMILY SIZE EXPECTATIONS AND BEHAVIOR

Nearly all of the first pregnancies to the mothers in our study were unplanned, and most were unwanted at the time conception occurred.[e] One year after delivery, the entire sample was asked when they planned to have their next child: Only 6 percent said they hoped to become pregnant again "soon"; at 3 years after delivery, only 7 percent said they were hoping to have another child at the time. Had the young mothers been successful in implementing their childbearing aims, the rate of second pregnancies during the study, particularly in its early years, would have been extremely low.

In fact, the gap between family size intention and experience was considerable. A year after the birth of the first child, almost 80 percent of the sample hoped to wait at least 2 more years before becoming pregnant again. Fewer than half of them managed to realize this goal. Not only did many women experience timing failures in the birth of their second child, but within 5

---

[e]Nine percent said that prior to the conception, they had not used contraception because they wanted to become pregnant. Twenty-three percent said that they had wished to become pregnant at "some time" when they engaged in sexual relations.

years after delivery, some women had already reached or exceeded
the total number of children they wanted to have ever, although
they were still in their early twenties. Asked at the time when
they would like to have their next child, more than one-quarter of
the young mothers declared "never."

Figure 11–3 shows that within 5 years of delivery of their
first child, 30 percent of the adolescent mothers had become pregnant again at least twice. (Within this subgroup, a substantial
proportion—10 percent of the entire sample—had had at least
three additional conceptions.) Thirty-seven percent of the respondents had one further pregnancy during the study period, and the
remaining third had not conceived again. As some indication of the
unacceptability of the repeat conceptions, the rate of abortion rose
sharply with increased parity, though most of the reported pregnancies came to term.

Table 11–3 presents a life table of the cumulative probability
of becoming pregnant a second and a third time. Nearly all of the
ever-married women were running well ahead of their desired family size schedules. Very few of the single women expressed a desire to have another child before marrying, yet most became pregnant again out of wedlock.

Within the total sample, nearly one woman in four became
pregnant again within 12 months of the birth of the first child.
By 3 years, half of the women with two children had become
pregnant a third time. Only one woman in five who had become
pregnant a second time within 3 years after delivery reported she
had been hoping for a second child; half stated that they had not

Table 11-3.—*Cumulative probability of subsequent pregnancies
among adolescent mothers, by marital status at Time 4 (1972)*

Month of exposure	Ever married	Never married	Total
Second pregnancy	(N = 199)	(N = 120)	(N = 319)
12	0.29	0.15	0.23
24	0.52	0.28	0.43
36	0.66	0.38	0.55
48	0.73	0.44	0.62
60	0.76	0.51	0.66
Third pregnancy	(N = 150)	(N = 55)	(N = 210)
12	0.26	0.32	0.27
24	0.41	0.35	0.39
36	0.52	0.47	0.47
48	0.60	0.40[a]	0.56

[a]Too few women for calculation of probability.

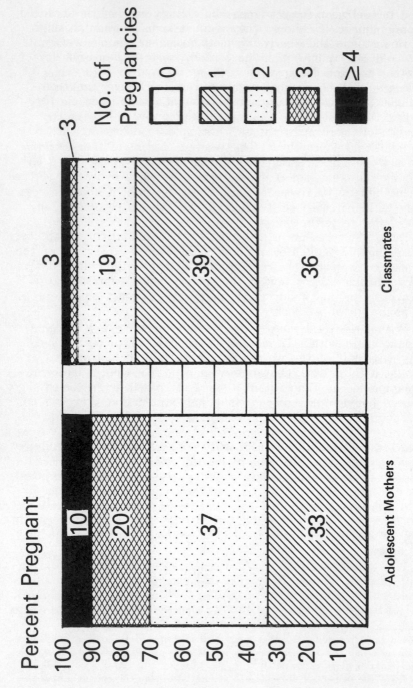

Figure 11-3.—Percent of adolescent mothers and classmates pregnant, by number of pregnancies in 1972

wanted to become pregnant again. Only 10 percent of those with three pregnancies had been planning to become pregnant a third time. In fact, most of the young mothers in our sample were not able to regulate their fertility to conform to their desires.

When the classmates were first interviewed in 1970, when they were about 19, nearly two-thirds had never been pregnant and almost all who had become pregnant had done so in the preceding 24 months. Two years later, slightly over half of the single classmates and four-fifths of those who were married had conceived at least once. Still they were well behind the adolescent mothers in number of pregnancies. By this time, two-thirds of the young mothers had had at least two pregnancies, and nearly one-third had had three or more. By contrast, only one-quarter of the classmates had become pregnant more than once, and only six percent had conceived three or more times. The young mothers who never married had, on the average, 1.09 more pregnancies than the single classmates; the difference among the marrieds was 0.66.[f]

EDUCATION AND CHILDBEARING PATTERNS

The women in our study most highly committed to education and those who returned to school immediately following the delivery of their first child were much less likely to experience a second conception in the 12-month period after the birth. Even after 4 years, the women who returned to school had lower rates of second pregnancy than those who did not.

Two-fifths of the women who quit school after their first child was born had at least two more pregnancies, while only one-quarter of the women who returned to school had an equally high rate of reconception. This was especially true for the unmarried.[g] Women may defer childbearing in order to attain their educational goals, but they may also discontinue their educations when they fail to prevent an unwanted pregnancy. Accordingly, we found (even holding educational ambition constant) that women remain in school (at least until graduation) if they are able to defer further childbearing.

It is often said that public assistance encourages childbearing out of wedlock because it provides a means of supporting additional children for unmarried women. The "broodsow myth," as Placek and Hendershot[29] so aptly labeled it, received no confirmation from

---

[f] Given equal fecundity, the classmates were somewhat more inclined to resort to abortion, although this tendency perhaps reflected the increased availability of abortion in the later years of the study.

[g] Half of the unmarried dropouts had at least two more conceptions during the study, as compared to only 11 percent of those who returned to school.

our data. The welfare mother was not significantly more likely to become pregnant again after she went on relief than the young mother who was not receiving public assistance. Among the single mothers, 42 percent of those on welfare 3 years following delivery became pregnant again within the next 2 years, as compared to 38 percent of the women who were not on relief. Among the ever-married women, the difference was somewhat larger, 50 percent versus 38 percent, but was still relatively trivial.

The similarity in fertility of the welfare and the nonwelfare groups suggests that there is no reason to single out the welfare mother as incapable of regulating her childbearing. She does about as well as her peers who are not on welfare.

BIRTH CONTROL EXPERIENCE

A substantial shift in knowledge and sentiments about contraception took place between the gestation period and the 1-year followup. A year after delivery, the adolescent mothers were much more likely to endorse birth control; they had fewer reservations about the effectiveness of contraception, and they were much more confident about the safety of birth control pills. The patterns of change had as much to do with general experience acquired during pregnancy as with participation in the prenatal clinics.

Initial use of birth control was high—88 percent of the young mothers practiced contraception during the year after their first child was born. Only two (four percent) of the nonusers reported that their abstention resulted from their desire to become pregnant again.

However, among those who began to practice contraception after the birth of their first child, more than one-third had abandoned birth control after 1 year; nearly two-thirds by 2 years. By the 5-year followup, only about one woman in five had used contraception continuously during the entire study. If those women who never used birth control are included, the figure drops still lower (see table 11-4).

Table 11-4.—*Cumulative probability of birth control continuation among adolescent mothers at Time 4 (1972)*

Month in clinic program	Total (N = 380)	Users only (N = 331)
12	0.56	0.64
24	0.33	0.38
36	0.25	0.29
48	0.20	0.24
60	0.19	0.22

All of the young women had attended one of the Sinai programs which offered contraceptive information and services. The
relatively low rate of contraceptive continuation after exposure to
the clinic programs is typical of the rates reported from family
planning programs for pregnant and postpartum adolescents
throughout the country.[26,30] Most participants discontinue contraceptive use after a short period. Typically, at least one woman in
three discontinues birth control within 1 year. The experience of
the young mothers in our study was consistent with these findings.

Overall, women who wed were much less likely to use birth
control at any given point in the study. Six months after delivery,
more than one-fifth of the ever-married women who had begun
using contraception stopped; one-tenth of the single women did
likewise. Close to half of the women who married during the study
had stopped using contraception by two years after delivery, while
more than three-quarters of the single women were still practicing
birth control. Therefore, the rate of continuation was about twice
as high for the women who remained single. It is little wonder
that the rates of pregnancy diverged so sharply in the two
populations.

Women with high educational goals and women who returned
to school were more likely to adopt some method of contraception
following delivery and to practice it more faithfully thereafter
than dropouts and women with low educational ambitions. However, even single women who returned to school or went to work
and explicitly expressed a desire not to become pregnant again
discontinued contraceptive use at a substantial rate. Three years
after delivery, more than half of these young mothers had stopped
using birth control.

REASONS FOR CONTRACEPTIVE TERMINATION

At each followup, the young mothers who had stopped using
contraception were asked why they had abandoned birth control.
As may be seen in table 11-5, it was rare for a young mother to
indicate that she had done so in order to become pregnant. Just as
uncommon was explicit expression of a casual or indifferent attitude toward the prospect of pregnancy. Even when combined, the
women in these two categories never constituted more than about
one-fifth of those who discontinued. Few women were deliberately
attempting to become pregnant again during the followup years.

As table 11-5 shows, only a small proportion stated that they
did not need to use birth control because they engaged in little or
no sexual activity. A few cited personal (mostly religious or moral)
reservations about contraception. But by far the most common
explanation for terminating use (reported by more than half of

Table 11-5.—*Percent distribution*[a] *of adolescent mothers reporting various reasons for discontinuation of contraception at Times 2, 3, and 4 (1968 to 1972)*

Reason	Time 2 (N = 96)	Time 3 (N = 137)	Time 4 (N = 76)
Desired pregnancy	6	9	15
Didn't care	16	7	8
Little or no sex	10	7	4
Personal reservations	4	8	8
Problem with method	51	58	55
Other	13	12	11

[a]Percents may not add to 100 because of rounding.

those who discontinued) was that specific problems had arisen with the method of contraception they were using. In some instances, women mentioned physical problems that they had encountered from the outset—a heavy menstrual flow, nausea, pain, or weight gain; but more often they referred to the fear of negative side effects—sterility, cancer, or thrombosis. From their comments, it is obvious that many had become frightened by reports in the mass media about the hazards of oral contraceptives or intrauterine devices.

Postpartum contact with the hospital was decidedly linked to contraceptive continuation. Discussions with the staff about how the birth control method was working out were especially critical for continued use. The number of discussions was related directly to the rate of continuation. Followup sessions provided an opportunity for the young mother to bring up problems she was having in using birth control, and gave her a chance to allay anxieties about physical reactions to the method of contraception. The discussions also reinforced the resolve to use birth control, countering the inclination to take risks. Many of the mothers needed this reinforcement in order to put up with the initial discomfort or inconvenience of using birth control methods.

After the first year, followup was very infrequent. It was up to the mothers to take the initiative in making contact. Few did, and those who continued to visit the clinic were a highly selective group consisting mainly of the single women who had remained in school. Consequently, this group had the highest rate of contraceptive continuation.

In view of the importance of followup, why did the clinics not make a greater effort to maintain contact with former participants? In the first place, the problem of maintaining commitment to birth control use was not foreseen by the individuals who designed the program. It was taken for granted that if the young mother wanted to prevent a subsequent pregnancy and was given contraceptive instruction, she would use birth control effectively until she was prepared to have another child. Her ability to use contraception was greatly overestimated, and the staff did not foresee the problems that arise when birth control is practiced by the inexperienced and wary. Finally, the program was designed to provide services in the prenatal and early postpartum periods, and it was not sufficiently flexible to extend services beyond the first year. Clearly, this "inoculation approach" did not work out very well.

EARLY PARENTHOOD AND SCHOOLING

Between one-half and two-thirds of all female dropouts cite pregnancy and/or marriage as the principal reason for leaving school.[31]

The policy of the U.S. Office of Education that every pregnant adolescent has a right to continue her education[32] has not as yet led to the creation of facilities and supportive services to ensure that right.[33] Opportunities for school-age parents vary enormously throughout the country. In some localities, teenagers are pressured to leave school as soon as it is known that they are pregnant, and no alternative education is provided. In other areas, special services are offered to the teenager who becomes pregnant, and she is encouraged to continue her education at home or in separate facilities for pregnant adolescents. Finally, an increasing number of school districts are permitting the expectant mother to attend regular classes.

While some educators justify their exclusion of pregnant teenagers on the ground that only special educational programs can meet their particular needs, relatively few programs of this nature exist. In 1967, there were 35 such programs throughout the country. By 1972, as a result of governmental efforts, the number had climbed to about 225, but these programs were serving only one out of five pregnant students.[h,34]

As may be seen in table 11-6, 5 years after delivery, the adolescent mothers in our sample were split almost evenly between women who had dropped out and those who had graduated from high school. Before terminating, nearly half of the dropouts had made some attempt to complete their schooling, and 16 percent of the nongraduates were still enrolled in school.

---

[h]There are no official estimates, but Shirley A. Nelson, director of the Consortium on Early Childbearing and Childrearing, estimates that by the beginning of 1975, there may have been 350 programs reaching one pregnant student in three.

Table 11-6.—*Percent distribution of adolescent mothers and of classmates premaritally pregnant (PMP) and not premaritally pregnant by educational achievement at Time 4 (1972)*

Education	Adolescent mothers (N = 323)	Classmates	
		PMP (N = 113)	Not PMP (N = 107)
Not high school graduate	51	18	11
Never returned	23	0	0
Returned, no longer in school	20	14	9
Returned, still in school	8	4	2
High school graduate	49	82	89
Never returned	7	0	0
Returned, no longer in school	33	65	62
Returned, still in school	9	17	27

It is obvious that pregnancy was not being used as a convenient excuse to drop out of school; 70 percent of the sample resumed school after delivery. It is equally apparent that teenage parenthood per se is not an insurmountable barrier to educational achievement; half of the sample completed high school, others were close to graduating at the 5-year followup, and a small minority had gone past high school.

Yet, against the young mothers' own educational goals, their achievements did not measure up quite so well. All but 10 adolescents reported that they hoped to complete high school, and nearly half looked forward to some type of higher education. While many conceded that in all likelihood these aspirations would not be realized, 84 percent still expected to complete high school, and over one-quarter anticipated finishing some higher education. A large number of the young mothers failed to reach their expected goals.

By contrast, 9 out of 10 of the classmates had completed high school by the time of the 5-year followup, and one-fifth of those who had not graduated were still in school. More than one-quarter of the classmates had obtained some amount of higher education. Perhaps it was merely coincidence, but after 5 years the classmates had achieved almost exactly the level of education that the young mothers in the initial interview had stated that they expected to reach by that time. This comparison indicates that the impact of pregnancy on educational achievement was substantial. On the average, the adolescent mothers had had approximately 2 fewer years of schooling than the classmates by the 5-year followup.

Our evidence consistently showed that the young mothers as a group were not conspicuously incompetent or disaffected students.

Three out of four were at the grade level appropriate to their age. The great majority reported that they enjoyed school, did moderately well, and wanted to return to school after delivery. Most did in fact return to school after their child was born. At the same time, ambition, academic performance, and family expectations all were highly predictive of whether the young mother remained in school until graduation. Most of those who did drop out had been marginal students before becoming pregnant, and probably some of them would have left school even if they had managed to avoid early parenthood. But nearly half of the dropouts were at least moderately able students and were unequivocally committed to obtaining a high school diploma.

If the first pregnancy disrupts the educational career of the young mother, additional childbearing generally brings it to an abrupt halt. With each successive pregnancy, the proportion of dropouts rose, and among those women who had three or more subsequent pregnancies, 85 percent had left school before obtaining a high school diploma. In contrast, only one-third of the young mothers who did not become pregnant again during the course of the study failed to complete high school. In most instances, multiparae managed to complete high school only if their schooling had ended before the birth of the second child.

ECONOMIC CAREER OF THE YOUNG MOTHER

The sterotype of the unwed mother as a welfare dependent serves to remind the public of the costs of a disorderly family career. Whether or not this sterotype is accurate is a separate issue. But to verify this assertion one must do more than show that a large number of women who are economically dependent have a history of premarital pregnancy.

At the 5-year followup, we asked the young mothers how much money they had received during the past year and where they had gotten it. One-quarter of the respondents had obtained most, if not all, of their income from working. Welfare barely edged out income from spouse as the second most common source of support.

Four types of support—self-support, welfare, husband's income, and economic partnership in marriage—encompassed all but about 4 percent of the women. Half the respondents were currently employed. About two-thirds of these women carried the major burden of supporting the family. In total, three out of five young mothers either were self-supporting or were nonworking women married to wage-earning males. These young mothers were clearly in an economically precarious position. Nearly half were living below the 1972 poverty level of $4,275 for a nonfarm family of four.

The classmates reported an almost identical number of income sources. However, they were more likely to be working (63 percent versus 48 percent) and were more often completely self-supporting if they worked. At the 5-year followup, only 15 percent of the classmates were receiving welfare payments, and only 5 percent depended completely on public assistance. This figure was just one-third as great as the proportion of adolescent mothers who obtained all of their income from welfare.

The dissimilarity between the groups became even more visible when we subdivided the classmates according to whether or not they had experienced a premarital pregnancy. While one-third of the young mothers were receiving at least one-fifth of their income from welfare, only 4 percent of the classmates who had not conceived premaritially relied at all on public assistance. Moreover, a much higher proportion of the classmates who had not had a prenuptial conception contributed substantially to their own support (70 percent versus 45 percent) through employment.

In addition, the median annual per capita income of the classmates who had not conceived before marriage ($1,000) was two-thirds greater than that of the young mothers ($600).

The young mothers divided evenly into those who worked and those on welfare. Almost two-thirds were on welfare at some time during our study. At the last followup, two-fifths of the women were receiving relief, so that 36 percent of the women who had had welfare experience were no longer on the rolls. Most of the women who were on welfare at the 5-year followup were not long-term recipients. Slightly more than one-half of this group had been on welfare for more than 12 months, and only one-third had been on welfare for 30 months.

Past work experience was not a shield against economic dependency when employment terminated. Five years after delivery, the young mothers who had been working at previous points in the study were just as likely to be on relief, if they did not then hold jobs, as were those who had no past employment record. Going on welfare is a specific response to unemployment, not a reflection of unwillingness to seek work; it is not motivation but jobs that are lacking. The vast majority of young mothers on assistance expressed an unequivocal desire to work if given the opportunity: 79 percent indicated that they would take a job immediately if offered one. Moreover, three-quarters indicated that they would be content to find an "unskilled" job, and very few expected to be hired for a job for which they were not then qualified. Almost two-thirds of the mothers on welfare stated that lack of child care facilities was the reason that they were unable to work.

Welfare mothers generally had large families and young children, a circumstance that decreased their ability to make use of child care options since it was difficult to arrange for care for several young children outside the home. Moreover, welfare mothers were less likely than working women to report that a relative in the home or nearby would be available if a job opened up. Most of the working mothers in our sample were able to call upon relatives to care for their children. Fewer than one-quarter had to resort to babysitters or day-care facilities. Since day-care arrangements are costly, it would seem that supportive kinship network is one of the critical factors in determining whether a young mother is forced to rely on welfare.

WORK PATTERNS

At the time of the first interview, only 5 percent of the adolescents were employed, and in most instances they held either part-time or irregular jobs. A year after delivery, one in four held a regular job. More than one-third were working by the 3-year followup, and at the last interview, just under one-half of the mothers were working—almost all (89 percent) of them full-time. About three-quarters of the women who were not employed at the 5-year followup were available for work. At that time, 43 percent of the young mothers who had not had an additional child had been employed steadily for the past 2 years, as compared to only about 10 percent of the multiparous women. Indeed, over half of the young mothers with at least two children had never worked during the five years of the study. Marital status was largely irrelevant to work patterns when childbearing was held constant.

Larger family size, of course, further complicates the already difficult problem of arranging for child care. The presence of a young child presents a further barrier to employment. Two-thirds of the women were working if they had no child younger than four. By contrast, only 20 percent of the mothers were employed when their youngest was not yet two. Having an additional child, however, regardless of his or her age, may deter employment. Since welfare benefits increase with each child, many women in our study found it impossible to locate a job that provided significantly more income than public assistance, especially if they lacked education and experience.

MANAGING MOTHERHOOD

From the three followup interviews and information from hospital records, we constructed a fairly complete history of mother-child separations. Formal separations were relatively rare, and in only a few cases were they permanent. Five years after delivery, just four of the young parents (one percent of the sample) had elected to give up their children for adoption. In addition to these cases, approximately 10 percent of the children were known to have lived apart from their mothers at one or more points during the study. At the time of the last interview, 21 children (6.8 percent of the 307 who were still alive) were not residing with their mothers.

A large number of mothers reported that another individual shared with them the responsibilities of caring for the child. Slightly fewer than half of the mothers said that they alone were the principal caretaker.

A single factor accounted almost completely for the pattern of caretaking that was established 5 years after the delivery. Only 5 percent of the women who were working reported that they were the principal caretaker; while nearly all (82 percent) of the nonworking mothers said that they took care of their children most of the time. The longer a woman had worked, the more likely she was to turn over child care responsibilities to someone else, particularly to a person who resided outside the home.

Most of the women who were not the principal caretaker managed to spend a good deal of time with their children. Our data indicate that the full-time mothers spent an average of only 10 hours a week more with their oldest child than did the mothers who shared child care with someone else. Once again, our findings appear to conflict with the argument that adolescent mothers prefer to entrust their maternal responsibilities to another person.

Relatively few of the young mothers could be classified by any standard as rejecting parents. Although most of the adolescents had negative reactions to becoming pregnant, 85 percent of them were rather content with motherhood after the child was born.

On the basis of our tentative results, it would be unreasonable to claim that adolescent mothers adjust to parenthood as easily as women who become pregnant when they are more mature. Our findings do, however, challenge the the assumption that early parenthood usually leads to childrearing problems.

PATERNAL INVOLVEMENT

More than three-fifths (63 percent) of the fathers were maintaining relations with their children at the five-year followup. While only one-fifth were actually living with their children, another fifth saw the children at least once a week, and the remaining fifth visited their children on an irregular basis.

A relatively high proportion of the couples who had never married maintained cordial relations—30 percent of the unmarried fathers who lived outside the home visited regularly. However, none of the children saw their fathers regularly, and only 7 percent had even occasional contact, if the mother had married a man other than the father.

Our data provide little support, however, for the contention that the absence of the father from the home adversely influences the mother's adaptation to parenthood. Neither marriage pattern nor paternal involvement was related to either maternal commitment or performance as reported in the 5-year followup interview.

SOCIAL POLICY AND THE TEENAGE PARENT

In our investigation we discovered a sharp and regular pattern of differences in the marital, childbearing, educational, and occupational careers of the adolescent mothers as compared to their classmates. The young mothers consistently experienced greater difficulty in realizing life plans; a gaping disparity existed between the goals they articulated in the first interview and their experiences following delivery. In contrast, we found that the classmates, especially those who did not become pregnant premaritally during the 5 years of our study, had a far better record of achieving their immediate objectives in life. The early pregnancy created a distinct set of problems for the adolescent parent that forced a redirection of her intended life course. In particular, we established a number of links connecting early childbearing to complications in marriage, to disruption of schooling, to economic problems and, to some extent, to problems in family size regulation and childrearing as well.

One of the most impressive findings was the diversity of responses to a common event. Although virtually all the participants in the study were low-income black females in their midteens who were premaritally pregnant for the first time, the outcome at the 5-year followup was enormously varied. Whether we look at their decision to wed, their marital stability, subsequent childbearing, work and welfare experience, or methods of childrearing, the young mothers were very dissimilar.

Some women had been able to repair the disorder created by an untimely pregnancy by hastily marrying the father of the child. When these marriages were successful, the situation of the young mothers closely resembled that of the former classmates who had delayed marriage and childbearing until their early twenties. Other young mothers developed innovative styles of coping with the problems caused by early parenthood. Rather than repair their family careers, they rearranged them, putting off marriage indefinitely and resuming their educations. When able to restrict further childbearing and make child care arrangements, these women often managed to achieve economic independence by the time the study ended. Still other participants were not so successful in coping

with the problems caused by precipitate parenthood. Their prospects of achieving a stable marriage were damaged by the early
pregnancy, and they were having great difficulty supporting a
family on their own. Poorly education, unskilled, often burdened by
several small children, many of these women at age 20 or 21 had
become resigned to a life of economic deprivation.

EXPLAINING DIVERGENT CAREERS

Every solution to adolescent parenthood has one element in
common: Each is an attempt to cope with the characteristic problems occasioned by early childbearing. Coping strategies, however,
simultaneously have the potential for problem producing and problem solving.

Nevertheless, some coping strategies typically work out better
than others. For example, young mothers who married the father
of their child, restricted their childbearing, and graduated from
high school generally were able to minimize the disruptive effects
of the unscheduled pregnancy.

Without question, the women who overcame many of the
problems created by an unplanned pregnancy were more capable
and committed than those who negotiated less successfully the
course of their later lives, but we must not fall into the trap of
concluding that the personal limitations of the young mothers explain why so many had difficulty in completing school, finding
rewarding employment, maintaining stable marriages, or restricting
childbearing. This reasoning is merely another version of what
might be designated the "fallacy of supermotivation." When they
possess "genuine" drive or a "real" desire to succeed, wom-
en/blacks/the blind/ex-cons/the mentally retarded are able to accomplish their goals. The socially advantaged need only be motivated; the disadvantaged must be supermotivated.

Almost all the young mothers in our study wanted to complete high school, but most were not so inspired to achieve educationally that they were prepared to remain in school whatever the
difficulties encountered or the sacrifices required. Similarly, with
few exceptions, the young mothers wished to avoid a rapid repeat
pregnancy, but few were so anxious not to conceive that they
continued to use birth control methods when events in their lives
made contraception difficult or frightening.

Even if all the participants in the study had been "supermotivated," most would nonetheless have experienced severe difficulties
in achieving their immediate life objectives. There was not a sufficient supply of highly eligible males to marry the young mothers;
caretakers and day-care facilities were not available to care for the
children of many of those who wished to return to school or enter
the labor market; and there was a shortage of stable and remu-

nerative jobs whose benefits equaled the income received from public assistance.

The few white women in our study, the adolescents from two-parent families, and the mothers in their late teens tended to be slightly favored when it came to marrying the father of the child, completing school, or obtaining work. However, these social attributes provided only a marginal advantage and seemed to have little more than a temporary influence on the life course of the adolescent mother.

SOCIAL PROGRAMS

The old saying that an ounce of prevention is worth a pound of cure may be hackneyed but it is also true. While the classmates who avoided an unplanned pregnancy were not necessarily destined to lead lives free of social and economic turmoil, their circumstances at the 5-year followup were clearly better than those of the young mothers. Yet there was, when we began this study, and still is today, a conspicuous lack of programs designed to reduce the pool of recruits to early parenthood. The general approach to social problems in American society is *reactive* rather than preventive. This posture might be understandable if preventive strategies were difficult to devise, but this excuse hardly seems to apply in the case of adolescent parenthood. We possess both the know-how and the techniques to reduce the incidence of early pregnancy and limit the number of adolescent mothers. Sex education, family planning programs, and abortion counseling and services, while imperfect strategies, can be effective preventive measures.

Despite some encouraging trends in recent years, one cannot help but be discouraged by the timidity of the approach toward prevention. Essentially, we still cling to the notion that provision of family planning services should be as cautious, unobtrusive, and inconspicuous as possible. Even though a clear majority of Americans favor birth control services for the sexually active teenager and endorse sex education in the schools, some institutional resistance and a great deal of institutional inertia have blocked the development of widespread and intensive sex education and family planning service programs for teenagers. Few populations are as potentially accessible to these services as are school-age youth. Yet school systems have been avoided, bypassed, and ignored as sites for pregnancy prevention programs.

In our discussion of the process of unplanned parenthood, we observed that potential recruits to early parenthood are reluctant to plan for sexuality or to take measure to avoid conception once they become sexually active; often they are tacitly encouraged to deny the possibility that their sexual actions may have negative consequences. Although a more open and accepting view of pre-

marital sexual behavior is developing in American society, vestiges
of the puritanical past persist. Family planners are still hesitant to
reach out aggressively to the population they purport to serve.

What we have said about the need for publicizing contraceptive information applies as well to abortion counseling and services.
Although many of the young mothers in our study were at least
equivocal in their attitudes toward abortion as a solution to an
unplanned pregnancy, they seemed poorly acquainted, even in the
1972 interview, with the specific procedures for arranging an abortion. Education about the alternatives to adolescent parenthood
must be part of any realistic prevention program. In order to
exercise these options, the teenager who becomes pregnant must
have easy access to counseling. Here again, the school is a potential site for pregnancy testing, counseling and referral programs,
and school health personnel should be trained for these purposes.

Perhaps the most prominent feature of existing intervention
programs is their crisis orientation. Most programs are designed to
supply emergency aid to help the young mother get through the
prenatal or early postpartum period. Such programs are based on
an ill-conceived notion that early parenthood is an affliction from
which one recovers in time. The young mothers in our study were
aided during pregnancy but abandoned when they became parents.
And they were by no means unique.[30] Most programs cease to
offer services at the point where many of the gravest problems
arise for the adolescent mother.

Educational, vocational, medical, or contraceptive programs are
certain to fail unless they continue to provide services for as long
as the need for services exists. In discussing the weakness of the
contraceptive program provided by Sinai Hospital, we made reference to the ideology of inoculation. Most programs for the adolescent parent are based on the premise that short-term assistance
will have a long-term impact. We discovered that short-term services produce short-term effects.

If we are to have any hope of influencing the career directions of adolescent parents, it is not enough to be present when
plans are formed at important junctures in the life course; we
must be available to ensure that these aims are implemented. Career plans are not binding contracts; they are subject to constant
renegotiation as new considerations arise. It is far less critical to
convince the young mother to stay in school, to use contraception,
or to look for a job than it is to help her realize these objectives.
As the young mother encounters unforeseen obstacles, it may be
necessary or convenient for her to reevaluate her initial goals. The
formerly firm decision not to have a second child may weaken
when she enters a new relationship, loses her job, or merely has
difficulty practicing contraception. It is not simply that commitments lose strength over time, but that people's ability to act on

their commitments may vary as circumstances in their lives change. Accordingly, unless programs for the adolescent mother extend past the early postpartum period, they are bound to have disappointing results.

Regretably, the delivery of services often is geared more to the convenience of the professional than to the needs of the client. For example, the trend toward specialization among professionals has led to a high degree of fragmentation in service programs. While there has been some encouraging movement toward the creation of comprehensive programs for the adolescent parent, the fact remains that segmentation of services continues to be more the rule than the exception. Educational programs typically do not offer day-care facilities, contraceptive clinics, job counseling, and employment placement, or pediatric and medical care. At best, several forms of assistance are provided under one roof, and weak ties are formed with agencies that can provide supplementary services.

One solution to the problem of service fragmentation is to make the assistance program mobile, as has been done with some family planning clinics. If these programs do remain stationary, then at least transportation should be provided for schools or day-care centers to them.

There can be little doubt from our results that the fate of the young mother and her child hinges partly on the situation of the child's father. If existing services do not actively discourage his participation, they provide few incentives to attract him. Practitioners are continually amazed by the interest unwed fathers show in their children. If programs were predicated on that interest, they might witness more of it.

Even worse than the fragmentation of services is the paucity of aid provided by programs for the teenage parent. We can point to few programs that come close to reaching a majority of the population in need of services, and those that do usually offer only token assistance. Educational programs reach, at most, one-third of school-age mothers. Family planning progams for teenage mothers are broader based, but have only brief contact with participants; their influence is usually temporary. The two services most needed, day-care facilities and job placement programs, are in short supply.

Without greatly expanding the scope of services, we are not likely to counter successfully the adverse effects of early parenthood. In particular, we cannot expect to modify the life course of the adolescent parent without providing substantial economic assistance, preferably in the form of stable employment for one or both parents; child care in order to permit parental educational and economic participation; and family planning services to prevent additional unplanned pregnancies.

Early parenthood destroys the prospect of a successful economic and family career not because most young parents are determined to deviate from accepted avenues of success or because they are indifferent to, or unaware of, the costs of early parenthood. The principal reason that so many young mothers encounter problems is that they lack the resources to repair the damage done by a poorly timed birth.

What would happen if service programs made it easy, not difficult, for women to restore order in their lives following an unplanned pregnancy? Let us imagine that there were truly comprehensive and extended services for young parents and their children. Suppose, for example, that family planning programs to prevent unplanned pregnancies and to counsel women who did have unwanted conceptions were established in the schools. Suppose that a woman who elected to bring her pregnancy to term would be granted a child care allowance to purchase day-care services or to pay a relative or friend to care for her child while she completed her education or entered the labor force. And whether or not she remained in school, took a job, or assumed full-time child care responsibilities, the young mother would receive an income sufficient to meet the needs of her family. Furthermore, suppose the father were invited to join special educational or job-training programs or were provided with a steady job. Our results indicate that under conditions of economic security, most fathers would contribute to the support of the family and willingly maintain a relationship with their children.

If the limited family planning program such as the one offered to the participants in our study had a modest degree of success, consider the possible effects of a more extensive service that maintained regular contact with participants over a period of years. While we cannot assume that such a program would completely eliminate unwanted conceptions, we can feel certain that a clinic that made more vigorous efforts to anticipate problems before they occurred, that reached out to participants when they encountered difficulties in using contraception, and that was prepared to establish a long-standing relationship with its clients would help to reduce drastically the number of unplanned births.

Providing easy access to social resources means that such resources will be used more readily. When services are difficult to utilize, they assist primarily the relatively privileged and the supermotivated. The privileged are in the best position to use them; the supermotivated are able to overcome barriers that normally discourage use. Making programs easy to use inevitably means that personal advantage plays a lesser part in determining who benefits from the provision of services.

ACKNOWLEDGMENTS

This chapter is adapted from an article that appeared in *Family Planning Perspectives,* 8(4):148–164, 1976.

REFERENCES

1. Kantner, J. F. and Zelnik, M. "Sexual Experience of Young Unmarried Women in the United States." *Fam. Plann. Perspect.* 4(4):9, 1972.
2. Zelnik, M. and Kantner, J. F. "The Resolution of Teenage First Pregnancy." *Fam. Plann. Perspect.* 6:74, 1974.
3. Zelnik, M. and Kantner, J. F. "Sexuality, Contraception and Pregnancy among Unwed Females in the United States." *In* C.F. Westoff and R. Parke, Jr., Eds., Commission on Population Growth and the American Future, *Demographic and Social Aspects of Population Growth,* Vol. 1. Washington: U.S. Government Printing Office, 1972.
4. Reiss, I. L. *The Social Context of Premarital Sexual Permissiveness.* New York: Holt, Rinehart and Winston, 1967.
5. Rainwater, L. *Behind Ghetto Walls.* Chicago: Aldine, 1970.
6. Rodman, H.: "The Lower-Class Value Stretch." *Social Forces.* 42:205, 1963.
7. Bowerman, C. E., et al. *Unwed Motherhood: Personal and Social Consequences.* Chapel Hill: University of North Carolina Press, 1966.
8. Kantner, J. F. and Zelnik, M. "Contraception and Pregnancy: Experience of Young Unmarried Women in the United States." *Fam. Plann. Perspect.* 5:21, 1973.
9. Rainwater, L. *Family Design: Marital Sexuality, Family Size and Contraception.* Chicago: Aldine, 1965.
10. National Center for Health Statistics. "Advance Report: Final Natality Statistics, 1974." *Monthly Vital Statistics Report.* Vol. 24, No. 2, Suppl. 2, 1976.
11. Weinstock, E., Tietze, C., Jaffe, F. S., and Dryfoos, J. G. "Abortion Need and Services in the United States, 1974–1975." *Fam. Plann. Perspect.* 8:58, 1976.
12. Center for Disease Control. *Abortion Surveillance, Annual Summary, 1974.* Atlanta: HEW, 1976.
13. National Center for Health Statistics. 1972 U. S. National Natality Survey. Unpublished data from P. Placek.
14. Tietze, C. and Bongaarts, J. Personal communication.
15. Pope, H. "Negro-White Differences in Decisions Regarding Illegitimate Children." *J. Marr. Fam.* 31:756, 1969.
16. Liebow, E. *Talley's Corner.* Boston: Little, Brown, 1967.
17. Schulz, D. A. *Coming Up Black: Patterns of Ghetto Socialization.* Englewood Cliffs: Prentice-Hall, 1967.

18. Staples, R., Ed. *The Black Family: Essays and Studies.*
    Belmont, Calif.: Wadsworth, 1971.
19. Christensen, H. T. "New Approaches in Family Research."
    Marr. Fam. Liv. 20:38, 1963.
20. Christensen, H. T. "Cultural Relativism and Premarital Sex
    Norms." *Am. Sociol. Rev.* 25:31, 1969.
21. Christensen, H. T. "Timing of First Pregnancy as a Factor in
    Divorce." *Eugen. Q.* 10(1):119, 1963.
22. Monahan, T. P. "Premarital Pregnancy in the United States."
    Eugen. Q. 7(3):140, 1960.
23. Lowrie, S. H. "Early Marriage: Premarital Pregnancy and As-
    sociated Factors." *J. Marr. Fam.* 27:49, 1965.
24. Coombs, L. C. and Zumeta, Z. "Correlates of Marital Dissolu-
    tion in a Prospective Fertility Study: A Research Note." *Social
    Probl.* 18:92, 1970.
25. Carter, H. and Glick, P. C. *Marriage and Divorce: A Social and
    Economic Study.* Cambridge: Harvard University Press, 1970.
26. Ricketts, S. A. *Contraceptive Use Among Teenage Mothers:
    Evaluation of a Family Planning Program.* Ph.D. dissertation,
    University of Pennsylvania, 1973.
27. Lewis, O. *The Study of Slum Culture: Background for La
    Vida.* New York: Random House, 1968.
28. Jaffe, F. S. and Polgar, S. "Family Planning and Public Policy:
    Is the Culture of Poverty a New Cop-out?" *J. Marr. Fam.*
    30:228, 1968.
29. Placek, P. J. and Hendershot, G. E. "Social Welfare and Public
    Planning: An Empirical Study of the 'Brood Sow' Myth." *So-
    cial Probl.* 21:658, 1974.
30. Klerman, L. V. and Jekel, J. F. *School-Age Mothers: Problems,
    Programs, and Policy.* Hamden: Linnet, 1973.
31. Coombs, J. and Cooley, W. W. "Dropouts: In High School and
    after School." *Am. Educ. Res. J.* 5:343, 1968.
32. Marland, S. P., Jr. "U.S. Commissioner of Education's State-
    ment on Comprehensive Programs for School-Age Parents."
    Sharing. March 1972.
33. Children's Defense Fund. *Children Out of School in America.*
    Cambridge: Children's Defense Fund, 1974.
34. Howard, M. *Multi-Service Programs for Pregnant School Girls.*
    Washington: Children's Bureau, 1968.

DISCUSSION

The following people were the major participants in the discussion: H. David, A. Rossi, and F. Furstenberg. The discussion
was short because of lack of time. Much of it centered around
questions concerning Furstenberg's findings and research methods.

A question was raised about the later adverse consequences of an out-of-marriage pregnancy on a teenage girl's life. An article by A. Campbell[1] states that when a girl had an early illegitimate birth, 90 percent of her life script was written. The figure, however, might more appropriately be 50 percent for the young people Furstenberg studied. Furstenberg believes their lives are so adversely affected by poverty and racism, that it is difficult to discover how much an early birth adds to their problems. Highly motivated, well-organized young women can overcome the possible negative effects of an early birth, Furstenberg's data reveal. Many return to high school and graduate, especially if they get child care help from their families. Problems in finding employment are probably more a function of the labor market than the individual characteristics of the young women.

In Furstenberg's study, the classmates of the very young adolescent mothers finished high school and had children somewhat later in life. It is a possibility that the classmates were affected by the fact that their mothers, on the average, had more education. The occupational status of the parents of the two groups appeared to be the same, however. Precise income data for the two sets of families appear to be lacking. Moreover, it is too early to tell what the long-range effects of early childbearing might be on the young people in Furstenberg's study.

In response to a question, Furstenberg said that he had been unable to get information from school records about the educational achievement of his respondents. Some of his respondents attended regular high schools. Some attended a special school for pregnant teenage girls. The effects of this latter school appeared to be fairly minimal when compared with the regular school. It seemed to be important for girls to continue in school during most of their pregnancy. They were more likely to return to school if they did that.

A number of young mothers thought motherhood had made them more mature and responsible. Interviewers also made these observations. Early childbearing, a few discussants remarked, need not be thought as always having negative effects. A pregnancy delayed long past the prime years of childbearing is an instance of a contrasting adverse consequence.

In discussing the effects of adolescent childbearing on the children of these adolescent mothers, Furstenberg said the measured level of cognitive development of the children was lower than that of a control group. These differences may well have been a result of the fact that all members of the control group were in a preschool, and their parents were of higher socioeconomic status. It was suggested that Furstenberg look at this data in terms of whether children who were in two-adult families (mother plus father or mother plus grandparent) had higher levels of cognitive development than children in one-adult families. Furstenberg said this was an excellent idea.

In discussing the lack of tested social adjustment differences between the children of the young adolescent mothers and those of the classmates, Furstenberg and others pointed out that comparisons were being made of children whose mothers were not greatly different in age and the measurements of social adjustment were poor (no adequate measures of this variable seem to exist for young children). It is difficult to tell what the long-range effects on social adjustment might be. Attempts to relate early behavioral traits to later ones (as at age 10 or later) are extremely difficult. Many intervening variables occur in the child's life during the developmental years. Possible adverse social and psychological consequences of early childbearing might well be reversed if adequate supports were given to young parents and their children, Furstenberg remarked.

Asked about the role of fathers in his study, Furstenberg replied that he had made many efforts to reach fathers. Nearly all of the young mothers eagerly agreed to have the fathers interviewed, but only half of the fathers could be reached for study. The majority of the fathers, though, were giving some assistance to the young mothers. About one-third of the couples married. Of the unmarried fathers, 20 percent were living in the home; another 20 percent were in frequent contact with the mother, and most of the remaining fathers were in occasional contact.

GENERAL DISCUSSION

This discussion of Furstenberg's paper was followed by reports by A. Campbell, W. Baldwin, and C. Chilman that summarized the major points made in the conference. Following these summaries, there was further general discussion.

Dr. Hill questioned earlier statements that marriage seemed to be increasingly irrelevant as a way of life. He felt that recent trends in lower marriage rates among young people might be a temporary phenomenon. These rates might represent deferred marriage rather than failure to marry. He suggested a historical review of marriage patterns over the generations in the United States and in other countries.

Dr. David pleaded for a broader look at adolescent sexual behaviors in all countries. For instance, data show that rates of early premarital intercourse have risen in European countries as well as in the United States. The age at first intercourse is decreasing in Europe; the general trend is to have premarital sex relations with relatively few people in, at least, serially monogamous relationships. Sex partners frequently marry each other as they get older.

David also commented that, in comparison with Eastern Europe, the abortion rate for single teenagers in the United States is remarkably high. Moreover, an increasing number of teenagers in the United States wait until the second trimester to obtain an abortion. Although some people have hypothesized that second trimester abortions would be more psychologically traumatic for adolescents than older women, available evidence suggests this is not the case. In general, not enough evidence to assess the long-range psychological effects of abortion exists.

A number of people emphasized the importance of recognizing the heterogeneous nature of the adolescent population of the United States and to study the consequences of adolescent childbearing for such groups.

Mr. Jaffe asked for the policy implications of the conference. He suggested the group go on record as supporting social policies aimed at the prevention of adolescent childbearing as well as supporting services for adolescent mothers and their children.

This suggestion was followed by a heated discussion by the participants. Some thought that the conference had been called to identify areas of needed research and research priorities, rather than to support policy statements. Others thought that, based on their research, social and behavioral scientists ought to define and support policies. In response to this point, a number of participants said that no evidence exists to state that adolescent childbearing has adverse consequences and that it should be prevented. Others thought that, although this might be true, the evidence did show that most teenagers who became pregnant did not want the child at that time. Therefore, the conference should support services that maximized freedom of choice about childbearing. It was suggested that this freedom be supplemented by counseling services that help teenagers make informed choices about childbearing.

The group appeared unable, or unwilling, to reach a consensus regarding a policy statement, although there seemed to be general support for policies that provided services that offered the widest freedom of choice and assistance to adolescent parents and their children. One person raised a question about public reactions to freedom of choice decisions when the results of this freedom often places a burden on society.

The lateness of the hour, the early departure of the Chairperson (Dr. Westoff), and questions as to the research goals of the conference seemed to preclude the reaching of a firm group decision regarding the advisability or inadvisability of a policy statement at that time. The majority seemed to agree that, at present, research evidence was inconclusive about the consequences of early childbearing per se. It is difficult to disentangle causes from consequences. Moreover, the consequences seem to be different for different people.

Some made a plea for research directed toward program evaluation of varying models of services, such as sex education, contraception, abortion, and prenatal and postnatal programs for unmarried parents and their children. Mr. Campbell pointed out that program evaluation was not in the domain of the Center for Population Research of NICHD. Responsibility for these kinds of studies had been assigned to other parts of the Department of Health, Education, and Welfare.

REFERENCES

1. Campbell, A. A. " The Role of Family Planning in the Reduction of Poverty." *J. Marr. Fam.* 30:236–245, 1968.

Chapter 12
A Theory of Teenage
Pregnancy in the United States

Kingsley Davis
University of Southern California

Fundamentally, the problem of teenage pregnancy is that in industrial societies the teenager is not a full adult and, consequently, not ready to undertake the grave responsibility of creating and rearing a human being. He is, of course, an adult from the standpoint of reproductive biology, a circumstance that creates the problem in the first place, but not from the sociologic, legal, and economic points of view. Ironically, as the age of biological adulthood has fallen (as seen in the younger age at menarche), the age of social adulthood has, for several reasons, become older. Not only does an advanced technology demand more skills and hence more training than an agrarian society, but alternative careers multiply and the information necessary to decide among them becomes more voluminous. Further, affluent societies can afford the luxury of a longer childhood, and as the life-span lengthens, the individual has less reason to foreshorten his youth. Of course, the incompatibility between organic and social adulthood is not the same throughout the teen years, because at puberty the maturation process moves swiftly. A boy of 15 is less ready for fatherhood than one of 19. But the community even tries to guide individuals aged 18 and 19 to protect them from fateful mistakes.

Because of their immaturity, childbearing by teenagers often has unfortunate consequences, not only for the girl, but also for the boy or man involved, the child that may be born, and others who are inevitably drawn into the situation or who indirectly must share the costs. Without doubt, some of the consequences come from factors *connected* with teenage pregnancy rather than from the pregnancy per se. Public policies, for example, influence the outcome, as do social developments not thought of as related to childbearing. It is therefore desirable, in studying both the consequences and the causes of adolescent childbearing, to view the subject broadly. In doing so, however, it is imperative that the criterion of relevance—teenage reproduction itself—be kept in view. For clarity's sake, anything else must be dealt with only insofar as it can be shown to be relevant to this topic. For instance, teenage sexual behavior, which is often dealt with at length under the heading of teenage pregnancy, is not itself at issue because it can vary independently of pregnancy. Intercourse, although a necessary element in pregnancy, is not in itself the crux of the problem. If this is granted, then sex education—depending on what is included under that rubric—often proposed as a "solution" to the problem of teenage pregnancy, may be no solution at all.

The costs of adolescent childbearing are both qualitative and quantitative. If only one girl in the United States becomes pregnant at age 14, that is too many. The fact that many girls have this happen to them magnifies the problem but does not create it. Nevertheless, the magnification is of great importance. To measure the problem quantitatively, one can use different gauges. Some of these gauges, such as pregnancy rates, are difficult to use because of deficient data. Others, with more data, are more feasible. If we look at births rather than pregnancies, the ratio of teenage births to all births in the Nation shows how much we depend on teenagers for population replacement. On the other hand, the ratio of teenage births to teenagers (the teenage birth rate), compared to the ratio for adults, shows how reproduction is figuring in the lives of teenagers compared to adults. Comparison of these measures at different periods and in different countries should prove instructive.

THE UNITED STATES DATA

The Number of Births to Teenage Mothers

For selected years, the absolute number of births to teenage girls in the United States is shown in table 12–1.[1,2] These figures reveal that the Nation is faced with an enormous problem. In 1977, there were 11,455 births to girls aged 14 or younger; 30,956 to 15-year-old girls; 70,050 to 16-year-old girls; and 112,782 to 17-year-old girls. Obviously, in most of these cases the baby was conceived when the girl was a year younger. Even the oldest teenage mothers (those who conceived their babies mostly at age 18) are too young to appreciate fully the responsibilities of parenthood. Evidence for this view is provided by figures on prenatal care (table 12–2).[2]

Table 12-1.—*Number of births that occur to teenagers in the United States*

Selected years	Number of births
1950	425,221
1957	557,593
1960	593,746
1965	590,662
1970	656,460
1974	607,978
1975	594,880
1976	558,744
1977	559,154

Source: References 1 and 2.

Table 12-2.—*Percent of mothers with no pre-natal care up to and through the 6th month of pregnancy, 1977*

Age of mother	Percent
Under 15	27.9
15 to 17	17.7
18 to 19	13.9
20 to 24	9.4
25 to 29	6.9

Source: Reference 2.

The Proportion of All Births Contributed by Teenagers

As the first column in table 12-3[1-4] shows, for more than 20 years (1952 to 1973), the teenage proportion of all births in the United States rose. After 1973, the proportion turned down again, especially for males. The turn-down was evidently due to the fact that in 1973, the number of adolescents in the population was at a peak because of the postwar baby boom, which reached its zenith around 1957.

Table 12-3 demonstrates that the proportion of teenage births is much higher among nonwhites. The rising trend, however, has been greater among whites. In the 1940's the teenage proportion of births was twice as high among nonwhites as among whites,

Table 12-3.—*Proportion of U.S. births occurring to teenagers, by race 1940-1977*

Year	Percent of births, all races		Percent of births, white population		Percent of births, nonwhite population	
	Teenage girls	Teenage boys	Teenage girls	Teenage boys	Teenage girls	Teenage boys
1940	12.9	1.8	11.2	NA	25.1	NA
1941	12.8	NA[a]	11.0	NA	25.3	NA
1942	12.3	NA	10.6	NA	25.2	NA
1943	11.8	NA	10.2	NA	24.5	NA
1944	10.9	NA	9.3	NA	22.6	NA
1945	10.4	NA	8.8	NA	22.2	NA
1946	9.9	2.1	8.5	1.7	21.0	5.6
1947	11.7	NA	10.3	NA	22.4	NA
1948	12.4	NA	10.9	NA	22.4	NA
1949	12.3	NA	10.8	NA	22.0	NA
1950	12.0	2.1	10.5	1.7	21.3	4.3
1951	12.0	NA	10.6	NA	20.8	NA
1952	11.5	NA	10.2	NA	20.1	NA
1953	11.8	NA	10.5	NA	19.9	NA
1954	12.1	NA	10.8	NA	19.9	NA
1955	12.1	2.7	10.8	2.4	19.6	4.5
1956	12.7	NA	11.4	NA	19.7	NA
1957	13.1	NA	11.9	NA	19.9	NA
1958	13.4	NA	12.2	NA	19.9	NA
1959	13.6	NA	12.5	NA	20.1	NA
1960	13.9	3.3	12.8	3.0	20.3	5.0
1961	14.3	NA	13.2	NA	20.2	NA
1962	14.6	NA	13.6	NA	20.6	NA
1963	14.5	NA	13.4	NA	21.2	NA
1964	14.7	NA	13.3	NA	22.2	NA
1965	15.9	4.5	14.3	4.0	23.9	7.0
1966	17.5	NA	15.6	NA	26.4	NA
1967	17.2	NA	15.0	NA	27.9	NA
1968	17.2	NA	14.8	NA	29.0	NA
1969	17.1	NA	14.6	NA	29.2	NA
1970	17.6	6.6	15.1	5.6	29.4	11.3
1971	18.0	6.6	15.4	5.7	29.6	11.1
1972	19.3	7.3	16.5	6.2	31.5	12.0
1973	19.7	7.4	16.8	6.3	31.9	12.2
1974	19.2	7.3	16.3	6.2	31.3	11.9
1975	18.9	5.7	16.3	5.4	30.3	NA
1976	18.0	5.2	15.5	4.9	28.7	NA
1977	17.2	5.5	14.7	4.6	27.3	NA

[a]Not available.

Source: References 1 to 4.

but by 1977 the proportion, for women, was only 59 percent higher. Because of the substantial percentage of births for which age-of-father is not given, the columns for males in table 12–3 are probably not accurate. For instance, in 1977 for the white population, 6.3 percent of the births provided no data on the father's age, and for the black population the figure was 37 percent. The nonresponses are probably higher for teenage fathers than for other groups. If so, to distribute the nonresponses by age in the same ratios as those who did respond is not accurate. In table 12–3, nonresponses are distributed in ratio to unknowns by mother's age, a better estimate but still not perfect.

Because the ratio of teenagers in the population is declining, the proportion of teenage births should also decline. In addition, adult women may be making up some of the births they postponed during the recent years of low fertility. Thus it seems likely that the teenage contribution to the total number of births will decrease. In the meantime, however, the proportion remains high, with one out of every 6.8 white births and one out of every 3.7 black births being to a teenage girl.

Naturally, the younger the age, the smaller is the proportion of all births contributed by girls of that age. However, when we look at the trend (table 12–4)[1-3] we find that between 1950 and 1973, the younger the girls the faster they increased their proportions of all births. In 1950, girls aged 17 or younger accounted for 3.72 percent of all births; in 1973, they accounted for 8.01 percent. Since 1973, however, girls in this younger age bracket have shown a slightly faster decline in their proportion than the older ones. In 1977, the younger girls accounted for 6.77 percent of all births, down one-sixth from the 1973 figure.

Table 12-4.—*Percent of all births and percent change in proportion, by age of mother, 1950, 1973, and 1977*

Age of mother	Percent of all births			Percent change in proportion	
	1950	1973	1977	1950-73	1973-77
14	0.14	0.41	0.34	192.9	-17.1
15	0.40	1.11	0.93	177.5	-16.2
16	1.07	2.48	2.11	131.8	-14.9
17	2.11	4.01	3.39	90.0	-15.5
18	3.47	5.34	4.62	53.9	-13.5
19	4.78	6.32	5.77	32.2	-8.7
Total	11.96	19.67	17.15	64.5	-12.8

Source: References 1 to 3.

The falling proportion of births contributed by younger girls in the recent period is due mainly to the reduction in number of these girls in the population. The number in these ages was the first to be eroded by the decline in the birth rate in the years after 1957. In 1970 and 1977, the proportion of all women 14 to 49 who were in specified adolescent ages was as follows:[a,5]

	Percent of Women 14–49		
Age of Girls	1970	1977	Projected 1985*
14–17	15.3	14.4	11.2
18–19	7.4	7.4	5.8

Owing to a falling representation of teenagers in the population, the proportion of births contributed by teenagers should decline sharply in the future. However, the degree of the fall will depend on another factor—namely, the fertility of teenagers relative to that of adult women. Let us turn to that topic.

Teenage Fertility

In the United States, as in all industrial countries, fertility is lower for teenage women than for women in their twenties and early thirties. Currently, for instance, the peak fertility among American women is found at ages 20 to 24. If we take that rate as 100, then the index of fertility at other ages is as follows:

Age of Women	Index of Fertility
20–24	100
25–29	99
18–19	71
30–34	50
15–17	30
35–39	17
40–44	4
10–14	1
44–49	0.2

American girls 15 to 17 have higher fertility than women 35 to 39, but a lower fertility than those aged 30 to 34. Thus, the problem is not that teenagers have a higher fertility than adult women, but rather that they, at least under age 18, have any fertility at all.

---

[a]This is the Series II projection.

Concerning changes, teenage fertility generally has moved in the same direction as fertility in general. This can be seen in table 12–5,[1-3] where the low and high points in American fertility since 1940 are depicted along with the rates-of-change. Between 1940 and 1957, when American fertility was rising, the rates for teenagers rose faster than for women in general. In the subsequent decline, between 1957 and 1976, the drop among teenagers was about the same, or perhaps less, than for all women. The result was that by 1976 teenage fertility was somewhat greater in ratio to the fertility of all women than it had been in 1940.

Although fertility of girls aged 10 to 14 is generally low, in 1957 to 1976 it kept on increasing against the general trend among whites; although it increased among blacks, it did so only slightly. Consequently, the ratio of teenage fertility to adult fertility has increased, especially among whites. Nonwhite teenage fertility is much higher than the white, particularly at the youngest ages. The ratio of nonwhite fertility to that of whites yields the following figures:

| | Nonwhite Fertility Divided by White | | |
| | Women's Ages | | |
Year	15–44	10–14	15–19
1940	1.33	18.5	2.69
1957	1.39	12.8	1.99
1976	1.41	7.2	1.91

Among nonwhites, the fertility rate for girls under age 15 is several times greater than among whites, and the rate for girls 15 to 19 is twice as great. However, the difference for both age groups has been lessening, whereas for all women 15 to 44, the difference has been increasing slightly. Perhaps this suggests that, with increasing school and housing integration, white youth are adopting some of the fertility behavior of the nonwhites; at least, the main factor in the convergence of teenage fertility between the races has been the rise in the white rates rather than a fall in black rates.

Table 12–5 also shows that the fastest increase in fertility between 1940 and 1957, and the slowest decrease after that, was among girls aged 10 to 14 and boys aged 15 to 19. However, this was, for girls at least, a white phenomenon. Among nonwhites, teenage fertility neither rose as fast during 1940–57, nor fell as slowly in 1957–76 as did general fertility. Additional insight is provided by birth rates for single years of age (table 12–6).[1-3] The rise in teenage fertility between 1950 and 1960 was less than the

Table 12-5.—*High and low points in the trends of teenage and general fertility since 1940*

Race and year	Births Per 1,000 Persons					
	Females			Males		
	15-44	10-14	15-19	15-54	15-19	20-24
All races						
1940	79.9	0.7	54.1	64.7	7.5	91.2
1957	122.7	1.0	96.1	98.4	22.3	198.5
1976	65.8	1.2	53.5	53.8	19.7	93.9
1977	67.8	1.2	53.7	55.7	19.3	95.1
White						
1940	77.1	0.2	45.3	61.7	5.5	81.9
1957	117.4	0.4	85.3	92.5	19.5	188.0
1976	62.2	0.6	53.5	50.3*	17.3*	88.0*
1977	64.0	0.6	53.7	51.6	15.8	85.9
Nonwhite						
1940	102.4	3.7	121.7	92.7	24.4	173.6
1957	163.4	5.1	170.1	137.7	44.3	272.4
1976	87.6	4.3	102.4	83.2*	43.2*	161.9*
1977	89.9	4.3	102.4	84.3	39.9	151.2
Black						
1977	89.8	4.7	107.3	84.1	42.3	163.6
	Percent change					
All races						
1940-57	53.6	42.9	77.6	52.1	197.3	117.7
1957-76	−46.4	20.0	−44.3	−45.3	−11.7	−52.7
White						
1940-57	52.3	100.0	88.3	49.9	254.5	129.5
1957-76	−47.0	50.0	−37.3	−45.6	−11.3	−53.2
Nonwhite						
1940-57	59.6	37.8	39.8	48.5	81.6	56.9
1957-76	−46.4	−7.8	−37.1	−39.6	−2.5	−40.6

*1975 instead of 1976.

Sources: References 1 to 3.

rise in the young adult age groups, and it was confined to the white population. Between 1960 and 1970, teenage fertility fell sharply—except at ages 14 and 15—and it fell even more sharply between 1970 and 1977.

Table 12-6.—*Fertility of teenage girls by single years of age compared with that for young women aged 20-24, United States, selected dates*

Age and race	Births per 1,000 girls in specified age				Percent change in rate*		
	1950	1960	1970	1977	1950-60	1960-70	1970-77
All races							
14	4.7	5.0	5.8	5.6	7.9	16.0	−3.5
15	13.1	14.3	15.1	15.0	9.3	5.1	−0.6
16	34.8	38.6	37.4	33.7	11.2	−3.2	−9.9
17	68.3	77.1	65.1	54.7	12.9	−15.6	−15.9
18	112.1	135.1	97.6	73.1	20.5	−27.7	−25.1
19	152.6	201.9	132.6	90.4	32.3	−34.4	−31.8
20-24	196.6	258.1	167.8	115.2	31.3	−35.0	−31.3
White							
14	1.8	2.2	2.5	2.7	21.3	17.3	4.3
15	7.6	9.1	8.7	9.8	20.7	−4.9	12.4
16	25.3	29.8	26.9	25.2	18.1	−9.8	−6.4
17	56.0	66.0	52.8	44.6	17.8	−20.0	−15.6
18	98.0	122.1	83.0	62.0	24.6	−31.3	−26.1
19	142.1	191.0	119.8	79.9	34.4	−37.3	−33.6
20-24	190.4	252.8	263.4	109.8	32.8	−35.4	−32.8
Nonwhite							
14	24.5	24.3	24.4	20.6	−1.2	0.7	−15.8
15	51.6	49.4	51.6	42.6	−4.2	4.4	−17.4
16	101.3	101.7	99.0	78.7	0.4	−2.7	−20.6
17	155.0	159.4	138.9	108.7	2.8	−12.9	−21.8
18	207.0	228.3	181.6	134.0	10.3	−20.4	−26.2
19	228.4	276.6	209.4	149.5	21.1	−24.3	−28.6
20-24	242.6	294.2	196.8	145.7	17.1	−33.1	−26.0

*Calculated on basis of figures less rounded than those shown in first four columns.

Sources: References 1 to 3.

In general, then, fertility in the youngest ages (14 to 16) seems to be less responsive to changing conditions than does fertility at older ages. Given this circumstance, the fact that the black-white differential is greatest in the youngest ages, and that a greater share of black births occur to women in those ages, means that black fertility is less responsive than white fertility. In the right panel of table 12–6, the change in the black rate is nearly always less than the change in the white rate. The peak rate of black fertility for a single year of age is a teen year—age 19 (according to the data for 1975, when births for single years of age are fully available), whereas for whites it is age 23. Although the races are converging somewhat, teenage fertility is still more characteristic of the black contingent.

An Index of Youthful Reproduction

By taking single-age rates into account, one can calculate an Index of Youthful Reproduction. If, say, 23 is chosen as the ideal age for a woman to bear a child, the birth rates of young mothers can be weighted by the square of the difference between their age and age 23. The sum of the weighted rates through age 22, divided by 1,000, yields the Absolute Index. When the sum is divided by the sum of the age-specific rates at age 23 and above, it produces the Relative Index. The Absolute Index varies with the level of fertility, but the Relative Index does not. The higher the Relative Index, the greater the role played by very young persons in a nation's overall fertility, regardless of how high or low the overall rate is.

When the calculation is made for the United States (table 12–7,[1-3] the Absolute Index is found to have varied with overall fertility. The index rose at the time that fertility was rising in the 1950's, and it declined in the 1960's. However, since the Absolute Index rose more rapidly and fell more slowly than overall fertility, the Relative Index rose throughout the entire period. For the whole population, the Relative Index was 18 percent higher in 1970 than it had been in 1950. The gain was greater for nonwhites than for whites, despite the fact that in the decade of the 1950's, the Relative Index actually fell for nonwhites.

DOES THE UNITED STATES HAVE MORE TEENAGE PREGNANCY THAN OTHER COUNTRIES?

Whether we take the teenage proportion of all births, the teenage birth rate, or an index that weights birth rates by degree of maternal youthfulness, we see that the United States has a substantial amount of teenage reproduction. Is this amount, however, more or less than is to be expected? After all, the average person is capable of reproduction throughout almost all of his or her teen years—in fact, the teen years make up 23 percent of the average women's reproductive span. By this standard, the

Table 12-7.—*Index of Youthful Reproduction in the United States, by race, 1950, 1960, 1970, and 1975*

Index by race	Values				Percent change[a]			
	1950	1960	1970	1975	1950-60	1960-70	1950-70	1970-75
All races								
Absolute index[b]	13.20	16.09	12.31	10.32	21.9	-23.5	-6.7	-16.2
TFR over age 22[c]	2.09	2.43	1.66	1.18	16.6	-31.9	-20.8	-33.2
Relative Index[d]	6.30	6.61	7.43	8.74	4.9	12.4	17.9	17.6
White								
Absolute Index	11.07	14.08	10.02	8.25	27.2	-28.9	-9.5	11.05
TFR over age 22	2.07	2.38	1.64	1.11	15.4	-31.1	-20.5	-32.58
Relative Index	5.36	5.91	6.10	7.46	10.3	3.2	13.8	22.24
Nonwhite								
Absolute Index	28.08	30.26	25.91	21.30	7.8	-14.4	-7.7	-17.77
TFR over age 22	2.31	2.80	1.76	1.65	21.2	-37.3	-24.0	-6.11
Relative Index	12.13	10.79	14.73	12.90	-11.0	36.5	21.4	-12.41

[a]Calculated on the basis of figures less rounded than those shown.
[b]Sum of birth rates at each age from 22 and less, weighted by the square of the distance of each age from 23.
[c]TFR is abbreviation for total fertility rate, which is the sum of the age-specific birth rates for women aged 23 and over, divided by 1,000.
[d]The Absolute Index divided by the TFR; based on figures less rounded than those shown.

Source: Calculated by the author from data on births by single years of age (references 1 to 3), and from census returns on the resident female population of the United States in those years.

17.2 percent of all births in 1977 that were contributed by teenage mothers is within normal range.

What is normal, however, cannot be judged solely in biological terms, nor can changes in teenage reproduction be explained in that fashion. Consideration should be given to social conditions in the United States compared to other countries. Is teenage pregnancy equally prominent and similarly fluctuating in other nations? If it is, the explanation must be sufficiently general to embrace other societies; otherwise, the explanation must rely on certain peculiarities of American society.

The Proportion of Teenage Births in the United States Compared to Other Countries

The proportion of births occurring to teenage mothers in the United States is extremely high compared to other countries. According to the data in table 12–8, the only countries that match the American proportion are the Latin American and Caribbean countries. Although the United States proportion is heavily determined by the black population, it is still true that the white population, taken alone, has a high proportion of births compared to most other nations.

Between 1963 and 1968 all regions included in table 1–8 show an increase in the proportion of births to teenagers, and most show an increase between 1968 and 1975. As both periods covered a time when fertility was experiencing an overall decline, it is clear that adolescent fertility was declining less than adult fertility. The fastest increase during 1963–68 was by the nonwhite population of the United States, but between 1968 and 1975 the nonwhite increase was exceeded by the white, and the white in turn was exceeded by the gain in the Latin American and Caribbean countries. The other advanced nations generally showed a slower rise in the teenage proportion of births than did the United States. Clearly, then, the United States is unique among industrial nations in its high proportion of births occurring to teenage mothers; but this may be partly due to its age structure rather than to adolescent procreativeness alone.

The Teenage Birth Rate in Comparative Perspective

For international evidence concerning the teenage birth rate, data for 50 countries (not including the United States) were assembled from the 1976 edition of the *Demographic Yearbook*.[6] The statistics refer mostly to 1974 or 1975, and none is earlier than 1970. As can be seen from the first two lines of table 12–9,[1,6]

Table 12-8.—*Percent of births by teenage mothers, selected countries, 1963, 1968 and 1975*

Countries	Percent of births to women under age 20 by year			Percent change	
	1963	1968[a]	1975	1963-68	1968-75
United States	14.50	17.16	19.15	18.4	11.6
White	13.47	14.75	16.45	9.6	11.5
Nonwhite	21.44	29.05	30.80	35.5	6.0
Asian Countries (Japan, Mauritius, Singapore, Sri Lanka, Taiwan)	6.49	7.52	7.39	15.9	-1.7
European Countries (Austria, Belgium, Czechoslovakia, England and Wales, France, Greece, Hungary, Ireland, Italy, Portugal, Romania, Sweden, West Germany)	7.63	9.26	9.91	21.2	7.0
Overseas European Countries (Australia, Canada)	10.81	13.18	11.13	21.9	-15.6
Latin American Countries (Chile, Costa Rica, El Salvador, Mexico, Panama)	13.70	14.51	17.44	5.9	20.2
Caribbean Countries (Barbados, Guadaloupe, Martinique, St. Kitts-Nevis-Anguilla, Trinidad-Tobago). .	14.54	17.07	22.53	17.4	32.0

[a]In some cases, the date is 1967.

the less developed countries have both a much higher general fertility and a much higher teenage fertility than the industrial nations, but the difference is wider for teenage fertility. With respect to general fertility, the less developed countries are 102 percent higher than the developed countries, but in regard to teenage fertility they are 160 percent higher. Thus, the United States shows up in table 12–9 as quite peculiar. Its white population has a general fertility rate substantially lower than the average for 26 other developed countries, and yet the teenage rate is substantially higher. The country's black population has a higher fertility in both categories than the developed nations generally, but the difference is greater with respect to teenage fertility. In

Table 12-9.—*Teenage birth rate by country category, circa 1974 or 1975*

Country category	Births per 1,000 women		15-19 as percent of 15-49
	15-19	15-49	
26 developed countries	36.1	70.6	51.1
24 less developed countries	94.0	142.7	65.9
United States			
All races	57.5	59.1	97.3
White	47.4	55.7	85.1
Nonwhite	113.4	80.5	140.8
Black	119.0	80.4	147.9

Source: References 1, 6.

fact, the Nation's black teenage fertility is so high that it eclipses that of the less developed countries. Clearly, the United States as an industrial nation has an unusually high teenage fertility, especially in ratio to its general fertility. The Nation is letting its adolescent girls bear a heavy share of its national reproduction. The theory of why this is so must rely on conditions somewhat peculiar to the United States.

Restatement of the Problem

The problem of teenage fertility in the United States, then, is not solely that the rate is high compared to other countries. Nor is it that, as one newspaper headline declared in April 1979, the rate has been "soaring" (actually, the rate has dropped drastically since 1957). In part, the problem is that in the United States an extraordinarily high *proportion* of the Nation's childbearing is borne by teenagers. This proportion has risen sharply in the last 25 years, and it has been twice as high among nonwhites as among whites, although the racial difference has diminished (see table 12.3). It is also clear from table 12–3 that since 1974, the proportion of teenage births among all births has been declining rapidly. This has been due more to shrinkage in the teenage population than to loss of teenage fertility relative to adult fertility. Whether one expects the recent relative decline in adolescent reproduction to continue depends on the interpretation one brings to the facts. Let us turn now to questions of interpretation.

Means versus Motives and Conditions

Following World War II, changes in teenage reproduction came mainly from changes in means of contraception, in sexual exposure, and in motivation to have children. In general, teenage fertility followed the direction of change in adult fertility, which means that it gained in the 1950's, and fell in the 1960's and 1970's. Teenage fertility gained more rapidly after the war and later declined more slowly, with the result that, until about 1970, the ratio of adolescent to adult fertility rose. After 1970, however, teenage fertility dropped more rapidly than adult fertility. The greatest tendency to gain is found in the youngest ages—14 and 15—where decline in fertility was not visible until after 1975.

During the 1960's and 1970's, contraceptives and abortion became available to teenagers on a scale never before realized. If other things had been equal, this would not only have reduced teenage fertility but also would have reduced it faster than adult fertility. Although teenage fertility did decline, it did not do so as fast as adult fertility until recently, and it did not decline at all in the youngest ages until after 1975. We must therefore give weight to the fact that sexual exposure among adolescents was rising during the period in question, and we must entertain the proposition that the desire to become pregnant was weakening less among adolescents than among adults. The rise in sexual exposure seems to have particularly characterized the youngest ages, where fertility has been most resistant to the downward trend. Less can be said about the desire to become pregnant, but circumstantial evidence indicated that it may have dropped less for adolescents than for adults. For instance, the rise in illegitimacy among teenagers implies an increasing willingness to bear a child out-of-wedlock.

Illegitimate Teenage Fertility

If teenage girls were highly motivated to avoid an illegitimate birth, the availability of contraception and abortion should have enabled them to reduce their illegitimate reproduction. Actually, it turns out that close to 50 percent of all illegitimate births in the United States are to teenage mothers, while only 13 percent of legitimate births are to such mothers. In 1977, of all births to teenage mothers, 44 percent were illegitimate, while of all births to mothers aged 20 and older, only 9.6 percent were illegitimate (table 12–10).[2,3] Among blacks, the proportion of illegitimate births was 83 percent for teenage mothers and 39 percent for adult mothers. The younger the mother, the greater the percentage of illegitimate births. At age 14, for example, 73 percent of white births and 99 percent of nonwhite births in 1977 were illegitimate. Even at age 19, over 70 percent of black births were illegitimate. Thus the problem of teenage pregnancy is largely a problem of illegitimate pregnancy.

Historically, the proportion of illegitimate births has risen sharply in the United States since 1940. Between that date and 1977, the percentage increased more than four times for the white population and nearly three times for the nonwhite population. For both whites and nonwhites the 1977 figures were the highest on record. Table 12–10 compares the figures for 1950 and 1977 by age of mother. The biggest percentage-point gains were made in the teen and the nonwhite population. For instance, the gain was 30 percentage points for women under 20, compared to 7 for women 20 and older.

The rise in the *ratio* of illegitimate births does not necessarily mean that illegitimate *fertility* has also risen. The latter (illegitimate births per thousand unmarried women) did show a steeply rising trend between 1940 and 1970, but after that it leveled off. Among white teenagers, however, the trend continued to rise after 1970, although at a reduced rate; and among nonwhite teenagers, the peak was not reached until 1972. Recalling that legitimate fertility peaked in 1957 and declined sharply after that until a low plateau was reached in the 1970's, one can see that illegitimate fertility has gained in comparison to legitimate fertility, especially among teenagers. During the period 1960 to 1975, births per 1,000 unmarried teenage women rose from 15.3 to 24.8.

The very size of the legitimate birth rate indicates that a high proportion of teenage marriages take place because the bride is pregnant. A decline in this rate and a simultaneous rise in the illegitimate rate may indicate that fewer girls are getting married when they are pregnant, and that some who would have married at an earlier period are now opting to have a baby out-of-wedlock. In any case, it is clear that overall teenage fertility is not "soaring." Among teenage girls, the decline in marital fertility between 1960 (when it was at its peak) and 1975 was 40.5 percent, almost identical with the decline among married women of all ages. The only soaring aspect of teenage fertility is illegitimate fertility, and its importance is due, not to its level, but to the fact that such a large proportion of teenage girls are unmarried. In 1960, the ratio of legitimate to illegitimate fertility among women aged 15 to 19 was 35 to 1; in 1975 it was 13 to 1. Among nonwhite teenagers, the ratio of married to unmarried fertility had dropped to 3.9 to 1 by 1975. Nevertheless, although married fertility greatly exceeds nonmarital fertility, there are so many single teenagers that even a modest illegitimate fertility means a large number of births. That is why some 28 percent of all white

Table 12-10.—*Illegitimate births as a percentage of all births, by race and age of mother, United States, 1950 and 1977*

Age of mother	All races		Whites		Nonwhites		Gain in percentage points		
	1950	1977	1950	1977	1950	1977	All Races	White	Nonwhite
14	63.7	88.2	41.4	72.8	74.6	98.8	24.4	31.3	24.2
15	41.6	74.3	19.5	56.2	62.6	95.4	32.7	36.7	32.8
16	26.1	68.0	11.6	42.9	50.8	90.6	41.8	31.2	39.8
17	17.2	59.2	8.2	32.9	40.4	84.9	42.0	24.7	44.5
18	11.6	39.6	5.8	25.0	31.0	76.5	28.0	19.2	45.4
19	7.7	30.2	4.0	17.8	24.3	67.3	22.5	13.8	43.0
Under 20	14.0	43.8	6.4	27.8	37.1	80.2	29.8	21.4	43.1
20+	2.6	9.6	1.2	4.8	12.9	33.8	7.0	3.6	20.9
All ages	4.0	15.5	1.7	8.2	13.9	46.5	11.5	6.4	32.5

Source: References 2, 3.

births and 80 percent of all nonwhite births to teenagers are illegitimate (see table 12–1).

Illicit Conceptions and Licit Births

Special note should be taken of the fact that marital fertility is higher below age 20 than at any other age, whereas the highest nonmarital fertility is found at ages 20 to 29. The high teenage marital fertility is due to premarital conception. In other words, for young girls, pregnancy is often the occasion for marriage rather than vice versa. If one-half of the babies born to mothers aged 15 to 19, and all of those under age 15 are illicitly conceived, this means that approximately 69.7 percent of all births to teenage mothers are conceived outside of wedlock. Similarly, almost as many girls who decide to carry their illicitly conceived babies to term manage to bear them in marriage rather than outside of marriage. The exact ratio is unknown, but on the assumption stated above, of the illicit conceptions resulting in live births in 1975, 44 percent led to marriage before the birth occurred. This estimate suggests that the desire among teenagers to confine reproduction to marriage is still strong.

Explaining the Facts

Any theory of teenage fertility in the United States must fit the salient facts brought out in the preceding analysis. It must account for the following:

- teenage births constitute a higher proportion of births in this country than in other industrial nations
- the proportion is especially high in the black population and, compared with other countries, in the youngest ages
- the proportion rose significantly between 1950 and 1973, but then fell somewhat
- the high proportion in the United States is not due to a higher fertility among teenagers than among women of more advanced age, but simply to a higher teenage fertility than other advanced countries exhibit
- teenage fertility as a whole has tended to follow the course of U.S. fertility in general—rising between 1940 and 1957 and falling thereafter—but the younger the girl, the lesser is the variation
- the principal difference in reproduction between teenage and older women is not in legitimate but in illegitimate births—the proportion of illegitimate births is nearly five times greater for women under 20 than for women 20 and older

- the illegitimacy ratio has risen more rapidly and more persistently among teenagers than among older women
- illegitimate fertility has risen steadily for adolescents while it has fallen for other age groups.

Some Proximate Factors

The availability or unavailability of contraception does not appear to be a prime consideration in explaining the above facts. Contraception does not appear to be more available to teenagers in other industrial nations than to those in the United States, nor did it become progressively less available to youth during the period when teenage fertility was rising. At most, it might help to explain the reduction in teenage fertility after 1957, but as noted in our data, this drop was greater for older women than for teenagers. Again, the availability of abortion apparently has had little effect. During the 1970's, when greater access to abortion was achieved, the fertility of teenage mothers declined more slowly than that of older women. The continued rise in the illegitimacy ratio among teenagers seems inconsistent with a greater role for abortion.

We are left, then, with the interplay between sexual exposure, willingness to take a risk, and readiness to bear a child as principal proximate factors. There is probably more sexual exposure among teenagers in the United States than in other industrial nations due to the higher proportion married in young ages and the greater amount of nonmarital exposure. The former has tended to be reduced in recent years. The proportion ever-married dropped between 1960 and 1977 from 5.4 to 2.5 percent for girls 14 to 17 years old, from 24.4 to 15.2 percent for girls 18 years old, and from 40.3 to 26.2 percent for girls 19 years old.[7] This drop in sexual exposure played a significant role in the drop in fertility among teenagers. However, sexual exposure outside of marriage has increased, especially among the youngest girls, at least partially compensating for the fall in marital exposure.

In addition to changes in sexual exposure, there are doubtless changes in the willingness to take a risk. Although direct data on such a phenomenon seem nonexistent, the fact that teenage illegitimate fertility has continued to rise, while falling in all other age groups, seems compatable with this supposition.

Finally, there appears to be greater willingness to bear a child out-of-wedlock. Less shame is attached to doing so than there used to be, as evidenced by the rising proportion of unmarried mothers who decide to keep their children. If so, this would help explain why during the 1970's, illegitimate fertility has risen in all age groups in the United States, not just among teenagers.[8] Within marriage, there has been less willingness to bear a child. The drop in marital fertility has been as sharp for adolescents as for older women, whereas the opposite is true for nonmarital fertility. The main cause appears to be a desire for low fertility. A subsidiary and more recent cause may be that premarital pregnancy is now leading less frequently to marriage and more frequently to illegitimacy. The proportion of first marriages in which the bride is pregnant, much higher for teenage girls than for adult women, rose steeply from 1952–56 to 1967–71 but fell after that.[7]

The Social Context

If our interpretation is correct that premarital sexual exposure, willingness to take a risk, willingness to bear a child out-of-wedlock, and early marriage, have been the main factors in the large share of adolescents in American reproduction, we must go on to ask how these factors happen to exist to an unusual degree in the United States. To answer that question, at least speculatively, let us begin by recalling the conditions of an earlier time, when teenagers played a lesser role in childbearing.

The key to the old system seems to have been that teenagers were held responsible for any children they engendered. They were held accountable by parents and relatives, by neighbors and acquaintances, and by official representatives of the community. Sanctions included use of force with respect to the father, if necessary, and ostracism and loss of reputation with respect to the mother.

Inasmuch as sex roles were clearly ascribed, the controls were different for boys and girls. It was in a girl's best interest to marry, because through marriage she gained a source of economic support and was privileged to bear children respectably. Her interest thus lay in marrying while she was still young and attractive, but the man frequently had to postpone marriage until he acquired the means to support a family. For this reason, the average age at first marriage was older than it is today, especially for the groom, and the age gap between husband and wife was greater.

Unless there was already a commitment to marriage, premarital sexual intercourse was perilous. For the girl it would mean a possible loss of reputation and the danger of pregnancy. For the boy, it carried a risk of retaliation either directly against him or indirectly against his family, not only by the girl's family but also by friends of her family and members of the community. If pregnancy occurred, the only way to escape retaliation was to leave town (itself a major step), secure a secret abortion for the girl, or marry her. Being young, the boy usually was not adept at finding an abortionist, and for him a forced marriage was often a major calamity because it meant assuming the obligations of a husband and father prematurely (perhaps with a girl he would not otherwise have chosen). With considerable surveillance of boy–girl relationships, the girl's local reputation (and hence her chances for a good marriage) depended upon avoiding the appearance of being a "loose woman."

Under the circumstances, the boy was highly motivated to avoid getting the girl pregnant. She, however, might or might not be so highly motivated, depending on whether she wanted to marry him and how she calculated the chances of marriage if she did become pregnant. At best, she had only a short period in which her chance of making a good match was at its maximum; hence, she could not wait long for the boy to "declare himself." Yet she had to be very careful about trying entrapment by means of pregnancy; if it failed in its purpose, she would be ruined.

A class factor was also involved. A boy did not have to be so afraid of retaliation if the girl were of a class distinctly lower than his, but in that case he had to be extra wary of being trapped into marriage.

Amid all of these factors, the combination of youthful passion and youthful inexperience made carefully calculated behavior difficult. Infatuation often led girls to behave recklessly, but more often it led them to indulge in incomplete sexual behavior, such as necking and petting. Girls were more likely to yield completely if marriage was definitely promised and symbolized by an engagement ring.

Informal controls of teenage children relative to sexual exposure included ignorance (discussion of sex was taboo at home and at school), fear (not only of pregnancy but also of venereal disease), and local surveillance (reducing opportunities). These controls got many girls and boys through the younger years without intercourse. Boys who were determined to experience sexual intercourse, as many were, had to seek out particularly vulnerable girls or prostitutes.

All told, the system did not preclude adolescent pregnancy, but it did keep it relatively low compared with adult pregnancy. In the United States, the male's reluctance to marry early was somewhat countered by the open opportunities of a new country.

The Special Case of Blacks

In 19th century America, black women represented a lower caste to which white males had access on a relatively cost-free, or irresponsible basis. Retaliation was difficult not only because the relatives were of lower caste, but also because black society was disorganized and itself characterized by male exploitation. Already at the bottom of the social ladder, the black female lost less by pregnancy than did her white counterpart. Both the original African culture and the experience of slavery engendered a tradition of consensual unions, strong mother-child bonds, and female economic independence—all of which freed the black male from responsibility for his offspring. Nevertheless, in the rural South where blacks were concentrated, community and family controls were gradually building up between 1890 and 1914. The occurrence of two World Wars, a major economic depression, and extremely rapid internal migration and urbanization subjected blacks to a loss of community controls.

How the Old System Was Lost

Apart from the special case of blacks, why did the old system of social control over teenage reproduction weaken? The answer can possibly be found in those social changes that have undermined the authority and power of the nuclear family, kin, and local community with respect to children. In the rising geographical and social mobility associated with industrialization and urbanization, the nuclear family has increasingly become dissociated from the wider circle of relatives. In dealing with the family's adolescent members, therefore, parents have little backing from uncles, aunts, cousins, and grandparents. More importantly, nonfamilial agencies, or third parties, have tended to intrude themselves between parents and children, taking over all or part of what traditionally were parental functions and hence assuming parental authority. These agencies, despite their protestations, often do not strengthen the family and may compete with it. They are, on the whole, achievement groups rather than inheritance groups. They are usually arms of the Government, and they justify their work in terms of the child's welfare or that of society at large. Schools take charge of the child's education, inculcating in him ideas that often contradict those of parents; courts decree the busing of children to schools outside of the neighborhood, regardless of parental wishes; social welfare agencies take over the support of mother and children, often ignoring the father; health agencies offer abortion and contraception to teenagers without parental consent; adoption agencies decide who can adopt children and who cannot.

Symptomatic of these kinds of intrusions by outside agencies is the growing tenuousness of the parents' hold over their children, and the subsequent reduced sense of responsibility of their grown children toward them (the parents) in later years. The old balance has been destroyed; the parent no longer has authority over the child to match his responsibilities. The parent's obligation to the child is not matched by a compensatory obligation of the grown child to the aging parents. Furthermore, the division of labor within the family is less clear. No division of labor on the basis of age is culturally recognized and there is in practice usually no reciprocity: the parents labor, the children play. The division of labor on the basis of sex has, more recently, also become problematic.

As a result, the child's emancipation from parental authority has been pushed steadily downward to a younger age. The median age at first marriage for males dropped from 26.1 in 1890, to 22.5 in 1956. By 1975 it had risen to 23.5, perhaps less because of caution about marrying than of carelessness about living together without marrying.

The Competition of Agencies Outside the Family

Currently, the competition between outside agencies and the family is seldom analyzed, because the goals of the outside agencies are seemingly sacred and cannot be criticized. Public schools, for example, may exist in part for the purpose of integrating and providing equal opportunity for different races and classes; therefore, their authority vis-à-vis the parent is not easily disputed. The school authorities represent a specialized group with specialized attitudes. They inculcate knowledge, ideology, and behavior patterns without reference to parents, and in some cases they encourage attitudes of neglect or defiance toward parents. The latest development in this struggle between parents and educators is the decline of neighborhood control (and hence parental supervision) over schools. School busing gives the public school apparatus greater control of children. Similarly, equalization measures, statewide standards in textbooks and teacher-certification, and unionization of teachers tend to take power from parents and give it to educators. In large part, this intrusion is precisely rationalized in terms of reducing the ascription of status—that is, reducing the influence of parents. Children living in neighborhoods where people are relatively successful do not reap any advantage from this fact. Not only is money from such districts siphoned off and given to poorer districts, but children from poorer districts are bused in while the neighborhood's own children are bused out.

Other Government agencies also intrude themselves between parent and child. Welfare agencies, for instance, during the 1960's and early 1970's were quick to respond to the possibility of substituting their financing for that of the father, making the father superfluous, and in fact, freeing him from parenting responsibility. This was happening increasingly with children of divorced and separated parents, and with children of unmarried or deserted mothers. Little effort was made to find the father and hold him responsible. The State simply became the economic father, but, of course, it could not become the moral and social father. In recent years a strong effort has been made to elicit support from fathers, but with the State as collector and distributor, and without an effort to strengthen the father-child relationship.

Public health agencies and the medical profession also take over authority with respect to the child. Teenagers are not only given birth control devices and abortions without parental consent, but are also given "sex education"—often conveying an implied approval of sexual relations among teenagers as long as a "method" is used.

In addition, numerous commercialized recreational agencies address themselves to teenagers. Even religion, which is profamily, competes with parents in furnishing recreation and in controlling young minds. Not only do new religious movements of a messianic character aim their hypnotic appeals specifically at gullible youths, but also old religions, in their rush to be avant-garde, may teach ideas to the young that contradict those of parents.

Parental Attitudes

Without doubt, many parents are satisfied to let others take over, as this frees them from responsibility. They can rest comfortably in the belief that other agencies are doing "the right sort of job" with their children. Indeed, the loss of parental authority has been facilitated by an ideological enthronement of "permissiveness" as a proper approach to dealing with children. Many parents take the attitude that it is the child who is to make the major decisions in life. He is to decide what occupation he will follow, what education he will get beyond high school, and when he will start engaging in sexual intercourse. Just what makes the child wise enough to make such important decisions is left unclear, but a laissez faire attitude is justified by references to democracy and "not interfering with the child's life." As the child, in fact, knows little of life, parental permissiveness actually means that the decisions are determined by others. These other decision makers are often the child's peers, who are as ignorant as the child himself; his teachers; and sometimes even drug peddlers, pederasts, or others whose interests are served by influencing children. In many cases the parent is afraid to interfere—afraid, that is, to cut the thin thread of personal relationship that remains after the intruding forces have had their way. Yet the child instinctively has little respect for parents who are too timid to exercise the function of parents—namely guidance and the use of authority in the child's interest.

Reproduction and Peer Relations

If this analysis is correct, it could explain why teenage reproduction has played an ever greater role in the Nation's overall birth rate. Deprived of the personal guidance and supervision that only a parent can provide, children often do what is biologically natural: they indulge in sexual intercourse. Although officials in impersonal agencies reason that such intercourse is harmless if the child is "protected" by contraception and abortion, the truth is that sexual intercourse is not something apart from, but is inevitably entangled in the interpersonal relations of the peer group. Moreover, if intercourse is justified because it is natural, then pregnancy is also justified. Indeed, for the girl there is no longer extreme disgrace in becoming pregnant, and in her childishness she often thinks that it will somehow strengthen her boyfriend's regard for her. In any case, as a pregnant adolescent, she is often the recipient of special attention and expensive services, and she is simultaneously producing a highly valued companion (or pet) for herself. For the boy, causing a pregnancy no longer carries a penalty. The family planning and female emancipation movements have placed the onus of contraception on the women, thus freeing the man from liability in the onset of pregnancy.

Social Change and Teenage Pregnancy Among Blacks

Blacks are being brought into the mainstream of American society just as that society is becoming increasingly disorganized. The already high proportion of illegitimacy and teenage reproduction among blacks has therefore tended to rise in approximate step with the rise in the white population. The same changes that have attenuated parental, familial, and community authority among whites have also affected blacks. For example, the rise in public welfare has tended especially to separate the black male from his offspring. The greater average poverty of blacks places more black families on welfare and thus provides more substitution for the father. Moreover, the rate of internal migration and urbanization has been greater for blacks than for whites.

Interpersonal Relations and Sexual Bargaining

Young girls are now exposed to sexual contact with boys in greater degree, with less surveillance and guidance, and with more effective privacy than ever before in civilized history. They usually lack firm goals to meet the situation because the goals conveyed by the different agencies that deal with adolescents are in conflict and doubt. Girls are advised in some circles that they should seek equality with males. But what does "equality" mean? One of the main advantages boys have is that they cannot get pregnant—an advantage girls can share only if they are sterilized. An even greater advantage that boys have is that they are not easily linked to their own offspring, whereas girls are. Whenever one group has built-in advantages, equality means inequality unless the weaker group is given compensatory advantages. This is not happening with respect to women because the other great plank in their emancipation is the opportunity to work. This opportunity, if childbearing is also involved, can become a new form of slavery. Instead of sharing more responsibility for children, the male in modern society is actually sharing less, with the consequence that the burden falls more squarely on the woman. Females must simultaneously participate in the labor force and assume greater liability for childrearing. Girls are rebelling against such newfound "freedom" by reducing the number of offspring. This accounts for the falling birth rate among adolescents aged 16 and older in the last few years.

At the same time, girls are aware that male company and attention depend on their "giving in." Yet a woman cannot adopt the same attitude as the male, because if she is ever to have children, it is she who will have to bear them, and this will, in the long run, prove extremely burdensome outside of a durable relationship. Her interest lies in establishing a durable relationship with a male, and she has a rather narrow span of years within which to do that satisfactorily. To accomplish that goal, however, she has nothing to bargain with, because the male, having been freed from constraint, is in a position of unparalled dominance.

Placed in this position of weakness, a girl has seemingly one advantage: she can get pregnant. Having been given responsibility for birth control, she can govern conception as she sees fit. Even though pregnancy is now a weak tactic, it at least has the merit of bringing to a head the girl's relationship with the boy, and preventing it from dragging on inconclusively during her best years. Furthermore, in getting pregnant, she has ready at hand an ideological justification: it is "natural." She has been told that sexual relations (and, by implication, pregnancy) are natural and therefore moral. When she is simultaneously urged to use contraception and abortion, she may feel that this is unnatural and hence of dubious moral value. Birth control also involves planning and foresight, both incompatible with young passion and impossible in some situations in which adolescents find themselves. A girl may take a chance rather than offend the boyfriend if she is unprepared for the intercourse that is demanded.

The motivation to avoid pregnancy is now relatively weak in any case. In some circles marriage is viewed as artificial, so that having children out-of-wedlock is all right. Indeed, in her relationship with the boy, the girl often may take the point of view that pregnancy is not only natural, but also an expression of love. A child represents "a gift to him."

These are some of the ideological, motivational, and circumstantial factors that have produced a substantial rate of adolescent pregnancy. The consequences, however, if not as disastrous for the girl as they used to be, are normally deleterious in the long run. The pregnancy may fail to cement the relationship with the boy. If it fails, it may do so at a time too late for a legal abortion. If it succeeds (either with or without marriage) the success may be temporary. In that case, if a child is born, the girl may become a single parent at a young age. The long-run disadvantages are apparently being realized by older girls because the rise of illegitimate fertility among them has been reversed in recent years.

If girls are led into early pregnancy by their involvement with a boy and their compulsion to hold on to him, what about the boy himself? He too wishes to have a stable relationship, and ultimately children, but usually at a much later age. If he is approximately the same age as the girl, his interest lies in avoiding a permanent commitment. Her interest, clearly, is to establish a durable relationship at a reasonably early age. To lose time in a long, but inevitably temporary relationship with a boy her own age is therefore emotionally satisfying, but economically and socially disadvantageous. Getting pregnant tends to bring the relationship to a head, but it usually does not resolve the underlying conflict, at least not in the girl's favor.

CONCLUSION

It is difficult to characterize trends in a complex society without seeming to exaggerate or caricature reality. What has been described as the social context underlying much teenage pregnancy in the United States is doubtless truer in some groups and in some regions than in others. Eventually, the Nation's dependence on teenage reproduction may produce its own reversal. If the analysis contains any substantial truth, it suggests that the problem of teenage pregnancy will not be solved by further promotion of contraception and abortion for children. Rather, the solution may lie in the direction of restructuring the institutional system governing male-female relations at young ages. A key element in such restructuring would be a division of roles between men and women that recognizes their differential participation in reproduction and their contrasting life cycles. Instead of freeing males from the responsibility for offspring, it would reimpose such responsibility. It would do so by new legal and institutional measures compatible with a modern economic system—measures rewarding the assumption of proper responsibility and penalizing its absence. In giving an economic role to women, it would avoid penalizing them for childbearing and parenthood within marriage, but would strongly discourage it outside of marriage.

By putting responsibility for children squarely on parents and giving them corresponding incentives for carrying out that responsibility, such measures would tend to rehabilitate the family, and additional strength would accrue to it from limitations on the power of other agencies dealing with the child. The schools could return to the purpose of education with social justice. Social welfare agencies could return to the principle of using family relationships, rather than ignoring them, in helping individuals. The medical authorities could confine themselves to matters of health rather than seeking to govern adolescent conduct.

Hardly anyone expects such restructuring to take place as a result of deliberate planning. Conceivably, it may take place by slow and unconscious evolution, as people try to avoid the misfortunes they see around them. In the meantime, unfortunately, the jungle of unregulated sexual and reproductive conduct is more traumatic for the young and their offspring than for the older generation that is ultimately responsible for the situation.

REFERENCES

1. National Center for Health Statistics. *Vital Statistics of the United States,* Vol. 1, *Natality.* Washington: U.S. Government Printing Office, 1960–1975.
2. National Center for Health Statistics. "Final Natality Statistics." *Monthly Vital Statistics Report.* Washington: U.S. Government Printing Office, 1976 and 1977.
3. National Center for Health Statistics. *Vital Statistics of the United States, Natality.* Washington: U.S. Government Printing Office, 1950.
4. U.S. Bureau of the Census. "Estimates of the Population of the United States by Age, Sex, and Race: 1970 to 1975." *Current Population Reports.* Series P-25, No. 614. Washington: U.S. Government Printing Office.
5. U.S. Bureau of the Census. "Projections of the Population of the United States: 1977 to 2050." *Current Population Reports,* Series P-25, No. 704, July 1977.
6. United Nations. *Demographic Yearbook, 1969 and 1976.*
7. U.S. Bureau of the Census. "Marital Status and Living Arrangements: March 1977." *Current Population Reports,* Series P-20, No. 323, April 1978.
8. U.S. Bureau of the Census. "Fertility of American Women: June 1977." *Current Population Reports,* Series P-20, No. 325, September 1978.

DISCUSSION

The following people were the major participants in the discussion: F. Furstenberg, W. Simon, K. Luker, E. Douvan, C. Chilman, D. Kallen, J. Kantner, and H. Presser. The major topics of discussion were the role of families in contemporary society, male-female sexual behaviors, female roles, and possible directions for future research.

It is generally recognized that urbanization and industrialization tend to undermine the power of the family role and its influence on the behavior of adolescents in contemporary society. Although the family used to be the major source of ascribed status, status is now achieved more through individual accomplishments than through family membership. This may be particularly true in the United States with its long tradition of individualism and its high level of industrial development.

A question was raised as to whether, in the earlier days in this country, parents, in general, actually controlled social institutions such as the school. Some studies reveal that some small, elite groups of parents have exercised such control. The educational wellbeing of children, however, may well be promoted more effectively by professional educators.

Inherent danger exists in the concept that stronger authority, vested either in parents or in the State, is needed to control such youth problems as illegitimacy, delinquency, and drug use. An excessive control of children and adolescents can prevent the development of their personal competence. Competence may be defined as "goodness of fit between the individual and the style of the larger society." Youthful incompetence, in the first place, leads to the kinds of problems that proposed authoritarian controls seek to prevent. Although stern repression might prevent some behavior problems, young people, as a result, would tend to grow into incompetent adults.

An objection was raised to the theory that the family is, necessarily, a conservative force preventing individual achievement and adequate adaptation to a rapidly changing society. Today, many parental attitudes, values, and behaviors also are changing in profound ways. Moreover, parents perform important psychological, as well as norm-setting, functions. An involved psychological support from parents can enhance the adolescent's sense of self-respect and self-worth. As shown by a number of studies, these self-attitudes have an important effect on premarital sexual behavior and contraceptive use. Families are important in providing guidance and motivation for self-discipline and "follow through" on tasks that need to be done.

Questions were raised concerning the effectiveness of verbal guidance and goal-setting as provided by parents. At least one study shows that what parents (notably mothers) *do,* especially in terms of family formation and educational and occupational behaviors, appear to have more influence on adolescent girls than what parents *say.* This study suggests that increased opportunities and guidance be offered to parents in, for instance, educational-occupational areas, so that the parents can be a more adequate role model for their children.

The discussion group was reminded that goal-setting for adolescent girls is useless unless society provides viable alternatives to early childbearing. More educational, vocational, and status-awarding opportunities are needed for young women. They also need ready access to contraceptive and abortion services so that they can control their fertility.

In the area of male-female sexual behavior, the lack of responsibility of contemporary males for their sexual behavior and reproductive outcomes of the behavior was discussed. Loss of family authority and loss of informal community controls was seen as part of the problem. On the other hand, several studies of low-income males indicate that many do have concern for their mates and children (legitimate or illegitimate), but the males are ofttimes unable to find employment to support their families. The 40 to 50 percent rate of youth unemployment in the urban ghetto is evidence of this plight. A counterargument was that young males should not have unprotected intercourse if they lack the resources for family support. The total life situation of low-income youth, however, tends to promote attitudes such as fatalism and alienation, which undermine the rational, planned use of contraceptive services.

Considerable discussion concerning male-female differences in sexual partnerships occurred. Some discussants felt that females engage in sexual bargaining. Adolescent women may try to obtain a commitment of affection and exclusivity from their partners in exchange for sexual favors. Older women may attempt to obtain a marriage commitment. Women might be under pressure to obtain this commitment while they are young, as women only have a few years in which they are considered highly desirable on the marriage market.

Strong exception was taken by some discussants to the concept of "sexual bargaining." This concept is considered part of the current but unfortunate mechanization of sex. When sex and love are disassociated, many problems arise. Females tend to see their sexuality as a package, alien to themselves, which can be stolen from them if they are not careful. If women give this package to a man (because he demands it as a condition for their partnership), they are fearful that they will be deserted because the man now has what he wants. Thus, women are in a "double bind" that leads to resentment, anxiety, and depression.

Males suffer from a depersonalization of sex, too. Male impotence appears to be a growing problem just as it was in France during the libertine period of the 18th century. At that time, flagellation became prominent in houses of prostitution. Impotent males needed to be sexually aroused through hostility because sex had been separated from love. These present times appear to have similarities to this earlier period.

Parents need to raise children to view sex as neither mechanical nor all-important, but as an ongoing part of life, closely linked to love relationships.

In plotting the directions for future research and in attempting to assess the effects of the family on adolescent sexual behavior (including early childbearing outside of marriage), it should be helpful to witness other urban, industrialized societies whose illegitimacy rates among teenagers are different from those in the United States. A strong word of warning was voiced, however, that cross-national comparisons require indepth knowledge concerning many aspects of the societies under consideration. All too often, comparisons are made with only a superficial understanding of the societies in question.